Laboratory Safety

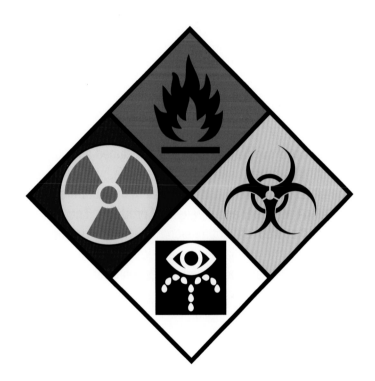

To my wonderful husband and children

Publishing Team

Adam Fanucci (illustration & graphics)
Tae W Moon (design/production)
Joshua Weikersheimer (publishing direction)

Notice

Trade names for equipment and supplies described are included as suggestions only. In no way does their inclusion constitute an endorsement of preference by the Author or the ASCP. The Author and ASCP urge all readers to read and follow all manufacturers' instructions and package insert warnings concerning the proper and safe use of products. The American Society of Clinical Pathology, having exercised appropriate and reasonable effort to research material current as of publication date, does not assume any liability for any loss or damage caused by errors and omissions in this publication. Readers must assume responsibility for complete and thorough research of any hazardous conditions they encounter, as this publication is not intended to be all-inclusive, and recommendations and regulations change over time.

American Society for
Clinical Pathology
Press

Printed in Hong Kong

13 12 11 10 9

Laboratory Safety

A Self-Assessment Workbook

Diane L Davis, PhD, MT(ASCP)SC,SLS, CLS(NCA)

Professor of Clinical Laboratory Science
Health Sciences Department, Salisbury University
Salisbury, MD

Contents

AN OVERVIEW OF CLINICAL LABORATORY SAFETY

PURPOSE OF THIS TEXT

1. In a teaching laboratory, a 22 year old clinical laboratory science student acquired *Salmonella typhi* which caused an intestinal abscess. In addition to antibiotic therapy, the abscess required two separate surgeries for drainage and creation of a temporary diverting ileostomy. The student also required hyperalimentation but was able to completely recover in six months, at which time the ileostomy was reversed. (*Laboratory Medicine*, "Typhoid Fever Acquired in a Medical Technology Teaching Laboratory", volume 19, number 3, March 1988.)

2. Prior to 1976, sodium azide was used extensively as a preservative in laboratory reagents and was disposed of in ordinary plumbing. Copper and lead pipes cause the formation of metal azides which are more explosive than nitroglycerin. Therefore, serious explosions resulted from the manipulation of pipes and drains in laboratories when this disposal hazard was unrecognized. (*Clinical Laboratory Safety,* by Susan L. Rose, J. B. Lippincott, 1984.)

3. "Eighty ml of diazomethane dissolved in ether detonated in a domestic-type refrigerator. The door blew open, the frame bowed out, and the plastic lining ignited, causing a heavy blanket of soot to be deposited far down the adjoining corridor." (*From Health Care Facilities,* NFPA 99, National Fire Protection Association, Quincy, MA 02269, 1990.)

4. A research facility hired students for the summer, and one of the jobs given to six students was to clean out a closed satellite lab. The students were given minimal instruction and were left to move equipment and dispose of chemical and biological wastes. When they were cleaning out the cold room, someone left some chemicals on the bench top at room temperature, and the students all went to lunch. A short time later, the chemicals exploded and a terrible odor necessitated evacuation of the entire building. The students had been working in the room without protective gear and would have been seriously injured if they had not been out of the room. (*Laboratory Medicine.* "In My Opinion," volume 27, number 5, May 1996.)

5. On September 20, 2000 an MRI technician died from a nitrogen gas leak at New York Presbyterian Hospital. Nitrogen is colorless and odorless, and levels incompatible with life can accumulate without anyone being able to detect it. (www.healthsafetyinfo.com, accessed September 28, 2000.)

6. A worker thought a can of sodium had completely converted to sodium hydroxide, so he decided to flush it with water. The remaining unconverted sodium reacted with the water and caused the can to explode. The resulting fire blocked the only door to the lab, so workers evacuated out the windows. Fortunately, the windows were on the first floor and a few weeks previously the security bars over the windows had been removed due to the safety department's insistence. (Furr, A. K., editor. *CRC Handbook of Laboratory Safety,* 5th Edition, CRC Press, 2000.)

The incidents above are real, and because all hazards can never be completely eliminated, lab accidents still occur regularly. Laboratory workers are often under pressure to produce results in a hurry, and they can become careless or be tempted to take short cuts. Even when laboratory workers are not under pressure, the familiarity with routine hazards may desensitize even conscientious workers to the need for appropriate caution.

The purpose of this text is to heighten the reader's awareness of safety issues and to promote the ability to:

1. Understand and apply the appropriate regulatory and professional requirements for safety, maintaining adequate records and documentation.

2. Establish standard operating procedures that routinely incorporate the appropriate safety techniques, monitor the management of hazards in a laboratory and properly dispose of waste.

3. Recognize potential safety hazards and/or hazards revealed through incidents and take action to prevent future accidents.

4. React promptly and correctly once an accident occurs.

This text is not intended to be all-inclusive. There are many special situations which require procedures not discussed herein, and this text will only address the most common hazards in a laboratory. Information cited in the text on the many safety regulations is accurate at the time of publication, but the reader should always check the most current version of any regulation before making changes in the laboratory. Resources from which current and additional information can be obtained are included in Appendix 1 at the end of this text. The reader is encouraged to consult these or other sources before embarking on any procedure which is unknown and therefore potentially dangerous.

LEARNING OBJECTIVES

Following study of the material contained in this text, the reader should be able to:

LEARNING OBJECTIVES (CONTINUED)

1. Explain the importance of each individual assuming some responsibility for complying with safety rules regulations

2. Discuss aspects of laboratory safety management such as the appointment of a laboratory safety officer, a safety committee and incident review committee and how these entities continuously formulate procedures, train staff, analyze incidents and reformulate procedures as necessary

3. Explain the role of the following governmental bodies/ regulations in laboratory safety:

   a. US Occupational Safety and Health Administration (OSHA), describing the requirements for employers under the general duty clause and with regard to the following OSHA standards and advisories:

      i. Hazard Communication Standard ("Right to Know")

      ii. Hazardous Chemicals in Laboratories Standard

      iii. Bloodborne Pathogens Standard (including changes mandated by Needlestick Safety and Prevention Act)

      iv. Formaldehyde Standard

      v. Personal Protective Equipment Standard

      vi. Control of Hazardous Energy Standard ("Lock out/tag out")

      vii. Ergonomics advisories

      viii. Tuberculosis advisories

   b. US Environmental Protection Agency (EPA)/ Resource Recovery and Conservation Act (RRCA)

   c. US Nuclear Regulatory Commission (NRC)

   d. US Department of Transportation (DOT)/ US Postal Service

   e. US Centers for Disease Control and Prevention (CDC)/National Institute for Occupational Safety and Health (NIOSH)/National Institutes of Health (NIH)

   f. US Department of Homeland Security (DHS)

4. Discuss fire hazards with respect to:

   a. the fire "quadrahedron"

   b. classes of fires, including examples of each class

   c. National Fire Protection Association (NFPA) graphic symbols for each class

   d. precautions for each class and fire prevention in general

   e. appropriate means to extinguish each class

   f. education and training

   g. lab design and design of optimal evacuation routes

   h. fire safety equipment, specifically the correct use of:

      i. fire alarms

      ii. sand buckets

      iii. fire extinguishers, including the "PASS" acronym

      iv. fire hoses

      v. fire blankets

      vi. respirators

      i. evacuation and emergency plans in cases of fire, including the "RACE" acronym

5. Discuss chemical safety with respect to:

   a. labeling of reagents, including interpretation of the following labeling systems:

      i. National Fire Protection Association (NFPA) labeling system

      ii. Hazardous Materials Information System (HMIS)

      iii. Globally Harmonized System adopted by US Department of Transportation

   b. classes of chemical hazards, giving examples or definitions of each of the following:

    i.   corrosives

    ii.   ignitibles- flammables and combustibles

    iii.   health hazards- carcinogens, teratogens, mutagens, sensitizers, irritants, hepato-toxins, nephrotoxins, neurotoxins

    iv.   unstable or reactive compounds including explosives and oxidizers

    v.   incompatible mixtures

    vi.   chemicals of particular concern in histology/autopsy suites

c. procedures for using, handling and storing chemicals

d. security of materials from theft and terrorism

e. proper use and maintenance of a chemical fume hood

f. information on Material Safety Data Sheets (MSDS) and procedures to use the information

g. regulations for using chemicals, particularly hazardous mixtures

h. proper methods for disposing chemicals

i. protective wearing apparel

j. chemical spill protocols, including the "CLEAN" acronym

6. Discuss electrical safety with respect to:

a. nature of electricity, conductors, insulators and circuits

b. effects of electricity on the human body

c. circuit requirement for shocks and the physical consequences of shock

d. the five essential principles of safe practice with electricity, explaining and give examples of each:

    i.   insulation

    ii.   grounding

    iii.   guarding

    iv.   circuit protection devices to include fuses, circuit breakers and ground-fault interrupters

    v.   safe work practices to include "lock out/tag out," emergency generators and proper use of electrical equipment

e. identification and prevention of electrical hazards

7. Discuss equipment safety with respect to:

a. glassware safety

b. safety with sharps to include needles, scalpels, bone saws, etc

c. centrifuge safety

d. steam sterilizer (autoclave) safety

8. Discuss biological hazards with respect to:

a. the universal biohazard symbol - color, where/how to display

b. types of biological hazards, including:

    i.   classes of microbes - viruses, bacteria, prions, protozoa and fungi

    ii.   microbe sources

    iii.   fomites

    iv.   aerosols - how they occur, how they are prevented

    v.   spills

c. essential components of a biosafety program

d. definition of CDC/NIH biosafety levels and basic requirements at each level

e. definitions of NIH and World Health Organization (WHO) biosafety levels

f. important examples in each CDC/NIH biosafety level

g. identification of critical agents associated with bioterrorism and providing security

h. CDC Universal Precautions, Standard Precautions and Transmission-Based Precautions

i. examples of common hazards and situations

j. precautions used to reduce risk for each type of biohazard

k. precautions unique to autopsy suites and histology labs

l. precautions for working with animals in the lab

m. special issues regarding individual pathogens such as hepatitis B virus, human immunodeficiency virus, hepatitis C virus, infectious prions (such as Creutzfeldt-Jakob disease) and *Mycobacterium tuberculosis* to include:

    i. signs of infections

    ii. typical means of acquiring infection

    iii. vaccine availability

    iv. testing for presence of infection

    v. treatment of workers exposed to organism

    vi. applicable biosafety level

n. physical containment requirements including:

    i. appropriate manipulation techniques

    ii. biosafety cabinets - proper usage, maintenance, selection of correct type

    iii. protective wearing apparel

    iv. design of histology/autopsy suites

o. biohazard decontamination to include:

    i. chemical agents

    (1) low- , middle- and high-level disinfectants

    (2) sterilants

    (3) antiseptics

    (4) proper use of bleach as mid-level disinfectant (concentration, expiration)

    (5) debulking material and sufficient contact time

    ii. heat, pressure, autoclaving

    iii. radiation - ionizing and ultraviolet

    iv. special procedures for infectious prions

p. treatment of spills

q. treatment of accidental exposures

r. methods for disposing biohazards

9. Discuss compressed gases with respect to:

a. definition and characteristics of compressed gases

b. correct labeling and color coding of cylinders

c. hazards associated with compressed gases

d. methods of transport, storage, usage and inventory

e. installing and reading a regulator on a compressed gas tank

f. methods of handling empty and full tanks

g. special precautions with cryogenic gases and gases for medical use

10. Discuss radioactive materials with respect to:

a. definitions of terms including:

    i. alpha, beta and gamma radiation

    ii. rems

    iii. Curies and Becquerels

    iv. half-life

b. effects of radiation on the human body

c. precautions including correct shielding (lucite for beta and alpha, lead for gamma)

d. storage and usage

e. methods of disposal and spill cleanup

f. regulatory requirements and documentation

g. environmental and personnel monitoring

h. the universal radiation hazard symbol

i. the "ALARA" principle to keep radiation exposure "as low as reasonably achievable"

j. managing radiation exposure by time, shielding and distance

k. security of materials from theft and terrorism

11. Discuss laboratory waste and waste management to include:

a. listed wastes and characteristic wastes

b. EPA categories of waste generation

c. infectious and medical waste

d. radioactive waste, including "decay in storage"

e. general EPA and RCRA requirements

f. importance of tracking and keeping waste manifests

g. definition of "cradle to grave" responsibility

h. waste disposal in the sanitary sewer

i. waste minimization including segregation, planning, reducing, reusing and recycling

j. protocols for accidental waste release

12. Define and give examples of the following OSHA terms: administrative controls, engineering controls, work practice controls

13. List important basic work practices that are common to all labs, giving examples, to include:

a. no eating, drinking, smoking and other hand-to-face contact

b. complying with policies on protective equipment, personal dress, working alone, etc

c. refraining from jokes, horseplay, drugs and alcohol

d. maintaining a neat and clean work area, decontaminating and removing trash as required

e. decontaminating hands to include glove removal, handwashing techiques, alcohol gels and segregating sinks

14. Explain the purpose for and correct techniques to select, install, maintain and use safety equipment to include:

a. safety shower

b. eye wash

c. personal protective apparel/equipment

    i. goggles and safety glasses with side shields

    ii. face shields

    iii. lab coats and aprons

    iv. footwear

    v. gloves - latex, nitrile, vinyl, chemical-resistant

    vi. masks and respirators

    vii. ear plugs and muffs

d. chemical fume hood

e. biological safety cabinet

f. containers for sharps and broken glass

g. telephones

LEARNING OBJECTIVES (CONTINUED)

  h. signage, including recognition of relevant symbols (eyewash, shower, etc)

15. Discuss the causes, signs, symptoms and prevention strategies regarding latex allergies

16. Discuss the importance of filing an accident report, the information which should be included in such a report and the analysis and action that should take place after an accident

17. Outline how and when OSHA should receive accident reports and what forms should be used

18. List and describe the "Check, Call, Care" first steps to take when encountering an accident situation

19. Discuss basic first aid in the following categories:

  a. clearing the airway

  b. restoring breathing

  c. restoring circulation - cardiopulmonary resuscitation (CPR) or automated external defibrillator (AED)

  d. stopping bleeding

  e. treatment for shock

  f. treatment for wounds to include:

      i.   chemical and thermal burns

      ii. bone, muscle and joint injuries

      iii. eye injuries

      iv. cuts and punctures

  g. recognizing and/or treating heart attacks and strokes

20. Identify graphic symbols or universal symbols corresponding to the following:

  a. chemical hazards - flammables, oxidizers, corrosives, poisons, explosives, etc

  b. biohazard

  c. radiation hazard

  d. compressed gas hazard

  e. laser hazard

  f. personal protective equipment - gloves, goggles, glasses, lab coats, etc

  g. safety equipment - deluge shower, eyewash, fire extinguisher, fire blanket, etc

21.* Given the location and type of work that a lab does, list and justify the appropriate safety equipment and contents of first aid kits for that lab

22.* Given the location and type of work that a lab does, formulate laboratory protocols that meet all applicable safety standards

23.* Given an accident case history, list the precautionary measures that should have been taken to prevent the accident

24.* Given an accident situation, list the appropriate remedial actions that should be taken

*Denotes terminal objective. The terminal objective indicates what the learner should be able to do upon completion of the text.

Exercise 1

INTRODUCTION TO SAFETY

Safety in the laboratory is the responsibility of every person who uses the facility. This obligation includes not only creating a safe environment for colleagues but also considering the safety of others in the institution and community. Serious accidents can injure innocent occupants of a building that houses a laboratory, and careless disposal of hazardous wastes can contaminate the environment of an entire community. Safety is unequivocally a serious duty for each person who practices laboratory science.

Some studies indicate that "just knowing" the institution's safety policies is not enough to ensure that they will be followed. The best defenses against a job-related accident are concentration on the work at hand and an attitude that an accident is always possible, even in the most innocuous procedures. Henry states that "while inexperience may be a cause for some accidents, others may be a result of ignoring known risks, haste, carelessness, fatigue or mental preoccupation" (*Clinical Diagnosis and Management by Laboratory Methods,* 2001).

An important first step toward safety in the work environment is strict compliance with standards established by regulatory/governmental bodies, research institutions and professional organizations.

Based on proper recommendations and requirements, procedures must be established, followed by adequate training and monitoring of all personnel. These actions will greatly decrease the chance of an accident occurring but must be regarded as the *minimal* requirements. Each facility has its own unique set of circumstances that may not be adequately addressed in recommendations from any organization. These circumstances should be scrutinized by safety management staff for additional necessary measures.

Each facility should have a person or a committee responsible for safety. In smaller laboratories, the laboratory director could handle the responsibility for safety, but in larger, more complex facilities it is more useful to have a safety committee consisting of representatives of each area. The person(s) who is (are) responsible for laboratory safety must have access to all recent and pertinent regulations/ recommendations and should have the freedom, authority, and budget to formulate policies based on the most current information. After implementation and personnel training, the procedures must be periodically reviewed, particularly if regulations have changed or if incidents have occurred. The safety officer and/or the safety committee should conduct periodic surveys/inspections of the facility (sometimes called "safety audits") to ensure that staff members are properly complying with procedures and that there are no unexpected hazards evident. "Near-miss" events and accidents, while unfortunate, are excellent opportunities to evaluate the validity of safety procedures and to identify areas that need improvement. As illustrated in **Figure 1-1**, safety must be viewed as a continuous process, rather than an event, as regulations change and accidents point out flaws in the current system.

The remainder of this exercise outlines some of the many bodies that set standards for safety. Some of these bodies have legal regulatory authority and others do not. It is helpful at this point to introduce terms that are often used in relation to meeting safety standards.

Local, state, and federal governments pass laws with general principles that must be followed. Many of these laws create and/or authorize regulatory agencies that make the detailed regulations or standards that ensure compliance with the law. These standards and regulations can be enforced by the agencies through licensing and/or mandatory inspections. Often, these agencies require licenses to perform specific operations. Because different governments can write laws that overlap in function, agencies may decide to grant equivalency or reciprocity to other government agencies. For example, the Environmental Protection Agency (EPA) regulates waste, but if a state has stricter waste regulations, then the EPA may grant equivalency to holders of the state license, and only the state regulations must be followed. By contrast, research institutions and professional organizations issue standards (not regulations) that are adopted entirely voluntarily. Instead of a license, these organizations can offer accreditation or certification. Laboratories can voluntarily conform to the standards, submit to an inspection, and gain the prestige of being accredited by some of these organizations.

Compliance measures are often characterized as engineering, administrative, or work practice controls. In general, an engineering control is a physical set-up or device that separates workers' exposure to a hazard. A chemical fume hood is an engineering control. Administrative controls are management techniques, such as employee scheduling, which minimize places and times that workers are exposed to a hazard. Finally, work practice controls are specifications to perform certain tasks in particular ways to minimize or eliminate hazards. Pipetting acid inside a sink next to an eye wash is a work practice control.

At the time of publication, every effort was made to be sure the descriptions of the regulations herein were accurate. The reader should be aware that

Lab Manager receives/obtains all regulations.

↓

Lab Supervisors/Safety Officer/Safety Committee- exact structure depends on size of lab.

↓

Establish Standard Operating Procedures (SOP), Chemical Hygiene Plan, Exposure Control Plan, etc.

↓

Train staff, document training, assess competency.

↓

Document accidents, near-misses and staff response to each.

↓

Analyze accidents for cause, staff training and prevention issues. Re-assess risk periodically even in the absence of incidents.

↓

Prevent incident recurrence - re-formulate SOP, re-train staff. New policies for new risks.

↓

SAFETY MANAGEMENT IS A CONTINUOUS PROCESS, NOT AN EVENT.

Figure 1-1

the regulatory agencies should be consulted for the most current version of each regulation before substantive changes in policy are made. Many changes in safety policy require considerable financial commitment and inconvenience, and safety officers will be most persuasive to managers if they can cite current regulations and specifications as justification for any changes. In many cases, safety officers may be asked to discriminate between the "nice to do" and "need to do" procedures. Laboratory hazards must be reduced to the least that are reasonably achievable, and safety officers must become skilled in risk assessment to determine the actual level of danger in each situation.

PART I: UNITED STATES REGULATORY AGENCIES WITH LEGAL JURISDICTION OVER LABORATORIES

A. Occupational Safety and Health Administration

The primary federal law dealing with safety in the workplace is the Occupational Safety and Health Act of 1970. Section 5(a)(1)of the act, known as "the general duty clause," states:

> **"Each employer – (1) shall furnish to each of his employees employment and a place of employment which are free from recognized hazards that are causing or are likely to cause death or serious physical harm to his employees; (2) shall comply with occupational safety and health standards promulgated under this Act.**
>
> **Each employee shall comply with occupational safety and health standards and all rules, regulations, and orders issued pursuant to this Act which are applicable to his own actions and conduct."**

The Act requires that employers minimize or eliminate hazards in the workplace and that employees follow the safety protocols set forth by the employers. The law created within the US Department of Labor a new regulatory agency, the Occupational Safety and Health Administration (OSHA), to oversee the establishment of safety standards for facilities, equipment, and procedures and to enforce adherence to those standards. An individual state may form its own occupational safety body if its requirements are as strict or stricter than the federal requirements. Approximately half of the states have elected to do this, and safety management staff must obtain information from the regulatory body under which they are operating. Laboratories in a state with an OSHA-accepted safety body are directly accountable for state regulations, not federal.

In general, OSHA requires employers to have a comprehensive safety policy which provides employees with appropriate safety equipment, adequate safety training, and free medical care in the event of an incident on the job. OSHA has posters that must be displayed in the workplace to inform employees of their rights. An important required poster, 3165, (see Appendix 2) and is easily obtained at www.osha.gov. Training sessions must be held during paid working hours and must be at an appropriate educational/language level for each employee. Documentation of all activities (hazard correction, training session topics, attendance roster for safety training, medical follow-up, accident investigation, and so on) is extremely critical. By law, safety training records must be kept for 3 years and overall employee records must be kept for the duration of employment plus 30 years. This is necessary to provide information in the event that an employee experiences a condition in the future that may be job-related. OSHA has also established guidelines for which incidents in these records are reportable to OSHA either immediately or within a specified time frame. More information on accidents and reporting is in Exercise 12.

If workers have complaints about uncorrected hazardous conditions or suspect that illness may be job-related, they should attempt to work with their employers. However, if they are not satisfied with the resolution of the issue, they have a legal right to report it to the local OSHA office. Employer retaliation or discrimination toward employees who report hazardous conditions is prohibited by law. As needed or after complaints, OSHA inspects working areas and issues citations to employers who fail to comply with the minimum safety regulations. OSHA does not accept expense or inconvenience as an adequate reason for failure to adopt an appropriate safety protocol. OSHA fines can be thousands of dollars per violation, so it is essential that laboratories comply with OSHA standards not only to make the workplace safe but also to avoid devastating financial penalties.

There are 2 general categories of OSHA standards. The first spells out requirements in great detail. Examples include safety showers which must be 100 feet or 10 seconds from any point in the laboratory and standards for safety glasses specifying the type of material to be used, the thickness of the material, the presence of side shields, and so on. Compliance with such standards is merely a matter of implementing the provisions or purchasing products manufactured to OSHA standards.

The second type of standard is a performance standard. The Bloodborne Pathogens Standard described later in this exercise is an excellent example of such a standard. It stipulates that employers must prevent employees from being exposed to human blood and body fluids. It does not specify the means by which facilities accomplish this goal, only that the goal be achieved. Therefore, one facility may elect to purchase work

shields behind which employees can work, and another facility may choose to dress employees in gowns, masks, and goggles.

A brief word of caution: Strict compliance with all published OSHA standards does not guarantee that OSHA cannot levy fines against an institution. Under its "general duty clause" of ensuring a safe working environment, OSHA can inspect and potentially issue fines based on obvious hazards for which standards do not yet exist. OSHA standards take time to develop into final form, but this does not absolve employers from doing what they can to abate a hazard before the final rule. Most wise employers, especially at high-risk facilities, immediately implement many proposed OSHA standards even without the final rule. For example, in recent years, workplace violence (homicides, assaults, etc) has been on the rise. Following OSHA's recommendation, many employers have instituted workplace violence prevention programs which include security provisions to protect against terrorism even though a specific standard for such is not in force.

The 6 OSHA standards and 1 pending standard described herein have significant impact on the clinical laboratory. Additional OSHA standards are discussed elsewhere. Postal and Web site addresses for OSHA appear in Appendix 1. Regional and state OSHA offices should be consulted by those operating under their auspices. In addition, OSHA provides "quick starts" for compliance associated with various industries. The link associated for health care may be useful (accessed February 19, 2008):

www.osha.gov/dcsp/compliance_assistance/quick-starts/health_care/hc_step1.html.

HAZARD COMMUNICATION STANDARD (CFR 1910.1200)

This standard requires that employers and industries inform employees about the chemicals to which they are exposed on the job and report for public record the chemicals they are disposing of in the environment. It has been referred to as the "Right to Know" standard. Every hazardous chemical used in a laboratory must have a material safety data sheet (MSDS) on file, which is accessible to the worker. An MSDS contains data on the hazards, composition, handling methods, and disposal of a particular chemical. (A sample MSDS is included in Exercise 3.) It must be documented that all workers have been informed of what chemicals are in the laboratory, where the MSDS's are located, how to handle the chemicals safely and what rights they have under the OSHA standard. Chemical mixtures that contain <1.0% of a hazardous chemical or <0.1% of a carcinogen are exempt, but this should be documented. Manufacturers will generally provide letters stating that products are exempt from MSDS requirements and these should be kept with the MSDS's for easy access.

HAZARDOUS CHEMICALS IN LABORATORIES (CFR 1910.1450)

The unique nature of laboratory manipulation of chemicals led to the implementation of this standard to address issues not adequately treated by the Hazard Communication Standard and other OSHA standards. At its inception, OSHA focused primarily on regulating large industries, and chemical manipulation in many of these facilities involves large amounts of a limited variety of chemicals. By contrast, laboratories handle smaller amounts of a vast array of chemicals, and many of the OSHA standards that had been written for industries did not easily apply.

The major requirement of this standard is the development and implementation of a chemical hygiene plan (CHP). A CHP must address virtually every aspect of the procurement, storage, handling, and disposal of chemicals in use in a facility. Exposure to chemicals must be minimized by establishment of standard procedures, requirements for personal protective equipment, engineering controls (fume hoods, air handlers, etc) and waste disposal procedures. For some chemicals, the environment must be monitored for levels that require action or medical attention. Procedures to obtain free medical care for work-related exposures must be stated. Finally, the means to administer the plan must be specified. Responsible persons for procurement and placement of MSDS's, organizing training sessions, monitoring of employee work practices, and annual revision of the CHP must be named. Additional information is provided in Exercise 3.

BLOODBORNE PATHOGENS (CFR 1910.1030)

This standard requires that a facility establish an exposure control plan (ECP) to minimize employee exposure to human blood and body fluids. This plan is similar to the CHP in that every aspect of employee contact with human materials must be addressed. Many provisions are identical, including requirements for personal protective equipment, engineering controls, training, medical care, and administration of the plan.

Major bloodborne pathogens of concern are human immunodeficiency virus (HIV), hepatitis B and C viruses, and Creutzfeldt-Jacob agent. Unique to ECP's is the stipulation that all employees with potential exposure to blood and body fluids be offered at no charge a vaccine against hepatitis B within 10 days of hire. Employees refusing the vaccine must sign a waiver. ECP's also must contain a task assessment in which the amount and types of potential exposures must be evaluated for every job category. The assessment must also state what measures will be taken to prevent the exposures from occurring. OSHA requires that "universal precautions" be used; in other words, every exposure is potentially infectious and must be prevented. Universal, standard, and transmission-based precautions and other information on biohazards will be discussed more thoroughly in Exercise 5.

On November 6, 2000, the Needlestick Safety and Prevention Act imposed additional requirements under the OSHA Bloodborne Pathogens Standard. All facilities must examine procedures that use needles and sharps to determine how safety devices such as self-sheathing needles can be incorporated to minimize injuries from contaminated sharps. There are documentation requirements for injuries caused by sharps, whether or not they are contaminated with blood and body fluids. More information on safety with sharps is contained in Exercise 4.

FORMALDEHYDE STANDARD (CFR 1910.1048)

Formaldehyde (the major ingredient in formalin) is used as a tissue preservative. It is an irritant and can cause allergic reactions (a sensitizer). Further, it has been implicated in causing cancer. This standard seeks to minimize formaldehyde exposure and requires monitoring of the environment for formaldehyde fumes. Areas that use formaldehyde-containing reagents such as surgical pathology, histology, and autopsy suites have to be sure that the chemical fume hoods/backdraft vents are in proper working order and that the ventilation systems provide an adequate number of air exchanges to ensure that the permissible exposure limits of formaldehyde are not exceeded.

PERSONAL PROTECTIVE EQUIPMENT STANDARD (CFR 1910.132)

The aforementioned standards require personal protective equipment for chemical and biological hazards, but the Personal Protective Equipment Standard is broader in that it recognizes these hazards as well as physical hazards such as heat (like Bunsen burners), light (such as lasers), sharps (needles, scalpels) and electricity. It requires a hazard assessment of the workplace, a written hazard certification, supplying the correct equipment, and training employees to use it. In general, equipment must comply with requirements set forth by the American National Standards Institute (ANSI). Specifications exist for gloves, goggles, face shields, helmets, footwear, respirators, and so on. Additional information is provided in Exercise 10.

OCCUPATIONAL EXPOSURE TO TUBERCULOSIS STANDARD (CFR 1910.1035)

A serious upswing in the number of tuberculosis cases caused by bacteria resistant to multiple drugs motivated OSHA to formulate a separate standard in 1997 for tuberculosis (TB) protection. Since then, the many protective measures that have been implemented have reduced the incidence of TB, so OSHA withdrew this standard in 2003. OSHA still recommends adherence to the guidelines of the Centers for Disease Control and Prevention (CDC), and the reader should refer to the United States Department of Health and Human Services Centers for Disease Control and Prevention (www.cdc.gov) 2005 publication discussed in Exercise 5.

ERGONOMICS

OSHA's definition of ergonomics:

> **"Ergonomics is a discipline that involves arranging the environment to fit the person in it. When ergonomics is applied correctly in the work environment, visual and musculoskeletal discomfort and fatigue are reduced significantly."**

20 to 40 inches

Proper position for using a computer

Figure 1-2

At the time of publication, the formal OSHA ergonomics standard was still withdrawn, but OSHA has made extensive recommendations on ergonomic safety issues on its Web site and in its publications. Various ergonomic work practices have potential application in the laboratory Some important issues are:

1. **Effects of long-term use of video display terminals (VDT's)** Increased use of computers in all areas of society makes this an issue to be seriously evaluated. Antiglare screens with adjustable positions are being used in many workplaces where employees spend many hours of the day using a computer. A screen slightly below eye level is easier to read than one above eye level. Users should look away from the screen every 15 minutes to reduce eye strain. In addition, as shown in **Figure 1-2**, users should be a proper distance away from the VDT (20 to 40 inches) with heads vertical, not at an angle. Users whose vision does not permit this distance may need to have their eyeglass prescription adjusted if the screen display cannot be altered.

2. **Hearing loss** The noise from all equipment being run simultaneously should not exceed 85 decibels over an 8-hour period. A general rule is that at 85 decibels one must virtually shout to be heard in conversation, so the noise level should be investigated.

3. **Cumulative trauma disorders caused by repetitive motion** Carpal tunnel syndrome may be a familiar example of this type of disorder. Excessive force for repetitive tasks and side-to-side twisting of the wrist should be avoided. Keyboarding and using a computer mouse are associated with repetitive task injury. There are specific recommendations for constructing workstations. For example, the position of the keyboard and computer mouse must be in the same plane as the hands when the elbows are at a 90° angle to avoid awkward wrist positions. The use of a wrist pad to maintain the proper position is shown in **Figure 1-3**. Repetitive use of pipetting devices can also cause injury. Several models of pipettes have been developed that fit more comfortably in the hand and require less twisting and/or force to operate. Use of these types of pipettes should be considered, especially for laboratories with a high volume of manual pipetting.

4. **Skeletomuscular disorders** Back strain and other skeletomuscular disorders are frequent reasons for job absenteeism. **Figure 1-4** To lift heavy objects, one should spread the legs shoulder-width apart for a wide base of support, face the object directly, bend at the knees, firmly hold the object close to the body with the chin

Use of a pad to maintain proper wrist position

Figure 1-3

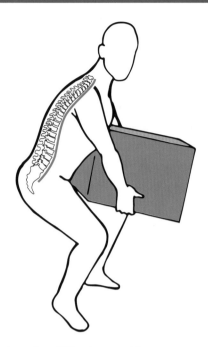

Proper poster when lifting heavy objects

Figure 1-4

tucked, maintain body symmetry, and lift with the legs avoiding any twisting motion. It is important not to ever lock the knees and to maintain body weight over the feet. The same principles hold when the object is put down. Heavy wheeled objects should be moved using a pushing rather than a pulling motion. Overhead lifting should be minimized since the leg muscles cannot be used and the back and arms must support the entire weight.

Laboratory chairs and computer workstations should be designed to be comfortable and supportive. Comfortable arm rests, back support, and laboratory chairs with 5 legs are recommended as shown in **Figure 1-5**. Chairs should be adjustable so that each user may get optimal support. There are microscopes available which prevent hunching over the eyepieces and have focus knobs positioned more comfortably for repeated wrist action (**Figure 1-6**). Using the telephone with the awkward posture shown in **Figure 1-7** can also cause problems, and if

employees must spend a significant amount of time on the phone, head sets should be considered. Even if a workstation is designed comfortably, staff should be encouraged to get up periodically and move around to avoid fatigue.

5. **Slips, trips, falls** Workspaces should be arranged so that they are easily navigable and that supplies, power cords, and furniture do not block the ordinary movement associated with work flow. Of course wet spills and other accidents must be cleaned up immediately or the affected area blocked off.

B. Environmental Protection Agency

Medical waste washing up on US beaches several years ago caused intense scrutiny of how laboratory waste was being discarded. The EPA regulates disposal of waste at a national level, and many state and local governments have additional restrictions on the manner in which laboratory

Chair with back support and 5 legs

Figure 1-5

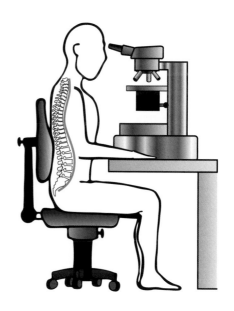

Proper posture when seated

Figure 1-6

waste can be disposed. Nothing should be flushed down the sink, thrown in the trash, incinerated, or autoclaved without checking with federal (EPA) and local laws. Laboratories should have protocols for waste disposal which comply with all governmental regulations, and these protocols should be reviewed before an item is discarded.

Some types of waste require removal by licensed waste handlers. Before sending waste out of the laboratory, however, it is important to thoroughly investigate the integrity of a waste handler. According to the Resource Conservation and Recovery Act (RCRA), every facility is responsible for its waste up until its *ultimate* disposal, regardless of the contractual obligations of the waste handler (the so-called "cradle to grave" principle). Huge penalties for improper disposal can be levied against institutions because of the damage that can be done

Improper posture for telephone use

Figure 1-7

to the community and the natural environment. Additional information is provided in Exercise 8.

C. Nuclear Regulatory Commission

The Nuclear Regulatory Commission (NRC) is responsible for the licensing and inspection of facilities handling radioactive materials. State and local governments may have additional restrictions on the use and handling of radioactivity which should be investigated in addition to compliance with NRC licensure. In general, the amount of radioactivity in the clinical laboratory is very small and minimally hazardous. This usually qualifies clinical laboratories for an NRC general license that is only slightly restrictive. Additional information is provided in Exercise 7.

D. United States Department of Transportation and US Postal Service

Transport and shipping of hazardous substances is regulated by the Department of Transportation (DOT) and US Postal Service (USPS). Many laboratory items are chemical, biological, or radioactive hazards that require special shipping and handling. If there is doubt about how to ship any item from a laboratory, DOT regulations should be consulted and/or help requested from the USPS. Penalties for noncompliance are very strict because of the risk of injury to innocent people who handle or open a hazardous package. If a private/commercial company is being used, its own specifications may include a policy against shipping hazardous material, so clear communication with these carriers is also essential.

In general, nonbreakable, leak-proof containers should be used. If breakable items must be shipped, they should be thoroughly padded and sealed before shipping. Liquid materials should be packed with enough absorbent material to soak up

leakage of the entire package. In some cases, such as shipping of biohazardous specimens, primary, secondary and tertiary containers are necessary to guard against leakage. The packages also must be clearly labeled as to the nature of the hazard within. DOT has certain codes for chemical materials, and the universal biohazard and radiation symbols can be used for dangerous biological and radioactive materials, respectively. **Figure 1-6** is an example.

On June 2, 2006, DOT published important revisions to 49 CFR Parts 171, 172, 173, and 175 which regulate the transportation of infectious substances. A link to a document containing the revisions is in Appendix 1. In essence, labeling requirements were changed to harmonize DOT regulations with United Nations and International Air Transport Association (IATA) regulations. Although USPS is not subject to DOT regulations, the departments are in substantial agreement. USPS published new regulations on November 1, 2006, and on September 25, 2007, published guidelines for mailing regulated medical waste, including sharps (39 CFR 111). The specifications from each agency are very complicated and include details such as the size of the package, labels that must be present, categories of infectious substances, the volume of infectious substance permitted, and information required on the packing slip. DOT labeling for chemicals will be discussed in Exercise 3. In September 2006, a new common shipping manifest for waste was issued that is now required by both DOT and EPA in all 50 states. The new manifest is in Appendix 3, and additional discussion of waste transportation is in Exercise 8. The reader is encouraged to become thoroughly trained in the exact regulations before attempting to ship any hazardous substance.

Both DOT and USPS recognize essentially the same three categories of biohazards. A good summary is the USPS Mailability Standard 601 (accessed February 19, 2008):

http://pe.usps.gov/text/dmm300/601.htm#wp1103548.

"Category A: An infectious substance transported in a form capable of causing permanent disability or life-threatening or fatal disease in otherwise healthy humans or animals when exposure occurs. Category A infectious substances are not mailable. A Category A infectious substance is assigned the identification number UN 2814 or UN 2900, based on the known medical history or symptoms of the source patient or animal, endemic local conditions, or professional judgment concerning the individual circumstances of the source human or animal.

Category B: An infectious substance that does not meet the criteria for inclusion in Category A. A mailpiece known or suspected to contain a Category B infectious substance must bear the proper shipping name "Biological substance, Category B" on the address side of the mailpiece and must be assigned to and marked with identification number UN 3373 or, for regulated medical waste and sharps medical waste, identification number UN 3291.

Specimens not being tested for infectious disease would usually be considered exempt and not subject to the labeling requirements for Category B substances, but they must be labeled "exempt human specimen."

Both Category B hazards and exempt specimens must be packaged as shown in **Figure 1-6**.

E. Clinical Laboratory Improvement Amendments of 1988 (CLIA '88)

The original Clinical Laboratory Improvement Act was passed in 1967. Two decades later, certain problems with quality of results from some clinical laboratories drove Congress to update CLIA '67

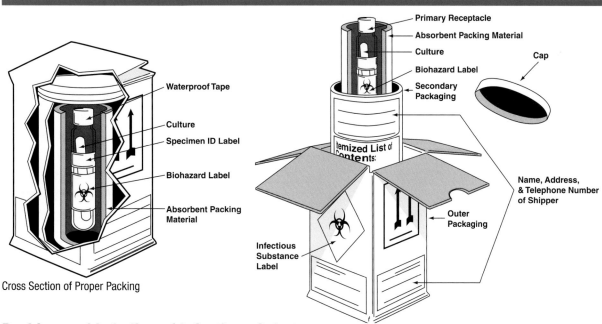

Cross Section of Proper Packing

Packing and Labeling of Infectious Substances

Triple packaging, absorbent material and proper labeling for shipping biohazardous materials (adapted from www.cdc.gov)

Figure 1-6

with a new and more stringent package of regulations (CLIA '88). This set of amendments governs all clinical laboratories. CLIA '88 empowers the Secretary of Health and Human Services to set laboratory and personnel standards (especially with regard to quality assurance and proficiency testing), to grant licensure, to perform inspections, and to invoke penalties for noncompliance. Small laboratories such as those in physicians' offices which perform tests that are "so simple and accurate as to render the likelihood of erroneous results negligible (CLIA '88)" may be granted waivers. Waivers to CLIA '88 licensure do not exempt a laboratory from compliance with safety standards.

F. US Department of Homeland Security

Potential acts of terrorism take many forms, and the Department of Homeland Security (DHS) is the central coordinating authority for antiterrorism measures in the United States. Laboratories can house chemicals and biological agents, so they are potential targets. DHS has developed standards for hazardous chemicals (further discussed in Exercise 3), and it supports bioterrorism standards from entities such as the Centers for Disease Control and the US Department of Agriculture. Laboratories may also need to implement many protocols for securing physical facilities and screening people. Even if laboratories do not possess particularly hazardous materials, many facilities could be targets for bombs or hostage situations, and the DHS is a good source for facility protocols. An example is the DHS Bomb Threat checklist in Appendix 4. The document is useful and free, and it contains information that is not readily apparent, such as the need to turn off all electronics/cell phones because they could be used as detonation devices during a bomb threat event. As a routine part of safety evaluation, clinical laboratories should consider the general security of the facility as well their ability to respond during emergencies and terrorism events

with appropriate specimen collection, handling, and testing.

PART II: PROFESSIONAL/ RESEARCH BODIES FOR VOLUNTARY COMPLIANCE

A. Centers for Disease Control and Prevention and National Institute for Occupational Safety and Health

The CDC conducts extensive research and monitoring of infectious diseases in the United States and throughout the world. Although it does not directly regulate most laboratories, its definitions of minimal accepted practice for biohazard handling are generally recognized by OSHA and other regulatory agencies. Barring other local and special regulations, it is prudent laboratory policy to practice the CDC recommendations for biohazards. A joint publication from the CDC and the National Institutes of Health (NIH) entitled "Biosafety in the Microbiological and Biomedical Laboratories" is an excellent source for the definition of biosafety levels and containment procedures for specific organisms. Extensive materials at www.cdc.gov can be downloaded at no charge, including virtually all of the CDC publications cited in this work. The National Institute for Occupational Safety and Health (NIOSH) is an important division of the CDC with regard to safety in the workplace, and a great deal of useful information can also be obtained at no charge at the NIOSH Web site. Addresses and contact information for both the CDC and NIOSH are listed in Appendix 1, and biohazard handling is further discussed in Exercise 5.

The CDC also coordinates the national Laboratory Response Network (LRN), which organizes medical laboratories in emergency events. In addition to the

DHS mentioned earlier, the CDC is a good resource for emergency response protocols for laboratories.

B. National Institutes of Health

Many of the health issues studied at the National Institutes of Health (NIH) relate to occupational illness, including the ergonomics issues discussed before. It is a valuable resource for new information on improving health and safety which may not yet be incorporated in OSHA standards.

C. National Fire Protection Association

The National Fire Protection Association (NFPA) publishes numerous, varied, and extremely useful publications. These publications provide fire prevention information for laboratory problems such as chemicals, electricity, and compressed gases as well as specifications for facility design and personnel training. Because the NFPA is a private professional organization, there is a charge for many of their publications. Additional information on fire safety is contained in Exercise 2.

D. Voluntary Accrediting Bodies

Many independent agencies that inspect hospitals and laboratories, such as the College of American Pathologists (CAP) and the Joint Commission (formerly JCAH), have safety standards that are useful guidelines for formulating policy and require that laboratories have protocols for emergency operations.

PART III: TRAINING

All staff must undergo thorough training in laboratory protocols on hiring or when procedures substantively change. Training materials must be at a language and educational level appropriate for each staff category, and trainers must hold appropriate credentials, as required. Generally, there is a common knowledge base for all employees (fire, first aid, accident reporting, etc) and then additional training can be tailored to particular job categories. At a minimum, annual updates are required, but they are not generally as detailed as initial training. In all cases, training should be documented, and staff should take a test after training to demonstrate competency. Staff must read employee handbooks and safety procedures and sign a form acknowledging that they have read and understood the material they have received.

Summary Table: Safety Regulatory and Accrediting Bodies

Topic	Comments
Compulsory regulatory terminology	Law, regulation, standard, license, inspection, reciprocity, equivalency
Voluntary accreditation terminology	Standard, inspection, accreditation, certification
Compliance measures	Engineering, administrative and work practice controls
Regulatory bodies with legally enforceable requirements	State and local jurisdictions may have additional requirements.
OSHA	Authority to insure safety in the workplace
	1. Hazard Communication Standard
	2. Hazardous Chemicals in Laboratories Standard
	3. Bloodborne Pathogens Standard/ Needlestick Safety
	4. Formaldehyde Standard
	5. Personal Protective Equipment Standard
	6. Tuberculosis Standard- withdrawn 12/31/2003 - see CDC
	7. Ergonomics recommendations
EPA	Authority to regulate waste disposal under RCRA.
NRC	Authority to regulate radiation handling and disposal.
DOT/U.S. Postal Service	Authority to regulate shipping and transportation of hazards
CLIA 1988	Law that regulates clinical labs
US Dept of Homeland Security	Coordinates general security and standards for at-risk facilities
Bodies with non-enforceable, voluntary standards	It is highly advisable to adopt these standards on a voluntary basis to improve safety
CDC	Standards for handling infectious microorganisms
NIH/NIOSH	Standards for occupational health and safety
NFPA	Standards for fire safety
Others	Joint Commission and CAP for clinical labs, for example

Exercise 1
Self-Evaluation Questions

1. ___ What is the first thing an employee should do if he or she finds an unsafe working condition?

    a. Report it to the supervisor
    b. Report it to the local OSHA office
    c. Assume that the supervisor will take care of it
    d. Conceal it so that OSHA does not issue a citation
    e. Ask other employees what they are doing to correct the problem

2. ___ How does OSHA govern the health and safety of employees?
    i. Sets minimum standards for performing hazardous jobs
    ii. Issues citations to employers who do not comply with standards
    iii. Inspects laboratories to ensure that they meet safety standards
    iv. Ensures that laboratory personnel are qualified to perform the tests they are doing

    a. i, ii, and iii
    b. ii, iii, and iv
    c. i and iii
    d. ii and iv
    e. All of the above

3. Match the OSHA Standard below to its major provisions. Choose 2 correct answers per item.

    ___, ___ Hazard Communication

    ___, ___ Hazardous Chemicals in Laboratories

    ___, ___ Bloodborne Pathogens

    a. Hepatitis B vaccine
    b. "Right to Know"
    c. Chemical Hygiene Plan
    d. MSDS's
    e. Exposure Control Plan
    f. Environmental chemical monitoring

4. ___ When lifting a heavy object you should:

    a. Bend at the waist
    b. Bend at the knees
    c. Hold the object with both arms extended away from the body
    d. b and c
    e. a and c

5. ___ Which of the following correctly describes the correct way to use a computer?

    a. Use a chair with a minimum of 3 wheeled legs
    b. Position the monitor so that you have to look up and not down
    c. Position the monitor so that it is not any farther away than 20 inches
    d. Maintain your arm at a 90° angle with your wrist straight and supported
    e. All of the above

6. ___ Your laboratory has added a new test which requires the use of a new chemical. Before you can dispose of this chemical, you must check:

    a. EPA regulations
    b. State and local regulations
    c. The MSDS for the chemical
    d. The facility's Chemical Hygiene Plan
    e. All of the above

7. ___ The most important reason to analyze accidents and near-misses is to:

    a. Discipline employees who are involved
    b. Try to hide the deficiencies from OSHA
    c. Prevent the accident from happening again
    d. Reduce worker's compensation insurance premiums
    e. Justify the purchase of equipment to respond to the accident next time

8. Match the entity below to its function in setting standards for laboratories.

___ CDC	___ EPA	a. Waste disposal
		b. Research on occupational injury
___ NRC	___ NIH/NIOSH	c. Clinical laboratory licensure
		d. Fire prevention information
___ DOT/US Postal Service	___ NFPA	e. Handling biohazards
		f. Voluntary accrediting bodies
___ CLIA '88	___ CAP/Joint Commission	g. Licensure for handling radioactive materials
		h. Regulates shipping of hazardous materials

List the entities above which have legal enforcement authority over laboratories:

_____

List the entities above with which laboratories comply on a voluntary basis:

_____

9. ___ You must mail a serum specimen from a healthy adult to a laboratory for cholesetrol testing. What will you do?

    a. You will put the specimen into sealed primary and secondary containers
    b. You will add enough absorbent material to completely soak up the full volume of the specimen
    c. You will clearly label the outside carton with the appropriate cautionary symbols and messages
    d. All of the above
    e. You will find another means of transportation, as serum/blood specimens cannot be mailed in the United States

Exercise 2
FIRE SAFETY

Four things are required for a fire to begin: oxygen (or oxidizing agent), fuel, heat, and a self-perpetuating chemical chain reaction. This is the so-called "fire quadrahedron." This is an important concept because lack of any one of the 4 components will prevent a fire or extinguish an existing one.

FIRE HAZARDS

A fire hazard is a substance that is easily ignitible, and many materials used in laboratories fit this definition. Fire hazards are classified by fuel type, and the means of extinction and control are different for each type (**Table 2-1**). Detailed specifications for fire-safe laboratory design and practice are present in the National Fire Protection Association (NFPA) Standard 45, which is aimed at laboratories. Clinical laboratories may also find NFPA Standard 99 for Health Care Facilities and Clinical and Laboratory Standards Institute (CLSI) GP18-A2 "Laboratory Design" useful.

Class A: Ordinary Combustibles

Ordinary combustible solids include paper, wood, fabric, and plastic. (Fuels that burn and leave "ash" are usually Class A.) Prevention of an ordinary combustible fire in a laboratory is best accomplished by good housekeeping. Combustible material must be kept away from burners, hot plates, and other heat sources and stored in its proper place. Unnecessary material must be discarded, and all unnecessary clutter should be eliminated. Smoking in the laboratory is absolutely forbidden at all times because it is a potential ignition source not only for the ordinary combustibles but also for the many flammable solvents in use.

A Class A fire can be extinguished with water, a dry chemical extinguisher, or sand. A carbon dioxide (CO_2) extinguisher is not hazardous to the user for Class A fires, but it is not considered optimal because the fire can continue to smolder while the CO_2 gas dissipates.

Clothing fires are Class A fires. Persons with burning clothing can be wrapped in a fire blanket or some other large material like a curtain or a sheet

Table 2-1: Types of Fire Extinguishers

Class of fire	Traditional NFPA symbol	New NFPA symbol	Water Extinguishers	Dry Chemical and CO$_2$ Extinguishers
Ordinary combustibles: Class A	A — Ordinary Combustibles		YES	YES, BUT CO$_2$ NOT CONSIDERED OPTIMAL SINCE GAS DISSIPATES
Flammable liquids and gases: Class B	B — Flammable Liquids		NO (SPREADS LIQUID AND FIRE)	YES
Energized electrical equipment: Class C	C — Electrical Equipment		NO (RISK OF SHOCK)	YES
Combustible metals: Class D	D — Combustible Metals	not applicable	NO (INTENSIFIES FIRE)	NO SAND OR SPECIAL EXTINGUISHING AGENTS REQUIRED

and rolled on the floor to eliminate the source of oxygen. (Do not allow a person wrapped in a fire blanket to stand because that might lead to the "chimney effect" of rising heat.) If a safety shower is available and there are no chemicals or electricity to contraindicate its usage, a clothing fire can be effectively extinguished in the safety shower. Laboratory staff should be instructed to "stop, drop, and roll" if their clothing catches fire, but a person on fire may begin running away in a panic reaction. This only worsens the fire, and it is best to restrain the person with force and roll the body on the floor until fire equipment can be used.

Class B: Flammable Liquids and Gases

Class B fires in the home are typically caused by oil, grease, paint, or gasoline. (Liquids can "boil" so they are Class B fires.) In the laboratory many organic solvents and compressed gases are potential Class B fire hazards. The main cause of ignition and spread of solvent fires is vaporization of the fuel, allowing it to mix with oxygen in the air. When this occurs, any source of heat can complete the "fire quadrahedron."

Many solvents are highly volatile and form a substantial amount of vapors, even at room temperature. A solvent's flash point is the temperature at which there are enough vapors to form combustible, potentially explosive mixtures with the air at the solvent's surface. Organic solvents should be used and stored with a knowledge of their flash points. **Table 2-2** gives examples of some common flammable solvents and their flash points. Note that all of the solvents shown except xylene exceed their flash points at normal room temperature. Solvents are classified as hazards based on their flash points. Class I solvents have flash points <100°F (38°C), Class II solvents have flash points between 100°F (38°C) and 140°F (60°C), and Class III solvents have flash points that exceed 140°F (60°C). The most dangerous solvents have the lowest flash points.

In addition to flash point, the hazard of a flammable is also assessed by its Lower Explosion Limit (LEL) and Upper Explosion Limit (UEL). LEL is the minimum concentration of vapor in air required to ignite a flame. At low concentrations of a flammable vapor, there is insufficient fuel to sustain a flame. The UEL is the maximum concentration of vapor in air above which a flame cannot be ignited. At this level, there is too much fuel in relation to the oxygen to sustain a flame. Therefore, the lower the LEL and the higher the UEL, the more hazardous a flammable is. **Table 2-2** illustrates that ethyl ether is the most hazardous flammable of those shown as it has the lowest flashpoint and the widest LEL/UEL range. Isopropanol and methanol have identi-

cal flashpoints, but methanol is more hazardous because of its higher UEL.

Because many flash points are below room temperature, it may seem that refrigerators should be used to store solvents. However, many domestic refrigerators have motors, lights, and heating elements (in frost-free models) which could provide heat/sparks to ignite any vapors confined in the refrigerators. In addition, many domestic refrigerators have drains that could connect chemical spills with motor components. If refrigerators are used for storage, they should be explosion-proof models specially adapted to flammable storage according to NFPA guidelines and hard-wired (not plugged in) to electricity.

Volatile liquids should be kept away from heat sources, sunlight, and electrical switches. Flammables must only be used around nonsparking equipment and explosion-proof heat sources, never open flames. All flammables should be tightly sealed to prevent accumulation of vapors anywhere, but especially when stored in the refrigerator because vapors generally cannot escape a closed unit. Room temperature storage areas must be vented, and vented cabinets or fume hoods should be used to store the liquids. Also recommended are specially-designed flammable safety cans with spring-closing lids to contain vapors, valves to

Table 2-2: Common Flammable Solvents and Their Flash Points

Solvent	Flash point (°C)	Flash point (°F)	Upper Explosion Limit, %	Lower Explosion Limit,%
Acetone	-20	-4	3	13
Ethanol	17	62	3	19
Ethyl ether	-45	-49	2	36
Heptane	-4	25	1	7
Isopropanol	12	53	2	13
Methanol	12	53	7	36
Toluene	4	39	1	7
Xylene	25	77	1	7

relieve pressure, and flame arresters in spouts to dissipate point heat sources (see **Figure 2-1**).

Flammable storage is designed to isolate flammables from ignition sources, especially so that they do not worsen a fire outside the storage area. Bulk supplies of flammables should be kept in specially designed storage at all times, and only the amount needed for the immediate work to be done should be removed. The Occupational Safety and Health Administration (OSHA) and NFPA have standards for the use and storage of flammable liquids, including construction standards and maximum permissible amounts in various storage facilities. If an area lacks a fire protection system such as sprinklers, no more than 1 gallon can usually be kept on open shelving and up to 2 gallons per 100 ft^2 can be kept in a safety can or cabinet. These limits change based on the flash point of the flammables being stored and the amount of fire protection provided. In general, laboratories should only keep the minimal amount of flammable solvents and gases on the premises necessary for normal testing needs.

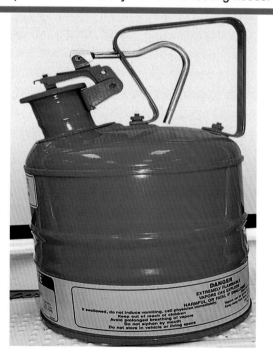

Flammable safety can

Figure 2-1

Small amounts of water-soluble flammables can sometimes be disposed of in the drain with cold water. Large amounts, however, must be stored in fire-safe containers until they can be picked up by a licensed waste-disposal firm which usually incinerates them under carefully controlled conditions.

In Exercise 10, alcohol-based hand gels will be discussed as a means to decontaminate hands without actual hand washing. Many medical facilities have installed numerous gel dispensers to reduce the spread of microbes. Unfortunately, the increased use of these alcohol-based gels has also resulted in an increase of small fires associated with them. Gel vapors are usually ignited by a spark from a device or an electrostatic spark, such as that created from walking across a carpet in low humidity. Staff who use the gels must be taught to let them dry thoroughly before using any electrical devices. Facilities that can maintain humidity over 50% will also reduce the risk.

Class B fires can be extinguished with the use of dry chemical or CO_2 extinguishers. Water should not be used because it can push the liquid and cause the fire to spread. In addition, many solvents are less dense than water and will float on top of it, continuing to burn.

Class C: Energized Electrical Equipment

Devices connected to a source of electricity are considered Class C fires. (Electrical equipment uses "Current" so they are Class C fires.) Frayed wires or malfunctioning equipment can provide the spark necessary to ignite flammable vapors or materials. A fire in or around equipment that is plugged in adds the hazard of electrical shock to fighting the fire. A non-electrical conductor must be used to extinguish Class C fires because conductors could carry the electricity back to fire fighter and cause electrical shock. Ordinary tap water contains ions which make it an excellent conductor, so water should never be used on a Class C fire. If it is possible, electrical power should be cut off from the area of the fire. If electrical power can be eliminated with certainty, then burning equipment can be considered a Class A fire and treated accordingly. If, however, there is any question that the equipment is energized, only dry chemical or CO_2 extinguishers should be used.

Class D: Combustible/Reactive Metals

Although rarely used, elemental metals such as magnesium, sodium, potassium, and lithium are not only combustible but also highly reactive, especially with water. For instance, pure sodium is stored in oil because it is capable of reacting with the water in ordinary environmental humidity. Logically, then, water and wet extinguishing agents must never be used on Class D fires. Therefore, these fires are difficult to control. In addition, they spread easily and could explode. Class D fires are controlled by scooping sand or dry-powder media onto the fire. It is important that buckets of sand stored in the laboratory for this purpose be checked periodically for the presence of cigarettes or other trash that tends to accumulate in them.

Class E: Uncontrollable

Class E fires cannot be put out or are likely to detonate and must be allowed to burn. An example might be a fire at a chemical factory. The only course of action is to evacuate and attempt to protect adjacent structures.

LABORATORY DESIGN AND EVACUATION ROUTES

Rarely does anyone have the luxury of designing a laboratory. However, there are some key elements to the floor plan that should be included in a new laboratory and adhered to even if the laboratory facility is inherited "as is."

The laboratory should have an adequate number of doors, exits, halls, and walk spaces to accommodate the number of workers who need to exit in the event of an evacuation. Exit signs, evacuation routes, and work spaces should all be well-lit, and emergency lighting should come on in the event of a power failure. This is particularly critical if the laboratory is housed in the basement and there are no windows. NFPA states that areas greater than 1000 square feet must have "at least two exit access doors remote from one another, one of which shall open directly onto a means of egress" (NFPA 99). The farthest point in the laboratory must be <75 feet from a door and hallways should be at least 96 inches across. Materials contained in exit corridors must not restrict the width of the passage and cannot be capable of feeding a fire (paper, coats, or trash). Walkways within occupied rooms should be at least 40 to 48 inches across, while storage rooms may have walkways of 36 inches across. CLSI recommends a clearance of at least 44 inches around instruments with 60 inches preferred. All exits should be well-marked and unblocked at all times. Exit doors ideally swing outward and are not ever locked in the exit direction. Dead-end doors or corridors that could easily be mistaken for an exit should be marked "not an exit." Doors should be made of fire-resistant material so that a fire can be contained for at least 1 hour in a specific laboratory area when the doors are shut. When possible, separate space should be built to isolate high-risk procedures.

Storage areas should be spacious and well vented with all electrical switches and receptacles of the explosion-proof variety and nonsparking. Fire-resistant construction materials are desirable wherever possible, but local fire codes can provide exact requirements based on the laboratory contents and purpose. Sprinkler systems must be considered on a case-by-case basis because of the increased potential of Class B and C fires in certain laboratories and the use of chemicals that should not exposed to water. Sprinkler systems that are activated only in the location of the fire are superior. In facilities with sprinklers, a clearance of about 36 inches must be assured around each sprinkler head. Regardless of the presence of sprinklers, adequate fire safety equipment must be easily available throughout the laboratory.

Once the laboratory is designed, a fire plan should be posted strategically around the laboratory. This plan must include a map of the laboratory, all of the nearest exits, the primary (optimal) and secondary evacuation routes from each location, the location of equipment (extinguishers, fire blankets, respirators, alarms, telephones, etc), and the actions that personnel should take (activate alarm or turn off gas, for example). Evacuation routes must not rely on elevators because fires can cause power interruptions. When possible, evacuation should proceed away from high-risk areas and toward low-risk areas. Good housekeeping, always critical in preventing fire, also extends to keeping evacuation halls and aisles clear; evacuation routes should be checked approximately once per month. Storage of hazardous materials along evacuation routes is forbidden.

The NFPA recommends that laboratories schedule quarterly fire drills so that every employee participates at least once per year. If 25% of the staff is designated at each fire drill to do a mandatory full evacuation, by year's end every employee will have participated in an evacuation with no interruption

in the laboratory work. An outside meeting place must be designated for all evacuees to verify that everyone has exited the building. Large facilities may wish to designate certain employees to bring out the current employee schedule so that they can identify all those who should have been in the building at that time.

FIRE SAFETY EQUIPMENT

All safety equipment must be properly located, easily visible, and well maintained. All fire extinguishers, alarms, and smoke detectors, etc, should be on a maintenance and inspection schedule. Each piece of equipment should have a tag on it documenting the last inspection.

Fire Alarms

Fire alarms must be scattered throughout a facility and be both auditory (for the visually impaired) and visual (for the hearing impaired). Auditory alarms and public address systems must be clearly audible from any part of the laboratory, including storerooms. If a facility has a central alarm system, the activation of any one alarm should be detectable at the central facility as well as the local emergency responders. Alarms should be tested at least quarterly, typically in conjunction with fire drills. If any alarms, such as smoke detectors, are battery operated, the batteries should be replaced or tested at regular intervals, typically every 6 months.

Sand Buckets

Sand can be poured on most fires to extinguish the source of oxygen without hazard. It is important to keep these buckets free of debris because they may be the most readily available tools at the onset of a fire.

Fire Extinguishers

Different types of fires need different fire extinguishers. Representative extinguishers are shown in **Figure 2-2**. Dry chemical extinguishers are the best all-purpose extinguishers and are the extinguishers of choice for most sites. The gas from compressed gas extinguishers such as CO_2 dissipates rapidly and should not be used in enclosed spaces. However, gas extinguishers are less damaging to electronics and may be useful in rooms in which computers are housed. Water extinguishers are limited to Class A fires, so they are used less frequently.

It is important to note that fire extinguishers are limited in their size, range, and amount of extinguishing agent and that fire extinguishers have only 2 purposes. They can be used on small fires such as fires in trash cans, frying pans, or table tops, or they can be used along an evacuation route to keep the path clear. If a fire has the following characteristics, an extinguisher should not be used and evacuation is the best course: 1) the fire is large and/or partially hidden, 2) flammable solvents and gases are involved, 3) flames exceed normal adult height, 3) base of the fire cannot be accessed from a normal standing position, 4) area is filled with smoke and/or breathing is difficult, 5) heat of the fire is too intense to approach it at the extinguisher

Water extinguisher (Class A)   Carbon dioxide extinguisher (Class B)   Chemical extinguisher (Class C)

Ordinary combustible   Flammable liquids   Electrical equipment

Types of Fire Extinguishers and Sample Label: Pressurized water extinguishers are usually silver in color while other types are generally red. The carbon dioxide (CO_2) extinguishers can be distinguished by their large discharge horns. Extinguishers are labeled as to how they can be used, generally having letters (A, B or C) and graphic representations. Icons for the 3 principal fire types are illustrated (www.osha.gov).

Figure 2-2

range, and 6) fire position could compromise evacuation route.

OSHA Standard 1910.157 requires a fire extinguisher within 75 feet for Class A fire risk and within 50 feet for high-risk Class B fire. In general, a fire extinguisher should be placed at every laboratory door, and a large room should have a second fire extinguisher in the area farthest from the door. Fire extinguishers should be visually inspected every month to be sure that the hose is intact, that the plastic seal on the pin hasn't been tampered with and that the gauge is showing a full charge (**Figures 2-3** and **2-4**). More detailed inspection and/or testing should occur annually.

"PASS" summarizes the essential features of operating a fire extinguisher. More detailed instructions on fire extinguisher operation are:
P: **PULL** out the pin
A: **AIM** the extinguisher
S: **SQUEEZE** the double handles
S: **SWEEP** the base of the fire

1. Check to see if you have an A, B, or C fire extinguisher and make sure the extinguisher you are using is proper for the class of fire that you are attempting to extinguish.

2. Pull out the locking pin located in the handle.

3. Before you approach the fire, squeeze the double handles briefly to make sure that the agent will discharge. It is dangerous to approach a fire with a nonfunctional extinguisher.

4. Make sure you have your back to an unblocked escape route.

5. Approach the fire and stand at the approximate maximum reach for the extinguisher you have. You can always move closer if the agent is ineffective at the maximum distance. If you are outside, attempt to stand on the upwind side of the fire. This side is cooler and the smoke is blowing away from you. The maximum reach and discharge time vary greatly with each

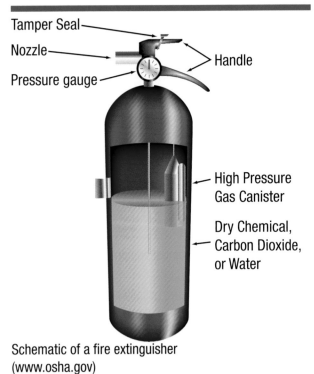

Schematic of a fire extinguisher
(www.osha.gov)

Figure 2-3

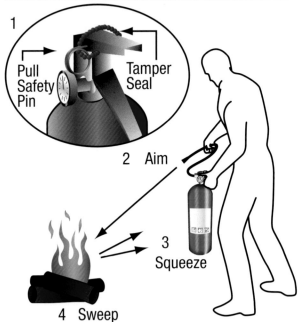

Illustration of the "PASS" process for fire extinguishers
(www.osha.gov)

Figure 2-4

extinguisher type and each extinguisher size. General guidelines are:

- Pressurized water extinguishers—maximum reach about 40 feet, maximum discharge time at full release about 60 seconds

- Dry chemical extinguishers—maximum reach 12 to 20 feet (only 8-10 feet for small home extinguishers), maximum discharge time at full release <30 seconds

- Gas extinguishers—because gas dissipates quickly, you must get very close to the fire. In addition, gas extinguishers should not be used in enclosed spaces because the gases will further reduce breathable oxygen

    - CO_2 extinguishers—maximum reach 3 to 8 feet

    - Halon extinguishers—maximum reach <16 feet

6. Aim the nozzle of the extinguisher. (Do not touch the discharge horn if using a CO_2 extinguisher because it can get extremely cold.)

7. Squeeze the double handle.

8. Direct the discharge at the base of the flame using a side-to-side, sweeping motion.

9. Continue to discharge the extinguisher even after the fire is out to prevent a reflash.

10. **Never** turn your back on the fire area, even after the fire is out. Walk backwards away from the fire area, watching for a reflash.

11. Recharge all fire extinguishers after use, even if the agent is not expended. Discharging the device opens the valves and gas or agent leakage may well prevent the extinguisher from working again.

A new class of fire extinguisher, Class K, has been developed for kitchens that use high-temperature oil fryers. Such fires respond poorly to water, CO_2, and Class C extinguishers. Class K extinguishers do not currently have any uses in the laboratory **Figure 2-5**.

Fire Hose (Class A Fires Only)

A fire hose should be pulled entirely off the rack for use. The hose should be as straight as possible to avoid interference of water flow. A fire hose uses high pressure so the operator should be braced, holding the hose with both hands while another person turns it on. Again, the base of the flame should be swept using a slow side-to-side motion. Continue spraying after the fire is out to prevent a reflash.

Fire Blanket

A fire blanket can be used to put out flames on a person's body, to contain a small area fire, or to aid

Symbol for Class K fire extinguisher.

Figure 2-5

in the evacuation of a fire area. For personal use, one should place the right arm through the rope loop and pull while turning the body to the left to wrap up in the blanket. One should crawl on the floor below the smoke to exit with the fire blanket over the back. If the fire blanket is being used to extinguish a clothing fire, it is essential to use the "stop, drop, and roll" technique. If the victim remains standing and the fire blanket is used, it will act like a chimney and direct heat and smoke upward to the victim's face. A graphic symbol for a fire blanket is shown in **Figure 2-6**.

Respirators

Respirators should be worn in the presence of toxic fumes. If respirators are not available, all personnel must be evacuated, and wet cloths may be used over the mouth and nose. Respirators must fit snugly onto the face to prevent any air from entering enter the mask. Personnel should be trained in the use of respirators and undergo fit testing to verify that they can wear them properly.

Symbol for fire blanket

Figure 2-6

PERSONNEL

The best evacuation plan and state-of-the-art fire fighting equipment are absolutely useless if the occupants of the laboratory are unaware of them. All personnel must be adequately trained in a laboratory's fire plan, and their training should be verified with periodic fire drills which include correct activation of alarms, knowledge of emergency phone numbers, ability to locate and correctly use fire equipment, and accurate knowledge of evacuation procedures. To avoid panic in patients and visitors, many hospitals do not announce fire directly and use terms understood by the staff such as "code red." It is essential that staff have such institutional codes memorized and that they assist in notifying nonemployee occupants of a building that they need to evacuate an area or the building.

The easiest personnel to overlook are often the new employees who are given a great deal of new information during training for a new job. This is particularly treacherous because new employees are unfamiliar with procedures and equipment and may be the ones most likely to accidentally cause a fire. After telling a new employee about fire and other safety plans during training, it is wise to reiterate it so that the information is not forgotten.

Some facilities, particularly large ones, may elect to provide special training to certain staff members for service in the "fire brigade." These staff members may act as first responders or experts in facilitating the evacuation of large numbers of people. Personnel also need to be trained to adhere to an institution's smoking policies and to remind visitors to adhere to smoking policies as well. "No Smoking" signs may be necessary in areas that are particularly hazardous.

What To Do In Case Of Fire

The guide below is a general plan for dealing with a fire—remember the acronym "RACE."

R: **RESCUE** – Be sure all people are out of danger
A: **ALARM** – Sound the alarm and follow up with a phone call
C: **CONTAIN** – Close doors, windows, etc. to confine the fire
E: **EXTINGUISH** – Attempt to put out the fire if it is small enough

Individual institutions or buildings may have certain other features unique to their fire plans. Individuals are responsible for knowledge of the fire plan in every building in which they live, work, or study.

1. People are always more important than property. Evacuation of everyone in immediate danger is the first priority in any fire. Alert all personnel in the immediate area of a fire, and make sure not to overlook the restrooms, storerooms, or small isolated nooks. Injured people, hospital/nursing home patients, and the elderly may not be ambulatory and will not be able to evacuate themselves. When wheeled beds and wheelchairs are available they can be used, but an excellent alternative is wheeled desk chairs. Avoid the elevators because fires can cause power interruptions. Be aware that in multistoried buildings, optimal evacuation may be "horizontal first, then vertical," as illustrated in **Figure 2-7**.

When possible, it is a good idea to designate a meeting place after evacuation to ensure that everyone has left the building. When the staff members vary from day to day, bringing the employee schedule to the evacuation site is useful to ensure that everyone expected to be in the facility is present.

2. The first person to see a fire, no matter how small, must report it immediately. What may

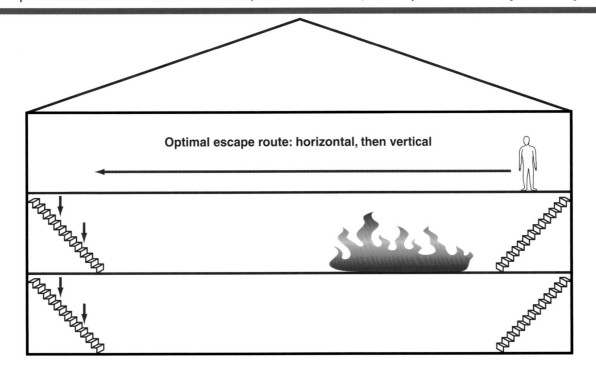

Optimal escape route: horizontal, then vertical

Figure 2-7

be a small fire could get rapidly out of control, and precious time would be lost if there were any delay in reporting. Notification might include activating the nearest alarm, calling an emergency number (such as 911), announcing a "code red" or verbally notifying all nearby occupants. Even if a central electronic alarm has been activated, confirm the fire by calling the appropriate emergency number. It is an unfortunate effect of fire plan rehearsals that alarms alone are sometimes thought to be just for testing the alarms or for a fire drill. It is important to remain calm and to clearly state the exact location and nature of the fire to the authorities.

3. Close the doors and windows as you leave a fire area. If it can be done safely, turn off the electrical current, especially if it is an electrical fire. When possible, close the valves of gas cylinders and the main gas shut-off valve. If the fire is in a hood, close the hood opening and turn off the fans to contain the fire.

   If the room is filled with smoke, leave at once by crawling out. The purest air is closest to the floor. If possible, cover your nose and mouth with a damp cloth. As you exit, close the door to contain the smoke.

4. If the fire is not extinguishable with the equipment on hand, shut the door and evacuate. Anything larger than a trash can fire may be too big for a fire extinguisher. For small fires, use the following:

- Class A fires (ordinary combustibles)— something to smother the fire such as sand, wet blankets, water, or the nearest ABC extinguisher.

- Class B (flammable liquids) and C (electrical) fires—the nearest dry chemical or CO_2 extinguisher, *not water.* Remember: flammable liquids include solvents, gas, oil, and grease; the use of water can spread a liquid fire or conduct electricity in an electrical fire.

Fight the fire by keeping yourself between the fire and the door and by staying as close to the door as possible. Never position yourself so that your escape route could be compromised.

5. Administer first aid to anyone suffering from burns or asphyxia.

6. Answer concisely any questions asked by fire response personnel. How the professionals deal with the fire greatly depends on information about the situation that you give them.

Sample Lab Evacuation Plan (Figure 2-8)

Note that there are both primary and secondary escape routes and that both escape routes go away from a high risk area.

1. When "Code Red" is announced, make sure all nearby persons are safe and evacuating the premises. Bring the staff schedule. Meet at the parking attendant kiosk and verify all staff on the schedule have evacuated.
2. For fire in the lab, as you exit dial "0" and announce, "Code Red, Lab." Pull the fire alarm in the hallway.
3. To the extent possible, turn off all instruments and gas jets as you exit. Close the doors behind you as you exit.
4. Do not try to use the fire extinguisher to put out the fire unless it is small and you can maintain a clear exit. If in doubt, let it burn.

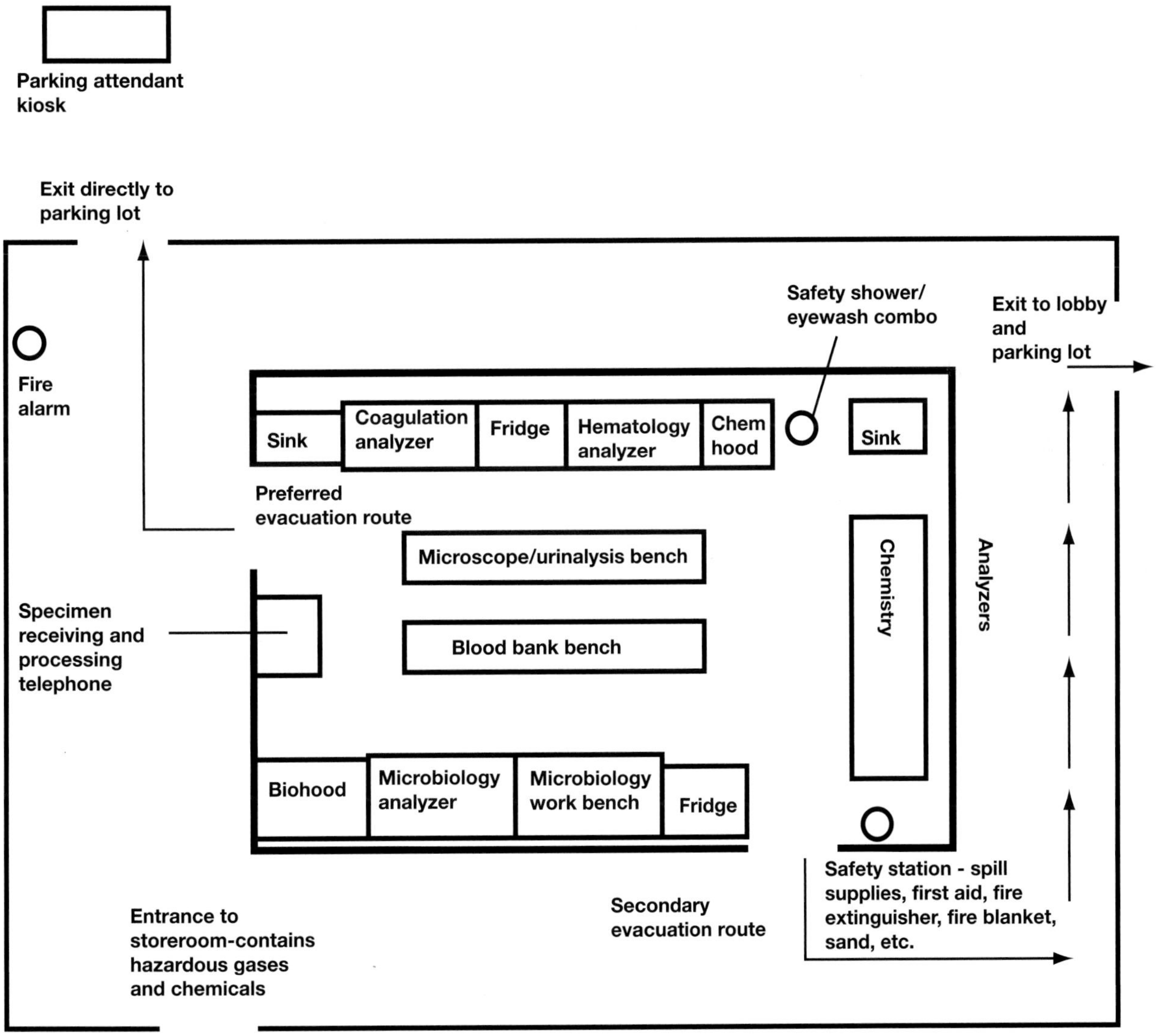

Laboratory evacuation plan

Figure 2-8

Summary Table: Fire Safety

Topic	Comments
Fire quadrahedron	1. Fuel, oxygen/oxidizer, heat, sustainable chain reaction
	2. Remove one of four, fire is prevented or extinguished
Fire hazards	1. Class A: Ordinary combustibles- use good housekeeping
	2. Class B: Liquids and gases - low flash points are the most hazardous, vented storage away from heat and electricity, use no water to extinguish
	3. Class C: Energized electrical equipment - use no water to extinguish, try to cut power to facility
	4. Class D: Combustible/reactive metals - use sand or special powder media only to extinguish. Water will make the fire burn even more
	5. Class E: Uncontrollable - evacuate and let burn
Lab design	1. Adequate number and size of doors, windows and hallways
	2. Well-marked, unobstructed exits
	3. Fire-resistant construction materials
	4. Adequate ventilation and storage areas
	5. No storage of materials in exit halls that is combustible or compromises width
	6. Lighted escape routes and exits, emergency lighting
	7. Clearance of 36 inches from sprinkler heads
	8. Clearance around instruments, desks, etc. to easily exit lab
Evacuation	1. Hold fire drills annually - do 25% of staff every 3 months
	2. Plan primary and secondary escape routes
	3. Evacuate toward low risk, not high risk, areas
	4. Check to see if "horizontal, then vertical" escape is better
	5. Bring staff schedule to know who should have been in building
	6. No elevators during evacuation
Fire equipment	1. Audible and visual fire alarms
	2. Sand buckets
	3. Fire hoses - Class A fires only- straighten hose and brace feet
	4. Fire extinguishers- only for small fires - limited reach and limited agent

	a. Water for Class A fires only; dry chemical and CO_2 for ABC
	   b. PASS - **P**ULL the pin, **A**IM the extinguisher, **S**QUEEZE the double handles, and **S**WEEP the base of the fire
	   c. Always recharge after any use, even if there is agent left

	5. Fire blankets- always use with "stop, drop and roll" for clothing fires
	6. Respirators- users must be fit tested
Fire plan	Train personnel on plan, post plan in a conspicuous spot and practice annually

	RACE: 1. RESCUE all people. Evacuation of people, not property, is first. Crawl below smoke to exit
	     2. ALARM. Set off the fire alarm and call emergency numbers to verify
	     3. CONTAIN the fire. Shut doors, windows, etc. Turn off gas and electricity
	     4. EXTINGUISH the fire. Keep yourself between the exit and the fire so that your escape route is not cut off

Exercise 2

Self-Evaluation Questions

1. Matching. Choose 2 correct answers per item.

    ___, ___ Class A fires

    ___, ___ Class B fires

    ___, ___ Class C fires

    ___, ___ Class D fires

    ___, ___ Class E fires

    a. Electrical
    b. Let it burn and protect adjacent structures
    c. Reactive/combustible metals
    d. Put out with sand or special powder agent only
    e. Uncontrollable
    f. Putting out with water may cause electric shock
    g. Ordinary combustibles
    h. Putting out with water may spread fire
    i. Flammable liquids
    j. Only type of fire on which water is acceptable

2. ___ What is the first step in using a fire extinguisher?

    a. Pulling out the safety pin
    b. Verifying that the maintenance is up-to-date on the attached tag
    c. Instructing all personnel to get out of the way of the extinguisher's line of fire
    d. Verifying that the extinguisher is appropriate for the class of fire on which it is about to be used
    e. Opening the doors and windows so that the extinguishing agent can be ventilated out of the room

3. ___ Care must be taken to avoid touching the discharge horn of a fire extinguisher because the horns of

_____ extinguishers get particularly cold.

    a. CO_2
    b. Halon
    c. Water
    d. Dry chemical
    e. Class K

4. ___ If a fire is small enough to be handled by the laboratory personnel, it is not necessary to:

    a. Pull the alarm
    b. Notify the fire brigade
    c. Evacuate other personnel
    d. Make the follow-up call verifying the existence of a fire, but the alarm should still be pulled
    e. None of the above; a fire is to be taken seriously no matter how small

5. ___ All of the following are necessary to do when evacuating an area with a fire **EXCEPT:**

    a. Close gas cylinder valves
    b. Crawl out below the smoke
    c. Carry out irreplaceable items
    d. Close the doors and the windows
    e. Turn off electricity and equipment

6. ___ The FIRST priority in any fire plan is:

    a. Dialing "911"
    b. Activation of the fire alarm
    c. Locating the closest fire extinguisher
    d. Ensuring the evacuation and safety of all endangered people
    e. Donning respiratory protection before smoke has had a chance to accumulate

7. ___ The safest institutions have:

    a. At least 1 fire extinguisher per room
    b. Detailed personnel training and frequent fire drills
    c. A window as well as a door in every room for a fire escape
    d. State-of-the-art alarm systems and automatic sprinkler systems
    e. Fire extinguishers for every class of fire to include A, B, C, D and K

8. ___ Because of the instrumentation and chemicals in many laboratories, which of the following is not automatically used in every laboratory area?

    a. A sprinkler system
    b. Fire-resistant doors
    c. Adequate number of well-marked exits
    d. Spacious and uncluttered aisles and hallways
    e. Ventilation systems which operate at a rate of 6-12 air changes per hour

9. Matching

a

b

c

___ Class A fire   ___ Class B fire   ___ Class C fire

10. ___ Which of the following actions in a fire is **CORRECT**?

    a. Responder uses a CO_2 extinguisher on a potassium fire
    b. Responder unwinds first 10 feet of a 100-foot-long fire hose to put out a nearby fire
    c. Responder wraps a victim in burning clothing in a fire blanket and walks him quickly out of the building
    d. Victim is on 5th floor, east wing. Fire is on 4th floor, east wing. Victim goes to 5th floor, west wing and then takes the stairs to exit the building
    e. All of the above are correct

11. ___ On which fire below can an extinguisher be used?

    a. Computer on fire
    b. Flames coming through a wall
    c. Floor to ceiling bookcase in flames
    d. All of the above
    e. None of the above

12. ____ Given the data below, which solvent is the most hazardous?

Solvent	Flash point, °C	Flash point, °F	Upper Explosion Limit, %	Lower Explosion Limit, %
A	−20	−4	2	28
B	17	62	3	19
C	50	122	1	47
D	-11	12	1	7
E	4	38	8	15

Exercise 3
CHEMICAL SAFETY

All laboratory workers, even those who do not work in "chemistry," use many chemicals in their work. This exercise reviews the general principles of safe chemical usage, and the topics discussed here should be covered in the chemical hygiene plan of a facility.

LABELS

All containers for chemicals or reagents must be clearly labeled. Manufacturers typically provide all the appropriate information on the product label in accordance with either the International Union of Pure and Applied Chemistry (IUPAC) or the Chemical Abstracts Service (CAS), and this information should never be defaced, damaged, or missing. It is often necessary to place chemicals in secondary containers or make mixtures of chemicals in other containers for use. Secondary containers must be clearly labeled with at least a minimal amount of information (see below). It is best to label the reagent bottle before it is filled so that there are no unlabeled chemicals in the laboratory even for a moment and there is no chance that a chemical could be mislabeled. Even containers of innocuous substances such as water should be clearly labeled so that they are not confused with more dangerous compounds.

At a minimum, a reagent label should include:

1. Identity: recognizable name(s) of the chemical and the concentration present

2. Dates: date of receipt, date reagent made, date of expiration

3. Personnel: initials of person who made or received the chemical

4. Hazards: major hazardous characteristics present (poisonous, flammable, etc)

5. Special: any unique instructions or cautions (refrigerator storage, keep from light, etc)

There are many chemical labeling systems. Although OSHA requires clear labels that employees have been trained to understand, it does not require the use of any specific labeling system.

Chemical Safety

Figure 3-1 illustrates the National Fire Protection Association (NFPA) diamond label for chemical hazards. Numbers placed in the red, blue, and yellow squares indicate the seriousness of the hazard according to the key in **Table 3-1**. The National Paint and Coatings Association developed a similar system, the Hazardous Materials Identification System (HMIS), shown in **Figure 3-2**. HMIS formerly had a reactivity hazard category like NFPA but replaced it with a physical hazard category. The HMIS white bar is to specify personal protective equipment. Ratings in the 2 systems are not identical, but either is appropriate in most cases.

Each of the hazard categories will be discussed in more detail in a later section. Many manufacturers as well as HMIS and NFPA will also employ icons, nonverbal pictures, or diagrams in conjunction with written instructions to communicate hazards. Examples are shown in **Figures 3-3** to **3-5**. With these systems, the chemical hazard can be rapidly interpreted, even by nontechnical personnel. It is

essential, however, that staff be thoroughly trained in any system if it is to be the exclusive means of chemical hazard communication. In addition, the Occupational Safety and Health Administration (OSHA) recommends that only 1 system be used at a time to avoid confusion.

Transportation of hazardous substances, including chemicals, is regulated by the Department of Transportation (DOT), which has its own labeling system. As discussed in Exercise 1, efforts have been made through the United Nations toward a globally harmonized system (GHS) of hazard labeling (http://www.osha.gov/dsg/hazcom/ghs.html, accessed January 14, 2008). The symbols shown in **Figure 3-6** are contained on both the OSHA and DOT Web sites and are currently being phased in by both agencies for chemical transport labeling. Participation in the GHS project is entirely voluntary, and each country can incorporate the new labeling on its own timetable. Canada has a labeling system called Workplace Hazardous Materials Information System (WHMIS). Some of the icons used are

Table 3-1: Key for NFPA Diamond

Health Hazard (Blue)	Fire Hazard (Red)
4. Deadly	4. Below 70°F
3. Extremely dangerous	3. Below 100°F
2. Hazardous	2. Below 200°F
1. Slightly hazardous	1. Above 200°F
0. Not harmful under normal circumstances	0. Will not burn

Specific Hazard (White)		Stability Hazard (Yellow)
Alkaline	ALK	4. May detonate
Acid	ACID	3. Explosive when exposed to heat, shock or water
Oxidizer	OXY	2. Capable of violent chemical change
Corrosive	COR	1. Unstable if heated
Use no water	W̶	0. Stable
Radioactive		

slightly different from those used in the United States (See **Figure 3-7**), in case the reader should encounter them. Canada and the European Union are participating in the global harmonization project and are still phasing in the new icons at publication time.

Many clinical laboratories provide specimen collection containers to patients which contain chemical

No smoking

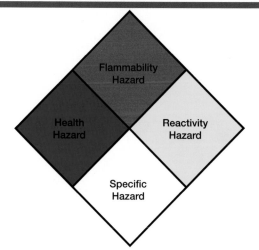

National Fire Protection Association (NFPA) Hazard Communication Label. Hazards are rated 0-4 with 4 most hazardous

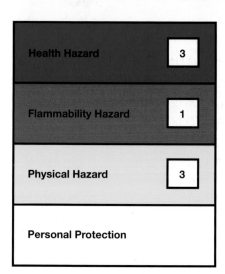

National Paint and Coatings Association Hazardous Materials Information Systems (HMIS). Hazards are rated 0-4 with 4 most hazardous

Wear gloves

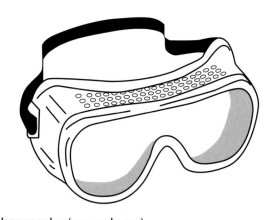

Wear goggles (www.cdc.gov)

Oxidizer Hazard

Health Hazard

Flammable Hazard

Poison Hazard

Extreme Health Hazard

Corrosive Hazard

Explosion Hazard

Environmental Hazard

Compressed Gas Hazard

Globally Harmonized System (GHS) Chemical Transportation Symbols adopted by United Nations and US Agencies OSHA and DOT

Figure 3-6

preservatives. An excellent example is jugs that patients use for 24-hour urine collections, which contain a chemical preservative to stabilize the specimen over 24 hours. These specimen containers also must be well labeled so that nontechnical laboratory personnel can understand the chemical contents and take the appropriate precautions. This may mean that they use labels that are more

detailed than those provided on reagent bottles used by laboratory personnel. The sole use of the NFPA or HMIS systems in these circumstances would not be appropriate.

It is important to note that chemical waste must be as meticulously labeled as unused chemical reagents. Many licensed waste handlers will not

Health Canada   Santé Canada

Canada

Do You Know These Vital Signs?

THE HAZARD SYMBOLS OF WHMIS

CLASS A
Compressed
Gas

CLASS D-2
Poisonous and
Infectious Material
(material causing
other toxic effects)

CLASS B
Flammable and
Combustible
Material

CLASS D-3
Poisonous and
Infectious Material
(Biohazardous
Infectious Material)

CLASS C
Oxidizing
Material

CLASS E
Corrosive
Material

CLASS D-1
Poisonous and
Infectious Material
(material causing
immediate and
serious effects)

CLASS F
Dangerously
Reactive Material

WHMIS provides you with information on the safe use, storage, handling and disposal of hazardous materials at Canadian workplaces.

Workplace
Hazardous Materials
Information System

For more information, consult the MSDS, and visit the Health Canada WHMIS Web site:
http://www.hc–sc.gc.ca/whmis

Figure 3-7

remove unidentified waste, and laboratories may face trouble and expense identifying unknown chemicals in waste containers.

STORAGE AND INVENTORY

The basic requirements of chemical storage areas and chemical laboratories are clear signs on entrance doors and storage units, good ventilation (at least 6-12 air changes per hour), temperature control, fire-resistant walls, doors and storage units, fire safety equipment, spark-proof electrical equipment, minimal electrical sources, and adequate space for the amount of stored chemicals. Air handling for laboratories should generally make air flow in a "clean to dirty" direction so that surrounding space is not contaminated. Ideally 100% of the "dirty" air is exhausted to the outside and not recirculated. Many designs require that laboratory doors remain closed when not in use. Most porous surfaces cannot be adequately decontaminated. Therefore all surfaces possible, particularly countertops and flooring, must be impervious to chemicals/fluids. Carpets are not permitted, and floors should have as few seams as possible with coved edges. Regulations and restrictions for certain stored chemicals may stipulate more elaborate requirements. The best design, however, cannot replace good housekeeping, inventory management, and organization in the storage area.

Chemicals should be stored in groups of similar reactivities and compatibilities. It may be easier to locate chemicals arranged in alphabetical order, but such an arrangement is potentially hazardous if 2 incompatible chemicals are mixed in an accident. A later section lists important chemical incompatibilities. Obviously, water-reactive chemicals should not be stored under automatic sprinklers.

Chemical stocks should be kept to the minimum amount possible to maintain efficient laboratory operations. Bulk chemical buying may be cost effective, but it poses additional safety issues. All chemicals should have a date of receipt on the label, and a "first in, first out" system of inventory management should be in place. Rotating the oldest stock to the front and placing new shipments in the back takes extra effort, but all staff must be trained and monitored for compliance with this policy. In many institutions, supply management is the responsibility of nontechnical staff who may not appreciate safety requirements such as these, so these employees should be included in almost all chemical training.

Large containers and hazardous corrosives must be stored as close to floor level as possible. Nothing dangerous should be on a high shelf because it could fall on someone. Supplies should not be stacked too high because of a tipping hazard, and a space of about 24 inches between the ceiling and the highest item is recommended. If supplies are stored on high shelves, nonskid ladders or step stools should be provided. Nothing should be stored close to a heat or electrical source. Whenever possible, particularly for large quantities, storage should be in metal safety cans or plastic coated glass. (Note: There may be a surcharge for coated safety glass, but it is usually nominal relative to the extra margin of safety it provides.) Storage of liquids in trays or on shelves with "lips" or raised edging prevents bottles from falling off and helps to contain liquid in the event of a spill. Specially vented safety cabinets are useful for storage of volatile liquids because they disperse dangerous fumes.

In the laboratory, metal safety cans and fume hoods can be used for the storage of working amounts of volatile chemicals. If hoods are used, they must be kept on at all times. As shown in **Figure 3-8,** a fume hood is enclosed on all sides with a window on 1 side for reaching in and working with the chemicals. It has an exhaust system that draws air up from the work surface and out

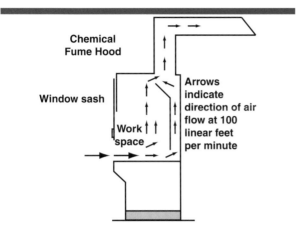

Schematic of a chemical fume hood (www.cdc.gov)

Figure 3-8

the top of the hood away from the worker and the laboratory. A special device is required to ascertain actual air flow in a chemical fume hood, and ideally a velocity sensor with an alarm is incorporated into a fume hood. In the absence of a sensor, however, a small object such as a piece of yarn can be taped to a spot in the hood that allows the operator to visually determine that air is flowing. Fume hoods must be maintained and inspected at least annually to verify that air flow is sufficient (face velocity of 100 linear feet per minute). To provide the correct amount of air flow, manufacturers generally require that staff keep the window shield on the fume hood pulled down as far as possible (about 12-18 inches) so that just the hands can enter the hood. Air flow is restricted if the hood is overloaded with objects, so typically supplies should be kept more than 8 inches from the hood face. Some laboratories even paint a bright line in the hood so that users know how far back to keep objects. For some procedures and equipment, deeper hoods may be required to keep air flow unrestricted. Air turbulence (such as foot traffic) at the hood face can reduce efficiency, so hoods should be placed out of traffic areas where they can draw air freely. Another issue is that workers cannot be crowded into too little hood space. With too many people at the opening, the hood draws poorly and workers are likely to

interfere with each other's work. OSHA recommends 2.5 linear feet of hood space per worker. Finally, since chemical fume hoods and biological safety cabinets are designed differently and cannot be used interchangeably, some laboratories may need to have both. Canopy hoods placed over work areas are also unacceptable because they exhaust fumes past a worker's face and do not protect against chemicals or biohazards. Backdraft hoods placed above the backsplash of a workbench are acceptable in some applications, particularly with chemicals that are heavier than air, as described later with formaldehyde and xylene.

The hazard of storing flammable chemicals in refrigerators was discussed in Exercise 2. Because vapors cannot escape a closed refrigerator, any ignition source introduced on opening the refrigerator (such as a light coming on) can cause a fire. Refrigeration of other chemicals that give off vapors may also be a poor idea if a vapor is toxic. The person opening a refrigerator with toxic vapors is likely to inhale a substantial amount. Chemicals that give off vapors should be tightly sealed at all times, but especially in a refrigerator. Screw-top caps are preferred because foil, plastic wrap, corks, and glass stoppers are more likely not to make tight seals. Food and drink should never be stored in a laboratory refrigerator.

Trash or unpacked shipments of laboratory supplies must not be allowed to accumulate in the aisles of a storage area. All persons who use the storage area are responsible for good housekeeping in the area. Personnel who enter the storeroom need to follow the same restrictions as laboratory personnel with regard to not smoking, eating, drinking, etc.

Only authorized personnel should be in a laboratory, and safety officers should assess the level of security required for a particular facility, including areas of chemical storage. Certain chemicals, drugs, biologicals, and equipment may be targets for theft by terrorists, drug dealers, and other criminals, so it may be necessary to lock storage facilities as well as limit laboratory access. The Department of Homeland Security (DHS) has published "Chemical Facility Anti-Terrorism Standards" and a list of "Chemicals of Interest." The chemicals list specifies the amounts of a particular chemical that require facilities to follow DHS standards. Clinical laboratories generally do not house sufficient amounts of chemical to follow these standards, but they do use some of the chemicals listed. Safety officers should verify the status of their particular laboratory at the DHS Web site (http://www.dhs.gov/xprevprot/laws/gc_1166796969417.shtm, accessed April 16, 2008).

MATERIAL SAFETY DATA SHEETS

Figure 3-9 contains a sample material safety data sheet (MSDS). Manufacturers are required by OSHA to provide an MSDS for every hazardous chemical they produce. The reader should note that the GHS abbreviation is SDS for Safety Data Sheet, and the term MSDS may eventually be replaced by SDS.

The essential function of the MSDS is to communicate the hazards associated with each chemical. OSHA Form 174 has the voluntary format for an MSDS:

1. **Chemical identity** This includes common, chemical, and trade names and/or chemical structures.

2. **Manufacturer's name, address, and contact information**

3. **Hazardous ingredients** Some chemicals are not considered hazardous and are not required to have MSDSs. If the use of these chemicals in a product is proprietary, manufacturers are not even required to name them. Chemical

mixtures need only list the characteristics of the hazardous chemicals.

4. **Physical and chemical characteristics** The physical nature (powder, liquid, etc) and the important features of chemicals are described.

5. **Fire and explosion hazards**

6. **Reactivity data**

7. **Health hazards**

8. **Precautions of safe handling and use**

9. **Control measures** This section includes information on how accidents and chemical spills should be handled and lists appropriate first aid measures.

Although OSHA's Form 174 still exists, it has been suggested that manufacturers move toward the American National Standards Institute (ANSI) MSDS specifications (ANSI Z400.1), which is becoming the international norm. There are 16 categories of information recommended by ANSI and these can be found on the OSHA Web site (http://www.osha.gov/dsg/hazcom/msdsformat.html, accessed January 14, 2008). The GHS specifications for SDS contain the same 16 categories used by ANSI. Many manufacturers are expected to begin converting their MSDSs to the new standard format and that chemical users can obtain the new versions thereafter. Currently, manufacturers can print their MSDS's in any way they choose as long as the correct information is included. Therefore, it is much more difficult to look up information such as first aid treatment quickly in an emergency situation. The new format requires emergency information to be closer to the front of the MSDS, and features like paper size, color, and margins are specified so that MSDS's will look more similar and be easier to use.

Figure 3-9 is an example of an GHS-compliant
MSDS taken from the OSHA Web site.

Sample MSDS compliant with the UN Global Harmonized System from www.osha.gov

1. Identification

Product Name: Chemical Stuff   **General Information:** 713-000-0000

Synonyms: Methyltoxy Solution   **Transportation Emergency Number: CHEMTREC:** 800-424-9300

CAS Number: 000-00-0

Product Use: Organic Synthesis

Manufacturer/Supplier: My Company

Address: My Street, My Town, TX 00000

2. Hazards Identification

GHS Classification:

Health	Environmental	Physical
Acute Toxicity - Category 2 (inhalation), Category 3 (oral/dermal)	Aquatic Toxicity - Acute 2	Flammable Liquid - Category 2
Eye Corrosion - Category 1		
Skin Corrosion - Category 1		
Skin Sensitization - Category 1		
Mutagenicity - Category 2		
Carcinogenicity - Category 1B		
Reproductive/Developmental - Category 2		
Target Organ Toxicity (Repeated) - Category 2		

GHS Label:

Symbols: flame, skull and crossbones, corrosion, health hazard

Hazard Statements	Precautionary Statements
DANGER!	Do not eat, drink or use tobacco when using this product
Highly flammable liquid and vapor	Do not breathe mist/vapors
Fatal if inhaled	Keep container tightly closed
Causes severe skin burns and eye damage	Keep away from heat/sparks/open flame
May cause allergic skin reaction	No smoking
Toxic if swallowed and in contact with skin	Wear respiratory protection, protective gloves and eye/face protection
May cause cancer	Use only in a well-ventilated area

Figure 3-9

GHS Label (continued):

Hazard Statements	Precautionary Statements
Suspected of damaging the unborn child	Take precautionary measures against static discharge
Suspected of causing genetic defects	Use only non-sparking tools.
May cause damage to cardiovascular, respiratory, nervous, and gastrointestinal systems and liver and blood through prolonged or repeated exposure	Store container tightly closed in cool/well-ventilated place
Toxic to aquatic life	Wash thoroughly after handling

3. Composition / Information on Ingredients

Component CAS Number Weight %

Methyltoxy 000-00-0 80

(See Section 8 for Exposure Limits)

4. First Aid Measures

Eye: Eye irritation. Flush immediately with large amounts of water for at least 15 minutes. Eyelids should be held away from the eyeball to ensure thorough rinsing. Get immediate medical attention.

Skin: Itching or burning of the skin. Immediately flush the skin with plenty of water while removing contaminated clothing and shoes. Get immediate medical attention. Wash contaminated clothing before reuse.

Inhalation: Nasal irritation, headache, dizziness, nausea, vomiting, heart palpitations, breathing difficulty, cyanosis, tremors, weakness, red flushing of face, irritability. Remove exposed person from source of exposure to fresh air. If not breathing, clear airway and start cardiopulmonary resuscitation (CPR). Avoid mouth-to-mouth resuscitation.

Ingestion: Get immediate medical attention. Do not induce vomiting unless directed by medical personnel.

5. Fire Fighting Measures

Suitable Extinguishing Media: Use dry chemical, foam, or carbon dioxide to extinguish fire. Water may be ineffective but should be used to cool fire-exposed containers, structures and to protect personnel. Use water to dilute spills and to flush them away from sources of ignition.

Fire Fighting Procedures: Do not flush down sewers or other drainage systems. Exposed firefighters must wear NIOSH-approved positive pressure self-contained breathing apparatus with full-face mask and full protective clothing.

Unusual Fire and Explosion Hazards: Dangerous when exposed to heat or flame. Will form flammable or explosive mixtures with air at room temperature. Vapor or gas may spread to distant ignition sources and flash back. Vapors or gas may accumulate in low areas. Runoff to sewer may cause fire or explosion hazard. Containers may explode in heat of fire. Vapors may concentrate in confined areas. Liquid will float and may reignite on the surface of water.

Combustion Products: Irritating or toxic substances may be emitted upon thermal decomposition. Thermal decomposition products may include oxides of carbon and nitrogen.

6: Accidental Release Measures

Keep unnecessary people away; isolate hazard area and deny entry. Stay upwind; keep out of low areas. (Also see Section 8).

Figure 3-9 continued

Vapor protective clothing should be worn for spills and leaks. Shut off ignition sources; no flares, smoking or flames in hazard area. Small spills: Take up with sand or other noncombustible absorbent material and place into containers for later disposal. Large spills: Dike far ahead of liquid spill for later disposal.

Do not flush to sewer or waterways. Prevent release to the environment if possible. Refer to Section 15 for spill/release reporting information.

7. Handling and Storage

Handling

Do not get in eyes, on skin or on clothing. Do not breathe vapors or mists. Keep container closed. Use only with adequate ventilation. Use good personal hygiene practices. Wash hands before eating, drinking, smoking. Remove contaminated clothing and clean before re-use. Destroy contaminated belts and shoes and other items that cannot be decontaminated. Keep away from heat and flame. Keep operating temperatures below ignition temperatures at all times. Use non-sparking tools.

Storage

Store in tightly closed containers in cool, dry, well-ventilated area away from heat, sources of ignition and incompatibles. Ground lines and equipment used during transfer to reduce the possibility of static spark-initiated fire or explosion. Store at ambient or lower temperature. Store out of direct sunlight. Keep containers tightly closed and upright when not in use. Protect against physical damage.

Empty containers may contain toxic, flammable and explosive residue or vapors. Do not cut, grind, drill, or weld on or near containers unless precautions are taken against these hazards.

8. Exposure Controls / Personal Protection

Exposure Limits: Component, Methyltoxy - TWA: 3 ppm (skin) - **STEL:** C 15 ppm (15 min.)

Engineering Controls: Local exhaust ventilation may be necessary to control air contaminants to their exposure limits. The use of local ventilation is recommended to control emissions near the source. Provide mechanical ventilation for confined spaces. Use explosion-proof ventilation equipment.

Personal Protective Equipment (PPE)

Eye Protection: Wear chemical safety goggles and face shield. Have eye-wash stations available where eye contact can occur.

Skin Protection: Avoid skin contact. Wear gloves impervious to conditions of use. Additional protection may be necessary to prevent skin contact including use of apron, face shield, boots or full body protection. A safety shower should be located in the work area. Recommended protective materials include:Butyl rubber and for limited contact Teflon.

Respiratory Protection: If exposure limits are exceeded, NIOSH approved respiratory protection should be worn. A NIOSH approved respirator for organic vapors is generally acceptable for concentrations up to 10 times the PEL. For higher concentrations, unknown concentrations and for oxygen deficient atmospheres, use a NIOSH approved air-supplied respirator. Engineering controls are the preferred means for controlling chemical exposures. Respiratory protection may be needed for non-routine or emergency situations. Respiratory protection must be provided in accordance with OSHA 29 CFR 1910.134.

9. Physical and Chemical Properties

Flashpoint: 2°C (35°F)

Vapor Density(Air=1): 1.7; air = 1

Autoignition Temperature: 480°C (896°F)

% Solubility in Water: 10 @ 20°C

Boiling Point: 77°C (170.6°F) @ 760 mm Hg

Pour Point: NA

Figure 3-9 continued

Melting Point: -82°C

Vapor Pressure: 100.0 mm Hg @ 23°C

Lower Flammability Limit: >3.00%

Upper Flammability Limit: <15.00%

Evaporation Rate (Water=1): 5(Butyl Acetate =1)

Octanol/Water Partition Coefficient: log K_{ow}: 0.5

Molecular Weight: Mixture

Molecular Formula: Mixture

Odor/Appearance: Clear, colorless liquid with mild, pungent odor.

Specific Gravity: 0.82g/mL @ 20°C

% Volatile: 100

Viscosity: 0.3 cP @ 25°C

pH: 7, 8% aqueous solution

10. Stability and Reactivity

Stability/Incompatibility: Incompatible with ammonia, amines, bromine, strong bases and strong acids.

Hazardous Reactions/Decomposition Products: Thermal decomposition products may include oxides of carbon and nitrogen.

11. Toxicological Information

Signs and Symptoms of Overexposure: Eye and nasal irritation, headache, dizziness, nausea, vomiting, heart palpitations, difficulty breathing, cyanosis, tremors, weakness, itching or burning of the skin.

Acute Effects:

Eye Contact: may cause severe conjunctival irritation and corneal damage.

Skin Contact: may cause reddening, blistering or burns with permanent damage. Harmful if absorbed through the skin. May cause allergic skin reaction.

Inhalation: may cause severe irritation with possible lung damage (pulmonary edema).

Ingestion: may cause severe gastrointestinal burns.

Target Organ Effects: may cause gastrointestinal (oral), respiratory tract, nervous system and blood effects based on experimental animal data. May cause cardiovascular system and liver effects.

Chronic Effects: based on experimental animal data, may cause changes to genetic material; adverse effects on the developing fetus or on reproduction at doses that were toxic to the mother. Methyltoxy is classified by IARC as group 2B and by NTP as reasonably anticipated to be a human carcinogen. OSHA regulates Methyltoxy as a potential carcinogen.

Medical Conditions Aggravated by Exposure: preexisting diseases of the respiratory tract, nervous system, cardiovascular system, liver or gastrointestinal tract.

Acute Toxicity Values

Oral LD_{50} (Rat) = 100 mg/kg   Dermal LD50 (Rabbit) = 225-300 mg/kg   Inhalation LC_{50} (Rat) = 200 ppm/4 hr., 1100 ppm vapor/1 hr

12. Ecological Information

LC_{50} (Fathead Minnows) = 9 mg/L/96 hr. EC_{50} (Daphnia) = 8.6 mg/L/48 hr.

Bioaccumulation is not expected to be significant. This product is readily biodegradable.

13. Disposal Considerations

Figure 3-9 continued

As sold, this product, when discarded or disposed of, is a hazardous waste according to Federal regulations (40 CFR 261). It is listed as Hazardous Waste Number Z000, listed due to its toxicity. The transportation, storage, treatment and disposal of this waste material must be conducted in compliance with 40 CFR 262, 263, 264, 268 and 270. Disposal can occur only in properly permitted facilities. Refer to state and local requirements for any additional requirements, as these may be different from Federal laws and regulations. Chemical additions, processing or otherwise altering this material may make waste management information presented in the MSDS incomplete, inaccurate or otherwise inappropriate.

14. Transport Information

U.S. Department of Transportation (DOT)

Proper Shipping Name: Methyltoxy   **Hazard Class:** 3, 6.1

UN/NA Number: UN0000   **Packing Group:** PG 2   **Labels Required:** Flammable Liquid and Toxic

International Maritime Organization (IMDG)

Proper Shipping Name: Methyltoxy   **Hazard Class:** 3 Subsidiary 6.1

UN/NA Number: UN0000   **Packing Group:** PG 2   **Labels Required:** Flammable Liquid and Toxic

15. Regulatory Information

U.S. Federal Regulations

Comprehensive Environmental Response and Liability Act of 1980 (CERCLA):

The reportable quantity (RQ) for this material is 1000 pounds. If appropriate, immediately report to the National Response Center (800/424-8802) as required by U.S. Federal Law. Also contact appropriate state and local regulatory agencies.

Toxic Substances Control Act (TSCA): All components of this product are included on the TSCA inventory.

Clean Water Act (CWA): Methyltoxy is a hazardous substance under the Clean Water Act. Consult Federal, State and local regulations for specific requirements.

Clean Air Act (CAA): Methyltoxy is a hazardous substance under the Clean Air Act. Consult Federal, State and local regulations for specific requirements.

Superfund Amendments and Reauthorization Act (SARA) Title III Information:

SARA Section 311/312 (40 CFR 370) Hazard Categories:

Immediate Hazard: X

Delayed Hazard: X

Fire Hazard: X

Pressure Hazard:

Reactivity Hazard:

This product contains the following toxic chemical(s) subject to reporting requirements of SARA Section 313 (40 CFR 372)

Component CAS Number Maximum %

Methyltoxy 000-00-0 80

State Regulations

California: This product contains the following chemicals(s) known to the State of California to cause cancer, birth defects or reproductive harm:

Figure 3-9 continued

49

Component CAS Number Maximum %

Methyltoxy 000-00-0 80

International Regulations

Canadian Environmental Protection Act: All of the components of this product are included on the Canadian Domestic Substances List (DSL).

Canadian Workplace Hazardous Materials Information System (WHMIS):

Class B-2 Flammable Liquid   Class D-1-B Toxic   Class D-2-A Carcinogen

Class D-2-B Chronic Toxin   Class E Corrosive

This product has been classified in accordance with the hazard criteria of the Controlled Products Regulations and the MSDS contains all the information required by the Controlled Products Regulations.

European Inventory of Existing Chemicals (EINECS): All of the components of this product are included on EINECS.

EU Classification: F Highly Flammable; T Toxic; N Dangerous to the Environment

EU Risk (R) and Safety (S) Phrases:

R11: Highly flammable.

R23/24/25: Toxic by inhalation, in contact with skin and if swallowed.

R37/38: Irritating to respiratory system and skin.

R41: Risk of serious damage to eyes.

R43: May cause sensitization by skin contact.

R45: May cause cancer.

R51/53: Toxic to aquatic organisms, may cause long-term adverse effects in the aquatic environment.

S53: Avoid exposure - obtain special instructions before use.

S16: Keep away from sources of ignition - No Smoking.

S45: In case of accident or if you feel unwell, seek medical advice immediately (show the label where possible).

S9: Keep container in a well-ventilated place.

S36/37: Wear suitable protective clothing and gloves.

S57: Use appropriate container to avoid environmental contamination.

16. Other Information

National Fire Protection Association (NFPA) Ratings: This information is intended solely for the use of individuals trained in the NFPA system.

Health: 3

Flammability: 3

Reactivity: 0

Revision Indicator: New MSDS

Disclaimer: The information contained herein is accurate to the best of our knowledge. My Company makes no warranty of any kind, express or implied, concerning the safe use of this material in your process or in combination with other substance.

Figure 3-9 continued

Although MSDS's are valuable, there are 2 major problems with relying solely on MSDS's as the primary tool for communication and policy formulation. Most MSDS's contain rather detailed technical information that may be difficult to interpret, particularly by staff with minimal chemical expertise. Secondly, MSDS's are often written for 100% pure chemicals. Thus, the MSDS for concentrated hydrochloric acid vastly overstates the hazard of a 5% solution used in the laboratory. While it is essential that MSDS's be available to all staff, it is appropriate for safety officers to interpret the information in the MSDS's to employees for clarity and for applicability to the concentration of chemicals in use. A "cover sheet," as illustrated in **Figure 3-10**, for each MSDS is also useful in summarizing the pertinent data and allowing employees to rapidly access institutional policy for a chemical.

As stated earlier, manufacturers are required by law to provide MSDS's to users of their products if the chemicals are hazardous. Some products composed entirely of chemicals not classified by OSHA as hazardous may not have a published MSDS (for example, urine dipsticks). In such cases, it is advisable to ask for a letter from the manufacturer stating why no MSDS is available and to keep it with the MSDSs to document that the absence of the MSDS is deliberate and not because of negligence.

In addition, OSHA requires MSDS's for consumer products with which employees come into contact more than a consumer would. For example, although consumers buy bleach, they would not use it as frequently as laboratory employees who decontaminate countertops with it daily. Thus, items like bleach, disinfecting hand soap, correction fluid, and copy machine toner could require MSDS's even though they are in general use by the public. Because laboratory procedures change over time, MSDS's for particular chemicals may no longer be necessary. Obsolete MSDS's should not be dis-

---

CHEMICAL HANDLING, STORAGE AND DISPOSAL SHEET

NAME OF PRODUCT: HDL cholesterol standard

PURPOSE OF USE: Calibrating HDL cholesterol procedures

ACTIVE INGREDIENTS AND CONCENTRATIONS WHERE SIGNIFICANT:

100 mg/dL cholesterol in 15% isopropanol, <1% sodium azide

POTENTIAL AS A HAZARDOUS MATERIAL:

Alcohol is flammable. Azides cannot come in contact with metals

DISTRIBUTOR: Manufacturer's name, address

METHOD OF STORAGE OR SPECIAL HANDLING WHERE NECESSARY:

Keep away from heat and light.

METHOD OF DISPOSAL:

Reacted material may be flushed into sanitary sewer as long as pipes are not metal

INSTRUCTIONS FOR USE OF THIS FORM:

1. Fill this form out upon receipt of ALL chemicals used in the lab and attach a copy of the Material Safety Data Sheet (MSDS)

2. Keep this form in the appropriate laboratory manual in the lab at all times

Figure 3-10

carded. They should be archived for up to 30 years in case of chemical exposure claims.

Finally, it is common practice for MSDS's and chemical inventories to be housed within the laboratory, close to the users for easy access. In the event of an emergency, the laboratory may be evacuated and the MSDSs would be difficult to access. It is good practice to have a duplicate set of documents elsewhere for access by hazardous materials teams.

HAZARDOUS CHARACTERISTICS

CORROSIVES

Corrosives are chemicals such as acids (low pH, especially <2.1) and bases (high pH, especially >12.5). Sometimes they are referred to as *caustics.* Certain dehydrating agents and oxidizers may also have corrosive properties even though they are not acids or bases. For example, bleach can be corrosive to metal.

Common laboratory acids include acetic, sulfuric, nitric, trichloroacetic, and hydrochloric acids. Common bases are ammonium hydroxide, potassium hydroxide, and sodium hydroxide. These chemicals can cause severe, irreversible injury to eyes and skin as well as the respiratory and gastrointestinal tracts when inhaled or ingested. When a corrosive agent comes into contact with the eye or skin, it must be flushed away immediately and thoroughly for about 15 minutes using a safety shower, an eyewash, or a special buffer provided for this purpose. Strong neutralizing agents *must not* be used because they produce a heat reaction and worsen any burn. Immediate medical attention is always required.

When working with corrosives, safety glasses should be worn and the chemical manipulated under a hood and near or in a sink. Large amounts of corrosive liquids or solids must not be added rapidly to a mixture because of increased likelihood of splashing and generation of heat. Automatic pipetting devices should *always* be used to add corrosive chemicals to water, not water to the corrosive. Slow pipetting of the corrosive down the side of the container into the water minimizes splashing.

IGNITIBLES

Ignitible liquids are characterized by their flash points. As stated in Exercise 2, a liquid's flash point is the minimum temperature at which it vaporizes sufficiently to produce an ignitible mixture with air near the surface of the liquid. Chemicals with flash points below 100°F (38°C) are called flammables or Class I solvents, and those with flash points between 100°F (38°C) and 140°F (60°C) are called combustibles or Class II solvents. Class I solvents, especially those with flash points below room temperature, are extremely hazardous and must be used under fume hoods and stored under vented conditions away from heat. Class II chemicals are less hazardous unless they are heated. Gases and solids may also be flammable and are handled similar to flammable liquids. Chemicals labeled as pyrophoric may spontaneously combust when exposed to air at <130°F and must be stored and handled carefully.

HEALTH HAZARDS

There are several categories of chemical health hazards, examples of which are listed in **Table 3-2**. Health effects can be acute, as in a large spill, or chronic, as in exposure to small amounts of chemical on a daily basis for several years. OSHA has many requirements for handling chemical health

Table 3-2: Examples of Chemical Health Hazards

Hazard	Definition
Poison	Is toxic to humans in some capacity
Hepatotoxin	Can damage the liver
Nephrotoxin	Can damage the kidney
Neurotoxin	Can damage the nervous system
Irritant	Can aggravating to body part in contact with chemical, but usually not toxic
Sensitizer	Induces allergic reaction
Mutagen	Can induce genetic mutation/DNA changes
Teratogen	Can cause birth defect in fetus
Carcinogens	Can cause cancer

hazards, but specifically targets carcinogens for special precautions. Lists of carcinogens can be found by consulting lists from OSHA, the National Toxicology Program (NTP), and the International Agency for Research on Cancer (IARC). Chemicals on any of these 3 lists must be handled as a carcinogen. The reader should note that many antineoplastic drugs found in clinical settings fall into this category. OSHA also publishes a list of hazardous chemicals that must be part of a medical surveillance program when they are used in the work place.

All chemical health hazards cannot be covered in this text or in employee training programs. In addition to providing MSDS's to workers, OSHA requires that a "target organ poster" be displayed so that workers know what signs and symptoms may be associated with chemical toxicities. A sample from the OSHA Web site is contained in Appendix 5. Certain toxic chemicals likely to be encountered in clinical laboratories are discussed in more detail.

Nitrogen

Nitrogen gas has been called "asphyxiating gas" because it can reduce oxygen in the air and create hazardous anaerobic conditions. (This can occur with other gases too.) It is critical that when working with gas cylinders of any type the valves be kept tightly closed when not in use and that all fittings be checked periodically for leaks. Immediate evacuation is necessary in the event of a large leak.

Mercury

Elemental mercury is extremely poisonous. Mercury can be absorbed through the skin, by inhalation, or by ingestion. It effects are cumulative, and chronic exposure to mercury can lead to serious toxic effects. Mercury spills of even small amounts are very dangerous because mercury has a very low vapor pressure and can contaminate an entire room with poor ventilation. Evacuation or respiratory protection is essential in the event of a significant spill of mercury. Ordinary vacuum cleaners can disperse mercury into fine airborne droplets that are not filtered by vacuum bags, so special clean-up procedures are required. Commercial mercury spill kits contain an absorbent powder that can convert mercury into a harmless amalgam in crevices, and they can be posted in convenient laboratory areas. Enclosed suction devices or vacuums specially adapted for mercury cleaning may also be used. Disposal of mercury and its compounds is highly regulated, and it is *never* acceptable to flush mercury down the drain or place it in ordinary trash.

Because of its low vapor pressure, mercury should only be used under a hood. Clinical laboratories rarely need to manipulate mercury, and the most frequent source is thermometers. The use of organic liquid thermometers may circumvent the need for mercury-handling procedures, and it is recommended that whenever possible mercury thermometers be replaced.

An additional source of mercury is fluorescent light bulbs. Not all fluorescent light bulbs contain mercury, but those that do may be regulated as a hazardous waste.

Chemicals in Histology/Autopsy Suites Paraffin, Formaldehyde, and Xylene

Histology laboratories use various chemicals and instruments to process, fix, and stain tissue. Paraffin is not particularly dangerous, but if cleaning protocols are poor, paraffin can build up on the floor and cause a slipping hazard. Equipment such as tissue processors must have a clearance of at least 5 feet from flammable chemicals in the histology section unless separated by 1-hour fire-resistant construction. Many chemicals in histology are toxic and/or flammable and should be handled with great care. Of particular importance are formaldehyde and xylene.

Formaldehyde is a strong chemical irritant. It can cause allergic reactions and is classified by OSHA as a probable carcinogen. The OSHA Formaldehyde Standard (29 CFR 1910.1048) outlines specifications for handling this chemical, including monitoring of environmental levels. To fix and preserve tissue, clinical laboratories frequently use formalin, a water, methanol and formaldehyde mixture, and formalin is covered by this OSHA standard. When mixed with hydrochloric acid, bleach, and other chlorine-containing compounds, formaldehyde can form bis-chloromethyl ether, an OSHA-regulated carcinogen. It is important to keep these compounds separate.

For certain chemicals, including formaldehyde, OSHA establishes permissible exposure limits (PELs) which are ambient levels of chemicals that

cannot be exceeded. To perform environmental monitoring, it is necessary for personnel to wear sampling devices during their work with the chemical in question. The amount of exposure is then determined from the sample collected, and it is compared to the PEL established by OSHA. Environmental monitoring is required at least once per year. Adequate ventilation (as in autopsy or histology suites), respiratory protection and/or containment (chemical fume hood) facilities must be provided to ensure that employee exposure is below an established PEL. At least 6 to 12 air exchanges per hour of 100% fresh air (not recirculated air) are necessary to keep formaldehyde exposure sufficiently low. As a general rule of thumb, if staff members can smell the formaldehyde, the area may be over the PEL.

Commercial spill kits are available for formaldehyde as well as respirator cartridges designed to block formaldehyde. It is important that staff members be trained in spill containment and waste disposal for this chemical and that the appropriate materials and protective equipment are provided.

Xylene has a low flash point, and it is toxic to various organ systems. Its PEL is 100 parts per million (ppm), but humans have the ability to smell xylene at 1 ppm. If staff members can consistently smell xylene in the workplace, environmental monitoring may be necessary.

Formalin and xylene are both heavier than air, so it is recommended that ventilation be used at the back of counter tops or at floor level. Ceiling vents for air circulation and/or updraft chemical fume hoods may not be as effective in keeping the PELs below acceptable limits. A common activity that causes formaldehyde levels to exceed PELs is pouring off liquid from specimens before their disposal. Appropriate ventilation adjacent to specimen disposal can easily rectify this problem.

Glutaraldehyde As HCN & Dry Ice

A limited number of high-level disinfectants are approved by the Food and Drug Administration (FDA) (http://www.fda.gov/cdrh/ode/germlab.html, accessed January 14, 2008). All high-level disinfectants that can also function as sterilants contain hydrogen peroxide, peracetic acid, and/or glutaraldehyde. These chemicals are important for sterilizing medical equipment that cannot be sterilized in another way (such as heat). However, because hydrogen peroxide and peracetic acid are somewhat corrosive, glutaraldehyde is far more widely used. In addition, glutaraldehyde can be used as a tissue fixative in histology or for film development in radiology departments. Unfortunately, glutaraldehyde is an acute irritant, a skin sensitizer, and a cause of occupational asthma. Acceptable levels for glutaraldehyde are recommended, and environmental monitoring may be needed to document exposure. A specific OSHA standard and PELs for glutaraldehyde do not exist at the time of publication. Because of the problems associated with glutaraldehyde, many manufacturers make high-level disinfection products that contain glutaraldehyde but with another chemical added so that the glutaraldehyde concentration is lower. The FDA has approved certain glutaraldehyde-free products for disinfection that are listed at their Web site.

As with its chemical cousin formaldehyde, if a worker can smell glutaraldehyde, the ambient levels could be too high. If glutaraldehyde products are not perfumed, most humans can detect it in the air at concentrations of 0.04 ppm; the lowest recommended exposure levels are 0.05 ppm. Occupational asthma is the most serious problem associated with glutaraldehyde. Therefore, good ventilation and containment are key to reducing exposure. Air exchange rates as high as 10 to 15 air changes per hour have been recommended if fume hoods are not used. Common sense measures such as tight fitting lids over instrument-soaking or tissue-fixing containers should also be used. For prolonged exposure, gloves known to be resistant to glutaraldehyde should be used. Certain glove materials, including latex, may absorb glutaraldehyde and are not recommended. Chemical neutralizers are available for significant glutaraldehyde spills or for disposal of waste glutaraldehyde when required. They should be placed strategically around laboratory areas in which glutaraldehyde is used.

Hydrogen Cyanide

Hydrogen cyanide is one of the most powerful poisons known to humanity. With an odor described as "bitter almonds," it is not detectable until the PEL has been exceeded; up to 60% of the population cannot reliably detect the odor. When working with cyanide compounds, it is best to use gloves to prevent absorption through the skin and work under a hood to prevent inhalation. Protocols for disposal of cyanide compounds should be strictly followed. These compounds should *never* be flushed down sinks with plumbing that interconnects throughout the laboratory. The cyanide compounds could mix with acids or other compounds in the pipes and form hydrogen cyanide gas, which could poison the entire laboratory. Therefore, cyanide compounds are classified as both toxic and reactive waste.

Dry Ice/Carbon Dioxide

The frozen form of carbon dioxide (CO_2) is referred to as dry ice because CO_2 gas emanates directly from the solid without an appreciable liquid phase in between. Dry ice is used to ship items that must be kept cold because the freezing point of CO_2 ($-78.5°C$) is below that of water ($0°C$), and unlike ice, it does not produce liquid upon melting.

Dry ice, however, is both a physical and chemical hazard. It is so cold that when in contact with unprotected skin, dry ice can "burn" or with prolonged exposure, can result in frostbite. Dry ice should always be handled with gloves, and if skin is inadvertently exposed, it should be warmed gently with tepid (not hot) water. Dry ice is also hazardous because as the gas is produced, it can: (1) "explode" a fully sealed package (the expansion ratio of CO_2 is 553 to 1), (2) reduce the oxygen level in an enclosed area to below breathable levels, and (3) because it is heavier than air, sink and reduce oxygen levels in lower levels of a structure. CO_2 concentrations of $\geq$11% in a room can lead to unconsciousness in about 1 minute, with only dizziness, headache, shortness of breath, or weakness as possible warning signs. CO_2 has no taste, color, or odor that would serve as a warning. Proper ventilation is essential when using dry ice.

OXIDIZERS

Oxidizers are materials that contain sufficient oxygen or oxidizing species to react with reducing materials and release energy. This group of chemicals includes oxygen, halogens, peroxides, and other compounds. Oxidizers will react with hydrocarbons and must be kept away from hydrocarbon oils and grease. Only the minimum amount required should be stored in the laboratory under sealed, dark, and cold (not freezing) conditions. Peroxides in the solid form are extremely sensitive to heat and mechanical jarring, so great care must be taken to ensure that refrigerator temperatures are maintained above a particular peroxide's freezing point. Oxidizers should be used under a hood with plastic, wooden, or glass materials, *not* metal. Oxidizers can be disposed of by dilution and the addition of a reducing agent if the amounts are small, but large amounts require special handling. MSDS's for each oxidixer have more detail.

Ethers are flammable solvents with low flash points. During storage, they combine with oxygen to form explosive peroxides. Storing ethers in refrigerators does not prevent peroxide formation and causes flammable vapors to be accumulated in a closed space. Ethers should be stored under a hood or in a vented cabinet in opaque containers. Each ether forms peroxides at a slightly different rate, but the rate is accelerated when the can is opened and the volume of ether declines in relation to the amount of air. Light also accelerates peroxide formation. Therefore, cans of ether should be dated upon receipt and upon opening so that they may be discarded after the appropriate amount of time. In general, unopened cans must be discarded after 1 year. Inventory management is critical for ethers so that an old ether can does not get pushed to the back of a group of reagents and go unnoticed. In addition, the smallest cans available should be purchased so that only 1 can of ether is opened up at a time and emptied quickly to prevent exposure to air. White deposits inside a can of ether or on the cap may indicate the formation of peroxide. The can should not be disturbed and must discarded by a professional.

EXPLOSIVES

Explosives are compounds capable of violent reaction under specific conditions of temperature, mechanical shock, or chemical reaction. Most flammables if heated sufficiently will explode. Peroxides formed from ethers are explosive as described earlier. Crystalline picric acid is an explosive hazard, so picric acid solutions must be protected from drying out. Perchloric acid explodes when mixed with reducing agents or organic materials and must not be used on wooden work benches. Dry perchloric acid is extremely explosive, so it is critical that spills be cleaned up properly and that perchloric acid only be used in specially designed and designated hoods. Perchloric acid fumes can form crystals in ordinary chemical fume hoods and turn a valuable piece of safety equipment into a bomb.

PHYSICAL HAZARDS

The GHS classification of physical hazards contains chemicals from every group discussed earlier. However, not every chemical in each class is a potential physical hazard. Some chemicals are natively physical hazards but others are only physical hazards if handled improperly. **Table 3-3** presents the chemical classes that pose physical hazards.

INCOMPATIBLE MIXTURES

Table 3-4 lists common laboratory chemicals that when mixed with other chemicals form hazardous mixtures. The MSDS for each chemical should list any major incompatibilities for that chemical and should be consulted before it is stored and used.

HANDLING AND USAGE

Glass containers must be held firmly around and under their bodies with 2 hands, never around delicate areas such as the "neck." Glass containers (especially those containing more than 500 mL of fluid) should be carried inside a rubber or plastic bucket to prevent breakage and/or contain a spill. When transporting heavy or multiple containers of chemicals from 1 area to another, a cart with a large rim should be used. Chemical spills in an elevator are very dangerous, so if chemicals must be moved within a building a freight elevator should be used. If a freight elevator is not available, only essential personnel should be in a public elevator when chemicals are being moved. Shipping chemicals from 1 location to another requires compliance with US Postal Service and/or DOT regulations.

Chemicals should never be tasted or purposely smelled. They should never be handled in non-laboratory areas. Chemical manipulation should be under a hood, over a sink, or on a nonreactive surface, as appropriate. Pipetting, pouring, and transferring chemicals should be done to minimize splashing, fumes, and/or aerosols, even if the operation is in a fume hood. (See additional information regarding fume hoods under "Storage and Inventory.") To the extent possible, high-risk activities should be isolated and segregated. Reagent caps or stoppers should *never* be placed on a work surface because caps could contain enough chemical to contaminate the surface and cause harm to personnel who later use the area. In addition, the cap could get dirty and contaminate the entire bottle of chemical. Chemicals should only be opened long enough to access the chemical, and then the container should be immediately closed. All work surfaces must be wiped off both before and after use. Automatic pipetting devices must *always* be used to transfer chemicals, and the appropriate safety apparel should be worn (see "Protective Wearing Apparel," p. 59). For similar reasons, bottles of picric acid and perchloric acid should be inspected for crystals around the top and handled as potential explosives if crystals are present.

Table 3-3: Chemical Classes That Pose Physical Hazards As Classified by the Global Harmonization System			
Flammable Gases	Flammable Aerosols	Flammable Solids	Flammable Liquids
Oxidizing gases	Explosives	Pyrophoric solids	Pyrophoric liquids
Gases under pressure	Organic peroxides	Oxidizing solids	Oxidizing liquids
Self-reactive chemicals	Self-heating chemicals	Water-reactive chemicals	Metal corrosives

Chemical Safety

Table 3-4: Important Chemical Incompatibilities

Don't mix this:	With this:
Acetic acid	Chromic acid, nitric acid, hydroxyl containing compounds, ethylene glycol, perchloric acid, peroxide, permanganates, xylene
Acetone	Concentrated nitric and sulfuric acids, amines, oxidizers
Ammonia (anhydrous)	Acids, aldehydes, amides, metals, nitrates, oxidizers, mercury, bleach, calcium hypochlorite, halogens sulfur and hydrogen fluoride
Azides	Acids, heavy metals (especially copper and lead), oxidizers
Cyanide compounds	Acids and alkalis
Formaldehyde	Hydrochloric acid, bleach & other chlorinated compounds
Hydrogen peroxide	Most metals and their salts, any flammable liquid, aniline and nitromethane
Hydrocarbons (benzene,butane, propane, gasoline, turpentine)	Halogens, acids, bases, oxidizers
Hypochlorites (bleach)	Ammonia, acids, activated carbon
Iodine	Acetylene, acetaldehyde, and ammonia
Mercury	Acetylene, fulminic acid, oxidizers and ammonia
Nitric acid	Acetic acid, aniline, chromic acid, hydrocyanic acid
Oxygen	Oils, grease, hydrogen, flammables, alkalis
Perchloric acid	Acetic anhydride, bismuth and its alloys, alcohol, paper, wood, grease, oils, organic amines or anti-oxidants
Strong acids	Strong bases (store acids and bases separately)
Sulfuric acid	Chlorates, perchlorates and permanganates

DISPOSAL

In general, there are 4 components to chemical waste management. Additional information on waste disposal is contained in Exercise 8.

1. Obey legal requirements. Consult the MSDS and regulations from the Environmental Protection Agency (EPA), state, and local authorities.

2. Reduce, reuse, and recycle. The least amount of chemical possible should be purchased and used, and if possible, it should be used repeatedly. Recycling may be difficult, but it is an option that should be investigated. Good organization and planning must be used to minimize chemical waste for any cause, including expiration.

3. Segregate and label wastes. Hazardous waste should not be mixed with nonhazardous waste because the entire resulting mixture would be classified as hazardous. The contents of every waste container should be clear.

4. Store and dispose waste properly.

SANITARY SEWER

Laboratory drains may be interconnected, so toxic, malodorous, or irritating chemicals that produce hazardous vapors should not be flushed. Cyanide salts in particular can form toxic hydrogen cyanide gas when mixed with acids. Cyanide compounds have their own unique disposal procedures, or the compounds can be collected separately in a safety can for licensed waste handlers.

Many laboratory reagents contain sodium azide as a preservative. These reagents should not be put in sinks with copper or lead plumbing. Copper and lead form explosive azides with sodium azide, and no reagents containing azide should be disposed of in sinks with metal pipes.

Proper disposal of strong corrosive types of chemicals is critical because improper disposal can cause damage to plumbing and can cause unexpected reactions in pipes containing incompatible chemicals from other laboratory areas. Before drain disposal, strong acids and bases must be diluted with large volumes of water and/or neutralized until the pH is greater than 3 and less than 10. Continue running water for several minutes after disposing of the diluted corrosive. However, this does not mean that any chemical can be sufficiently diluted for sanitary sewer disposal. Some types of plastic pipes are damaged by strong chemicals, so evaluate the exact type of plumbing in a facility before disposing of any chemical down the drain.

Chemicals that are candidates for sink disposal are aqueous, neutral solutions that do not contain heavy metals or organic solvents. Buffers and surfactants are good examples. Most chemicals that may be disposed of in the sanitary sewer should be flushed with generous amounts of cold water between chemicals. Chemicals that can be flushed may still need to be segregated because, as stated before, if laboratory plumbing is interconnected, incompatible chemicals may be mixed. Once the chemicals are disposed, it may be necessary to triple-rinse the empty containers before final disposal.

LICENSED WASTE HANDLERS

Chemicals requiring special disposal should be labeled and segregated from ordinary trash for removal by licensed waste handlers. Storage requirements are essentially the same as those for the pure chemical, but if waste is kept in the same place as unadulterated chemical, it should be clearly marked so that it is not inadvertently used.

INCINERATION

Incineration should generally be done only by professionals in an EPA-approved facility.

LANDFILL OR SOLID-WASTE DISPOSAL FACILITIES

Some chemicals may be placed in the "regular" laboratory trash for disposal in a public landfill while others must be placed in the EPA's hazardous waste sites. Personnel training is essential to prevent hazardous chemicals from reaching a public landfill.

PROTECTIVE WEARING APPAREL

Clothes should be protected by a laboratory coat or apron. For some chemicals, particularly corrosives, fluid-proof aprons should be worn. Sandals, open footwear, and cloth shoes must *not* be worn. Goggles, face shields, or safety glasses are often necessary, particularly when using concentrated chemicals. Because chemical fumes can penetrate under contact lenses, in some cases they cannot be worn. Eyeglasses also do not suffice in all situations, and it may be imperative to wear goggles over corrective glasses because fluids can still splash under or over corrective glasses. Toxic and corrosive chemicals demand fluid-proof gloves, and insulated gloves are prerequisites for handling hot objects. Gloves should be changed when a leak or tear develops or if they are grossly contaminated. Certain chemicals can dissolve certain glove materials, so caution must be used when selecting gloves for a particular task (see Exercise 10). Finally, if chemicals with toxic fumes are not maneuvered under a hood, respiratory protection may be in order.

CHEMICAL SPILLS

The Emergency Preparedness and Community Right-to-Know Act, also known as Title III of the SUPERFUND Amendments and Reauthorization Act (SARA, Title III), requires certain chemical users to plan for emergencies, report chemical use to adjacent communities, and report accidental release of toxic chemicals. At the time of this publication, research and medical laboratories are exempt under SARA, Title III, regulations. The OSHA regulation pertaining to chemical spill management is 29 CFR 1910.120, Hazardous Waste Operations and Emergency Response, often referred to as "HAZWOPER." This regulation is primarily geared toward large-scale industrial spills, but all laboratories should rehearse emergency procedures for chemical spills. "CLEAN" is a useful acronym describing the handling of chemical spills.

C **CONTAIN** the spill
L **LEAVE** the area
E **EMERGENCY EQUIPMENT** - eyewash, shower, medical help
A **ACCESS MSDS**
N **NOTIFY** a supervisor and/or emergency personnel

A more detailed version of the general sequence of events is as follows.

1. Remove all personnel from harm's way, evacuating and quarantining the spill area as necessary

2. Contain the spill if possible during the evacuation

3. Perform the appropriate first aid on injured personnel

4. Notify hazardous spill teams or emergency health authorities, as appropriate

5. Put on the necessary personal protective equipment

6. Stop the spill or leak

7. Turn off heat and electrical sources. If toxic or flammable fumes are present, turn on ventilation

8. Contain the spill by spreading absorbent material around its perimeter

9. Clean the spill

10. Document the incident

11. Analyze the incident for appropriate emergency response and measures to prevent recurrence

Commercial kits for most types of spills are available and can be posted in strategic sites around the laboratory. All-purpose absorbents like kitty litter, vermiculite, and sand can easily be stored in buckets and distributed around the laboratory. This allows for immediate spill containment because absorbent material can be placed around the perimeter of large spills to form "dikes" around them and prevent spreading. Small spills can be completely soaked up. Cloths and paper towels frequently are not useful because they may be hazardous if soaked with chemicals, particularly flammables. If the spill is large (more than 1 gallon of hazardous material) or contains a physical or health hazard, personnel should be evacuated immediately, and the cleanup should be handled by professionals or by personnel with the appropriate equipment. A good example might be the presence of toxic fumes that require a respirator. When possible, heat and electrical sources should be turned off, especially after a flammable spill. Flammable spills also require that the area be ventilated to prevent fire from accumulated fumes.

If the spill involves a person's clothing and skin, all affected clothing should be removed immediately and the affected areas flushed with water. If clothing must be removed by pulling it over the victim's head, it should be cut off to prevent contamination of the eyes. A safety shower should be used for body spills, and an eye wash is adequate for eye and face splashes. If the spill does involve an eye, every effort should be made to remove contact lenses while flushing with water because chemicals will remain trapped under the lenses. Prompt medical attention is always necessary for any serious spill affecting the body.

It is critical that laboratory workers know the proper procedures for each chemical with which they work. Information on specific chemicals should be obtained from manufacturers, OSHA, the EPA, or local health and environmental departments *before* they are used, and this information should be placed in the standard operating procedures of the chemical hygiene plan.

Summary Table: Chemical Safety

Topic	Comment
Labels	Label before filling. Includes waste and non-hazardous substances like water
	1. Name and concentration of chemical 2. Dates: receipt, made, expiration 3. Initials of person who made or received the chemical 4. Hazards present (poisonous, flammable, etc.) and special instructions
	NFPA Descriptive Labels (Scale of 0 - 4. 0 no hazard, 4 maximum hazard.) RED- Fire Hazard BLUE- Health Hazard YELLOW- Stability Hazard WHITE-Specific Hazard
	HMIS Descriptive Labels (Scale of 0 - 4. 0 no hazard, 4 maximum hazard.) RED- Fire Hazard BLUE- Health Hazard ORANGE- Physical WHITE-Personal Protective Eqpt
	Pictograms 1. Learn symbols. Examples: personal protective eqpt, hazard classes, no smoking symbols 2. Learn DOT hazard symbols 3. Learn GHS hazard symbols (see text)
Storage	1. Follow government and NFPA regulations. Use MSDS & CHP. 2. Inventory: Minimize stocks, organize chemicals to separate incompatibles, "first in, first out" 3. Keep storage area labeled, clean, temperature controlled, ventilated and secured. 4. Store dangerous material on low, "lipped" shelves 5. Use refrigerator storage cautiously. Fumes can accumulate inside 6. Ensure fume hoods maintain 100 linear feet per minute air flow: low traffic areas, maintenance, sash low, objects away from air intake. May need backdraft hood for vapors heavier than air
MSDS	1. Comprehensive source of information on a chemical 2. Required for all hazardous chemicals. Document non-hazardous status of others 3. Maintain obsolete MSDS's for 30 years
Chemical classes	1. Corrosives - strong acids and bases 2. Flammables (flash point <100°F) and combustibles (flash point >100°F) 3. Health hazards - toxins, carcinogens, teratogens, mutagens, irritants, sensitizers 4. Oxidizers 5. Explosives 6. Physical Hazards
Incompatible mixtures	1. MSDS for each chemical and CHP should list major incompatibilties 2. Consult MSDS and CHP before using or storing a chemical 3. Review exercise for examples of incompatible chemicals
Handling and Usage	1. Use cart with raised sides for transporting 2. Move glass containers inside rubber or plastic bucket 3. Hold containers firmly around and under their bodies, not by slender "necks" 4. Hold bottle cap in other hand. Do not lay on countertop unless inverted 5. Always use automatic pipetting device. Add acid to water, not water to acid 6. Do not eat, drink or smell chemicals 7. No splashing or aerosols. Use fume hoods when appropriate or if airborne drops/fumes present 8. Decontaminate work surfaces and wash hands when work complete

Exercise 3

Self-Evaluation Questions

1. ___ All of the information below is essential when labeling a secondary reagent container **EXCEPT:**

   a. Date reagent made
   b. Concentration of reagent
   c. Manufacturing source of reagent
   d. Initials of person who made reagent
   e. Hazards of the reagent and special handling required

2. ___ Which of the following needs to be labeled?

   a. A beaker of water
   b. Chemical waste that will not be reused
   c. A reagent that contains non-hazardous chemicals
   d. A squirt bottle of bleach being used to clean a countertop
   e. All of the above

3. ___ According to the NFPA diamond below, this chemical's most significant hazard is

   a. Health
   b. Reactivity
   c. Instability
   d. Flammability
   e. Radioactivity

4. ___ Which chemical type below best fits the HMIS label as shown below?

   a. Mutagen
   b. Corrosive
   c. Sensitizer
   d. Teratogen
   e. Pyrophoric

5. Match the GHS symbol to its hazard class.

___ Corrosive
___ Explosive
___ Oxidizer
___ Severe Health Hazard

A   B   C   D

6. ___ Each item below is stored **CORRECTLY EXCEPT**:

a. Ether in a fume hood
b. Class I solvent in a vented safety cabinet
c. Solid sodium chloride on room-temperature shelving
d. Concentrated hydrochloric acid in an overhead shelf with a lip for containing spills
e. Peroxide in an explosion-proof refrigerator at a temperature *above* its freezing point

7. State 3 important principles of chemical inventory management.

_____

_____

_____

8. ___ When fume hoods are in use:

a. Air flow should be maintained at 100 linear feet per minute
b. At least 1.5 feet of linear work space should be allowed per person
c. The sash should be in the fully up position to draw in the maximum amount of air
d. Objects should not be pushed to the back of the hood. They should be close to the front for easy reach to prevent users from leaning into the hood space
e. All of the above

9.___ All of the information below should be found on an MSDS **EXCEPT**:

a. Flammablity of a chemical
b. Emergency spill procedures
c. Health hazard of a chemical
d. Common name of a chemical
e. Closest disposal site for a chemical

10. ___ Each technique below is **CORRECT EXCEPT:**

    a. Add acid to water
    b. Wear gloves when using poisons
    c. Work under a fume hood with flammables
    d. Carry bottles of chemicals firmly by the neck
    e. Use respiratory protection when cleaning a mercury spill

11. ___ If you can smell ___, it is likely that its environmental concentration is too high for safety.

    a. Xylene
    b. Formaldehyde
    c. Glutaraldehyde
    d. Hydrogen cyanide
    e. All of the above

12. Matching

    ___ Corrosive   a. Flash point below 100°F
    ___ Health hazards   b. Reduces compounds and releases energy
    ___ Class I, flammable   c. Irritants, poisons, sensitizers and carcinogens
    ___ Class II, combustible   d. Strong acid or strong base
    ___ Oxidizer   e. Flash point above 100°F
    ___ Explosive   f. Detonates under specific stress, for example, high temperature

13. Ethers should be discarded after 1 year because they can form explosive

    _____.

    If this has occurred, you may see

    _____.

14. ___ In what way(s) is perchloric acid dangerous?

    a. It is corrosive
    b. It will react with wood
    c. The dried acid is explosive
    d. Fumes will crystallize in fume hood duct work and crystals are explosive
    e. All of the above

15. Crystalline _____ acid is explosive.

16. The preservative _____ must never be flushed down a drain with metal plumbing.

17. Oxidizers should never contact_____.

18. If permissible, flush chemicals down the sink with large amounts of _____.

19. List the 4 ways that chemicals can be disposed:

    1. _____

    2. _____

    3. _____

    4. _____

20. ___ A chemical that is known to harm an unborn baby is a:

    a. Mutagen
    b. Corrosive
    c. Sensitizer
    d. Teratogen
    e. Pyrophoric

21. ___ A chemical that is known to induce allergies in some people is a:

    a. Mutagen
    b. Corrosive
    c. Sensitizer
    d. Teratogen
    e. Pyrophoric

22. ___ Dry ice can be hazardous because

    a. Its cold temperature is a physical hazard
    b. It may reduce the breathable level of oxygen to below safe limits
    c. It is colorless, odorless, and tasteless, so high levels are difficult to detect
    d. Its large expansion ratio may cause confined dry ice to explode its container
    e. All of the above

23. ___ In the event of a chemical spill, which action below should generally be done first?

    a. Ventilate the area
    b. Quarantine the area
    c. Create a "dike" around the spill to contain it
    d. Put on personal protective equipment
    e. Ensure that all personnel are safe, evacuating them as needed

24. The chemicals _____ and _____ are heavier than air and may be best controlled using a backdraft hood.

25. A chemical particularly harmful to the liver would be classified as a

_____.

Exercise 4

EQUIPMENT AND ELECTRICAL SAFETY

The proper procedure for using laboratory equipment—from the simplest piece of glassware to the most complex analytical instrument—is essential to prevent accidents. This unit will cover in a generic way the proper use of electrical equipment, identification of electrical hazards, glassware safety, centrifuge safety, safety with sharps (such as needles and scalpels), and steam sterilizer/autoclave safety.

NATURE OF ELECTRICITY

In simplest terms, electricity is the movement of electrons. Materials through which electrons can easily flow are called conductors. Those which resist electrical flow are called insulators. In general, metals that loosely hold their valence electrons, water-containing ions, and human beings make excellent conductors. (Very pure water is not a very good conductor.) Materials that tightly hold their valence electrons such as dry wood, plastic, glass, rubber, and ceramics are good insulators. The number of electrons flowing down a path is expressed in amperes ("amps"), and the force of the electrons is expressed as voltage ("volts").

Electricity travels best in closed circuits. A circuit is composed of an electron source (a battery, for example), and a conductor which makes a complete circuit from the electron source and back again. Humans experience electrical shock when they inadvertently become part of the electrical circuit, and current enters one part of the body and leaves via another. The severity of the shock is related to the amount of electrical current, the path through the body, and the length of time the current is experienced. Even low voltages can cause injury if they are of sufficient duration and affect essential organs such as the heart. Therefore, *no amount of electricity is considered "safe."*

As shown in **Table 4-1**, electrical shocks range from a faint tingling sensation to cardiac arrest, burns, and death. Electricity can cause muscular contractions which "freeze" the victim to the electrical circuit or cause involuntary movements leading to injury. Burns are the most common manifestation of electrical shock. Therefore electrical injury should always be considered in an unconscious victim with burns. In addition, the heat generated by electrical malfunctions creates a fire hazard for the entire facility.

Equipment and Electrical Safety

GENERAL MANAGEMENT OF ELECTRICAL HAZARDS

The Occupational Safety and Health Administration (OSHA) recommends 5 means to manage electrical hazards:

1. **Insulation** Electrical wires should never be exposed, and frayed insulation should be replaced before any equipment is used. Insulation on devices should never be intentionally compromised.

2. **Guarding** High-voltage electrical equipment should be placed in areas of restricted access so that only qualified personnel may work around them. Unqualified laboratory personnel should not be allowed to operate or maintain laboratory instruments and equipment.

3. **Grounding** By virtue of its size, the earth can absorb large amounts of charge and remain electrically neutral. When an instrument is connected to the ground by a wire that easily conducts electricity, any excess electricity it accumulates will preferentially pass into the earth and not onto a laboratory worker. All equipment must be grounded, usually with 3-pronged plugs. (The only exception is certain

double-insulated sealed plastic devices that have polarized plugs to orient the prongs of the plug to the socket correctly.) A schematic of a 3-prong plug is shown in **Figure 4-1**. The 2 flat prongs carry current, and the large round pin connects the instrument to a grounding wire. The grounding pin of an electrical plug should never be cut off or bypassed. Even if an instrument is grounded and coated with an insulator, however, it should never be assumed that it is incapable of causing shock. Grounding and polarity on all electrical outlets should be checked at least annually, and all electrical equipment should be on a maintenance and inspection schedule.

4. **Circuit protection devices** Fuses, circuit breakers, surge protectors and ground-fault circuit interrupters (GFCI's) are devices that automatically shut off electrical flow in the event that excess current has been detected. These devices should be clearly labeled and easily accessed. Circuit breakers, GFCI's, and some top-model surge protectors shut off current mechanically and can be reused. Fuses and less expensive surge protectors contain wires that melt when too much current travels through them and must be replaced when they are used. Fresh fuses have zero resistance to

Table 4-1: Effects of Electricity on the Human Body

Current level (milliamperes)	Probable effect on human body
1 mA	Perception level. Slight tingling sensation. More dangerous if skin wet.
5 mA	Slight shock felt; not painful but disturbing. Average individual can let go. Strong involuntary reactions (muscle contractions) can cause injury.
6-30 mA	Painful shock, muscular control is lost. This is called the freezing current or "let-go" range.
50-150 mA	Extreme pain, respiratory arrest, severe muscle contractions. Individual cannot let go. Death is possible.
1000-4300 mA	Ventricular fibrillation (the rhythmic pumping action of the heart ceases). Muscular contraction and nerve damage occur. Death likely.
10,000 mA	Cardiac arrest, severe burns and probable death.

(www.osha.gov)

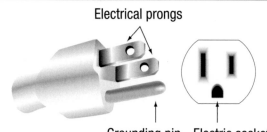

Electrical prongs

Grounding pin   Electric socket

Schematic of an electrical plug

Figure 4-1

electrical flow, and as long as excess current is not entering an instrument, power should flow in freely. A schematic of a fuse is shown in **Figure 4-2**. As indicated, fuses are rated for amperage and voltage. The amperage rating is the upper limit of current that can pass through the fuse without melting it. The voltage rating is the lower limit of voltage that is sufficiently strong to "jump" the gap in the fuse created by the melted wire. Manufacturers select fuses that are appropriate to the amount of electricity an instrument can tolerate, so ideally, a spent fuse should be replaced with another fuse of identical rating. If an identical fuse is unavail-

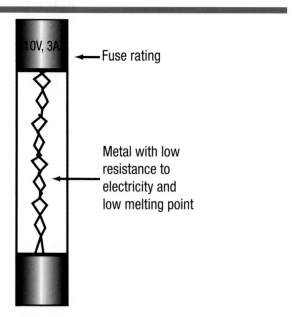

10V, 3A ◄── Fuse rating

Metal with low resistance to electricity and low melting point

Schematic of a fuse

Figure 4-2

able, it is possibly acceptable to use a fuse with *higher* voltage or *lower* amperage, but never the other way around. If any of these devices shut off current, the cause of the current surge should be determined before reactivating the circuit or replacing the fuse. Repetitively tripped circuits and blown fuses indicate a problem that should be corrected.

5. **Safe work practices** The major safe work practices recommended by OSHA are "deenergizing electric equipment before inspecting or making repairs, using electric tools that are in good repair, using good judgement when working near energized lines and using appropriate protective equipment." These issues will be discussed herein as they relate to the laboratory.

LOCKOUT/TAGOUT

The OSHA Standard "Control of Hazardous Energy," CFR 1910.147 is also known as the "Lockout/Tagout" standard. Electrical and machine maintenance can be hazardous if electrical current is accidently turned back on or if equipment is activated. During maintenance staff members must often turn off the electricity to a particular area, and during this time access to electrical panels or instruments should be denied (a "lockout") or prominent signs should be displayed to prevent inadvertent reactivations (a "tagout"). Only the person who initiated the lockout/tagout is permitted to remove the lock/tag when the work is safely completed. Therefore, all lockouts/tagouts must bear the name of the person who initiated them. All staff members who must initiate lockout/tagout protocols or who would encounter the lockout/tagout must be thoroughly trained in the protocols used at their institution. During electrical maintenance in an area, special precautions may be needed, such as foregoing the use of metal step stools and ladders while

Equipment and Electrical Safety

wires are exposed. Although OSHA does not call it "lockout/tagout," similar protocols should be used when an instrument is malfunctioning and is removed from service. Special attention may also be required in institutions such as hospitals where continuous uninterrupted power is a patient safety requirement. For example, emergency generators must be in operation within 10 seconds of power loss in a hospital, therefore 2 emergency generators are required to allow servicing of one without violating the 10-second requirement.

EMERGENCY GENERATORS

During power supply interruptions, many homes and public facilities have the capability of restoring power with generators. Generators should only be installed by qualified electricians who can then train the users on proper protocols for that generator. In most cases, the main circuit breaker should be locked out in the "off" position so that there is no connection to the power lines while the generator is operating. When a generator is connected to the normal power lines, a serious problem called *backfeed* can arise. Backfeed is when a portable generator unexpectedly sends power to the power lines. Repair workers in the vicinity of those lines can be fatally electrocuted in a backfeed event. To prevent backfeed, generators should never be plugged directly into a wall outlet unless special power transfer switches have been installed.

Laboratories wired to emergency generators often have particular outlets that are identified as uninterruptible power supplies (UPS). Sometimes these outlets can be color-coded or red. Staff should be familiar with how the laboratory should be powered in the event of an outage to prevent any loss of valuable equipment or electrical injury caused by nonstandard situations.

USE OF ELECTRICAL EQUIPMENT

Because some instruments and heating devices use large amounts of electric current, laboratory electrical requirements may be significantly different from domestic power needs. Laboratories, however, are often located in facilities originally intended for other purposes. Electrical wiring and power sources in a laboratory facility should be inspected by experts to ensure that dangerous inadequacies do not exist. GFCI's are the surge protectors of choice in high-risk areas, especially for outlets near sources of water, and should be considered if guaranteed separation of electrical supply and fluids is impossible.

Surge protectors should be used to protect delicate equipment, but all surge protectors are not created equal. The higher priced models generally provide increased protection against excess current. Using a surge protector rated for the highest amperage and voltage possible is often a wise investment.

Electrical equipment for laboratories should conform to stipulations set forth by bodies such as Underwriters Laboratories, Inc (Northbrook, IL). Many laboratory instruments are specially designed to operate spark-free in environments likely to have flammable solvents, so substitutes of domestic consumer goods such as ovens, blenders, hotplates, etc, may not be appropriate. The user's manual is a valuable resource for an instrument's proper operating procedure. Users must consult it if they have never, or not recently, used a particular device. Directions for cleaning and servicing the instrument are particularly important. The wrong cleaning agent, such as acetone or water, can decrease the effectiveness of insulating materials and cause shock. In addition, insufficient maintenance of an instrument may cause not only interference in the instrument's function but also hazardous conditions to the user. Instruments should be on a maintenance schedule and be checked annually for proper grounding and current leakage. A procedure manual or user's manual should be readily accessible to every individual who operates an instrument.

When an instrument is not in use, it should be turned off, unplugged and dried thoroughly unless the manufacturer explicitly directs otherwise. Any electrical equipment, especially a motor, that is operated in an area with flammable vapors, must be nonsparking and explosion-proof. This includes any temporary equipment brought into the area such as a floor polisher or a vacuum cleaner.

Water, unless specially treated, contains ions that make it highly conductive of electricity. Liquid around electrical equipment is to be avoided at all costs. Wet wires must *never* be plugged into a circuit. Electrical equipment must *never* be handled with wet hands or while standing in or near water. Wet motors and instruments must *never* be operated.

Permanent extension cords are not permitted, and circuits should never be overloaded with too many pieces of equipment (no "octopus" outlets). Wires and extension cords are rated for the amount of amperage and voltage that they can support. If extension cords must be temporarily used, users must check that they are rated for the amount of current used by the equipment. Like surge suppressors, extension cords generally increase in cost as they increase in their ability to sustain higher currents. Extension cords conducting current in excess of their capacity get extremely overheated and are a serious fire hazard.

IDENTIFICATION OF ELECTRICAL HAZARDS

Any malfunctioning equipment or equipment that produces a "tingle" should be unplugged and marked "OUT OF SERVICE" or "DO NOT USE." Arrangements for service should be made promptly. Only persons qualified for instrument repair should work on malfunctioning equipment. Instruments that have been turned off sometimes have high voltage points that remain from the previous "on" cycle, which can cause shock. Certain types of malfunctions in medical equipment must be reported to the Food and Drug Administration (FDA), and staff should be aware of these guidelines when there are instrument problems.

User's manuals often include guides to troubleshooting. The directions in the user's manual must be followed explicitly when any repair is attempted. Repairs that are not listed in the user's manual should *not* be attempted. Some general rules to follow when troubleshooting instruments are:

1. Turn off the power, and unplug the instrument whenever possible. Occasionally troubleshooting may require that the instrument remain on (for example, to check if a light bulb is burned out). It is especially important to follow directions for correct troubleshooting when an instrument remains on.

2. Most jewelry conducts electricity. Remove all jewelry and follow the "one hand in pocket" rule. If both hands are on an instrument, a completed electrical circuit is made which will pass current through the chest if electricity is present. This practice is still advisable even if the instrument is off in case any high voltage points remain.

3. Have a clear path to the master switch or breaker box in case power needs to be interrupted quickly. A minimum clearance of 3 feet in front of electrical panels is required at all times. In the event of shock, try to cut power to the entire laboratory. Use a *nonconductor* to separate an electrical shock victim from an electrical source, *not* the hands. Burns must be treated with cool water, but only far away from the source of the electrical problem.

Exposed instrument parts, frayed wires, and electrical cords can cause shock or fire. All worn cords or plugs should be replaced immediately by persons qualified to do so and with the correct replacement part. An important source of strained and frayed wires is repeated unplugging of an instrument by grabbing the cord rather than the plug itself. All users should unplug equipment by pulling on the plug and should be particularly alert for exposed wires adjacent to the plug.

Electrical fires *cannot* be extinguished with water and should only be controlled with the use of a carbon dioxide or dry chemical extinguisher. (See Exercise 2 for more details.)

GLASSWARE SAFETY

Glassware, even when handled correctly, is a frequent laboratory hazard because it is easily breakable. Any glassware that is cracked, chipped, flawed, or otherwise showing signs of stress should be discarded. When glass connections or stoppers become stuck, they should never be forced. It is important to keep glass connections lubricated and to use appropriate hand protection for making glass connections. (Caution: Certain chemicals, such as oxidizers, should not come into contact with lubricants.) Glass should not be put where it can easily be struck. For instance, pipettes sticking out of the tops of flasks or glassware left close to the edge of a work surface can easily be knocked over.

Mouth pipetting is not acceptable, so appropriate devices must be attached to the tops of slender glass pipettes. When inserting a glass pipette into an automatic pipetting device, the pipette must be grasped very close to the end that is being inserted into the device. Holding the pipette opposite to the end that is being inserted applies a force that could cause the pipette to break in the middle (see **Figure 4-3**).

Glassware should be made of borosilicate glass such as Pyrex® or some other heat-resistant material, and heated glass should only be handled with gloves or tongs. Rapid heating and cooling should be avoided because this stresses virtually all glass. As shown in **Figure 4-4**, glassware should be handled from the bottom or around the body. The "neck" of most glass is fragile. This particularly applies to volumetric flasks with long, delicate necks that are easily broken. Glass under pressure (such as that used with suctioning pumps) should be housed in wire jackets.

Glassware must be cleaned thoroughly after each use. If a chemical or biological hazard has been in a particular piece of glass, it is important to neutralize the effects of the hazard *before* cleaning. If an automatic washer is not in use, it is desirable

Correctly inserting pipette into bulb

Figure 4-3A

Incorrectly inserting pipette into bulb

Figure 4-3B

Correctly holding filled flask at top and bottom

Figure 4-4

to wear rubber gloves and to line the sink with a rubber mat when washing glassware. The gloves will improve the grip on the soapy, wet glass and will protect hands in the event of breakage, and the mat will "soften" the sink surface. It is safer to let glass air dry than to towel dry it because the wet glass is slippery and more easily dropped.

In the event of breakage, broken pieces of glass should never be removed by hand. Mechanical means, such as sweeping, tongs, or forceps, must be employed. If the glass breaks during washing, the water in the sink should be completely drained before cleanup. Broken glass must be disposed into a specially designated puncture-resistant container. Broken glassware in ordinary trash can puncture garbage bags and harm unsuspecting individuals. Also, because broken glass in vacuum cleaner bags is a hazard, removing broken glass with a vacuum cleaner is unacceptable.

Thin, delicate glass objects should be treated like sharps and disposed accordingly. This includes glass slides, Pasteur pipettes with long slender ends, capillary tubes, and the like. When possible, these should be replaced with plastic. Plastic tubes for blood collection are currently available

as well as plastic capillary tubes for tests in which the plastic does not interfere. Plastic beakers and flasks are also readily available, but because some chemicals can dissolve plastics, it is important to check any container before it is used for a particular chemical.

SAFETY WITH SHARPS

Sharp objects like needles, syringes, scalpels, microtomes, cryostats, and bone saws may be used in a laboratory and require disposal or cleaning. These objects present not only a physical hazard but also an infectious hazard if they are contaminated with biological material. Safety-engineered devices generally cost far more than conventional devices. Because both disposable sharps and their protection devices usually must be discarded, the volume of hazardous waste and disposal costs are also increased. Employers have no choice, however. The Needlestick Safety and Prevention Act went into effect in November 2000. As part of the Bloodborne Pathogens Exposure Control Plan, safety managers must incorporate as many safety devices as is reasonable to minimize employee exposure to injury from sharps. In many ways these practices are cost-justified. In 2005, the Centers for Disease Control and Prevention (CDC) estimated that accidental needlesticks cost between $900 and $5,000 to treat. If an employee acquires a disease from an accidental exposure, the American Hospital Association estimates employer costs in excess of $1 million. The OSHA enforcement procedures document CPL 2-2.69 (www.osha.gov, accessed January 15, 2008) states that sharps devices must meet the following criteria:

1. A fixed safety feature provides a barrier between the hands and the needle after use.

2. The safety feature should allow or require the worker's hands to remain behind the needle at all times.

3. The safety feature is an integral part of the device and not an accessory.

4. The safety feature is in effect before disassembly and remains in effect after disposal to protect users and trash handlers, and for environmental safety.

5. The safety feature is as simple as possible, and requiries little or no training to use effectively.

Examples of devices with the features outlined are skin-puncturing sharps that automatically retract after use and "self-sheathing" needles and scalpels. **Figure 4-5** illustrates one such device. Employees who try to circumvent safety devices should be disciplined or terminated.

In addition to the aforementioned devices, work practices should be scrutinized to minimize hazards. Sharp devices should never be used when a nonsharp or alternate method can be substituted. For example, in some situations, blunt-tip suture needles can be substituted for sharp-tip needles. Syringes have some of the highest accident rates of all sharp devices. Drawing blood directly into

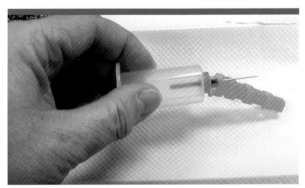

Safety needle cover. Cover can be flipped onto needle with one hand behind the sharp at all times

Figure 4-5

evacuated tubes rather than using syringes is preferable. When possible, plastic capillary tubes and plastic test tubes can be substituted for glass. Blade guards and locks must be engaged properly in cutting devices (cryostats and microtomes) and blades must be cleaned, replaced, and discarded with great care.

Safety-engineered devices are usually designed to be single-use and discarded as a single unit because removal of the sharp and reuse of the device could constitute an OSHA violation. Reuse of devices can also cause biohazard contamination. The use of a safety device does not change the sharp device into a nonsharp one in terms of handling and waste disposal. Sealed sharps must still be discarded in puncture-resistant containers and handled as sharp waste.

Most needles are disposable, and it is prudent to avoid the use of reusable needles if possible. Recapping or shearing needles by hand is extremely dangerous and is forbidden unless employers can prove medical necessity. This would be extremely rare. More commonly, needles and other sharps are used once and discarded into a puncture-resistant container. It is dangerous to overfill sharps disposal boxes. Once they are approximately 3/4 full, they should be sealed and removed for final disposal.

Disposal boxes for sharps should be within arm's reach of the site of use. Mounted disposal boxes must be at an ergonomically acceptable height for manipulation and viewing of the disposal portals. This generally means 38 to 42 inches above the floor for seated work stations and 52 to 56 inches high for standing. This can generally be achieved in laboratories. However, OSHA recognizes that this may be a problem in some patient-care situations. Patients in pediatric units, psychiatric units, and correctional facilities, for example, should not have access to sharps, and staff may need to lock down sharps disposal boxes or have them in another

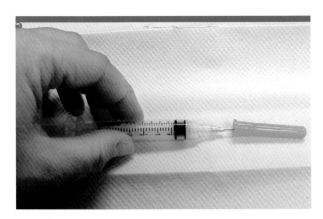

The "one-handed scoop" to cover needles safely

Figure 4-6

room. Because it is dangerous to walk any distance with an exposed sharp, devices that automatically resheathe must be used. If the use of a traditional needle and cap-type device is unavoidable, the user should use the "one-handed scoop", shown in **Figure 4-6**, to cover the sharp. Using only the hand with the needle, the cap is "scooped up" and covered until it can be disposed.

Used sharps devices must be autoclaved or incinerated to remove infectious hazard. Most states have regulations for medical waste, and in some cases needles must not only be disinfected but also destroyed beyond recognition to prevent reuse and/ or accidental puncture.

After use, reusable scalpels may be placed in a pan of disinfectant until they can be autoclaved. The entire pan should be autoclaved to prevent removal of dirty scalpels by hand. If disposable scalpels are used, the entire scalpel should be put into a puncture-resistant disposal box.

Facilities are required to keep "sharps injury logs" to keep track of employee incidents. Such logs are used to evaluate the safety devices in use and work practices that led to injuries. Detailed analysis is done to prevent such injuries in the future. OSHA requires that employees who are actual users of safety-engineered devices give input into the purchase decisions. This is to prevent managers from buying cheaper devices that may not be the safest or easiest to use. On an annual basis, employees must be surveyed as to their satisfaction with the performance of current devices and these surveys should be considered simultaneously with injuries incurred during the year to determine if new devices are likely to improve safety. Manufacturers often introduce new products or change prices, so annual surveys of new technologies are also required. For example, some manufacturers have begun introducing various "needleless systems" that would be highly preferable. The appendices of the OSHA document CPL 2-2.69 contain sources of evaluation forms and criteria that can be used.

CENTRIFUGE SAFETY

Centrifuges are common laboratory instruments that spin rapidly to achieve separation of materials based on density. Centrifuges should only be operated with their covers closed, as shown in **Figure 4-7**, because hair, clothing, or jewelry could

Centrifuge with closed cover

Figure 4-7

become entangled in the moving parts. In addition, liquids under centrifugation can produce hazardous aerosols. Therefore, not only should the cover be closed, but all containers in the centrifuge should be capped or covered. This especially applies to flammables that can accumulate fumes in a centrifuge if they are not contained.

"Items in a centrifuge must be balanced evenly with regard to weight," as shown in **Figure 4-8B**. This also means that carriers in the centrifuge need to be balanced. Carriers frequently vary because of manufacturer imprecision. Unbalanced centrifuges, as shown in **Figure 4-8A**, shorten the life of the motor, but when they are spinning they can also "walk" off the edge of a countertop. Unusual noise or motion frequently indicates that a centrifuge is out of balance, and the devices should be turned off immediately. If no brake is available, centrifuges should be allowed to stop on their own, *never* by hand.

Visibly cracked or flawed containers must not be spun. If the sound of breakage is heard, the centrifuge should not be opened until it has come to a complete stop. If the centrifuge contains biohazards or respiratory chemical hazards, delay the opening for 30 minutes to allow aerosols to settle. If flammables are present, immediate opening of the centrifuge may be necessary to prevent the buildup of fumes. Breakage should be cleaned carefully

using the same techniques specified for regular maintenance and cleaning. Even if no breakage occurs, all centrifuges should be on a maintenance schedule to keep the carriers smooth and to keep the rubber cushions clean. This will lengthen the life of the centrifuge and minimize the chances that items in the centrifuge will burst.

STEAM STERILIZER/AUTOCLAVE SAFETY

Steam sterilizers/autoclaves sterilize material using a combination of high pressure and high temperature in the form of steam. A representative unit is shown in **Figure 4-9**. They can sterilize metal, plastic, glass, wood, and organic material. Caps and covers on all items to be autoclaved should be loose to prevent them from bursting. Solvents, bleach, and strong oxidizers should not be autoclaved because oxidizers and bleach can combine with organic material in an autoclave and cause an explosion. Flammable solvents should never be subjected to high temperatures, so they can never be autoclaved. Because autoclaves discharge steam to the environment at the end of each cycle, breathable hazards such as toxic chemicals and radioactive isotopes also should not be autoclaved.

Open centrifuge showing improperly balanced load

Figure 4-8A

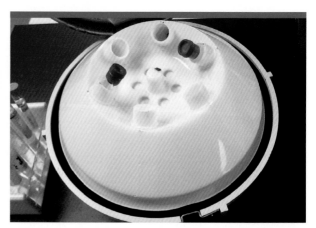

Open centrifuge showing properly balanced load

Figure 4-8B

An autoclave should always be operated according to the manufacturer's instructions. In general, water must be placed into the appropriate reservoir(s) to provide steam, and devices such as heat-sensitive tape must be included to verify that the instrument reached the proper temperature. To properly sterilize a device, steam must completely penetrate objects. Therefore, autoclaves should not be overstuffed, and objects with heavy layers of caked-on material may need to be cleaned before sterilization. In addition, spores from heat-resistant quality control organisms such as *Bacillis stearothermophilus* must be autoclaved every week to ensure that all organisms are being killed. It is a good idea to place the quality control organisms deep in the middle of the autoclave load to verify that the steam is penetrating. Once the autoclave is loaded properly, the door is latched firmly shut, and the autoclave is turned on for the appropriate amount of time.

During the sterilization cycle, the autoclave reaches high temperature and pressure. An open or leaky door will result in forceful blasts of steam. Clearly, an autoclave must *never* be opened until the pressure has returned to ambient. Even when pressure and temperature gauges indicate that it is safe to open the autoclave, the worker must stand to the side of the instrument and turn his or her face away in case a gauge is malfunctioning.

Ideally, all items from the autoclave should be allowed to return to room temperature before they are handled. If they must be removed immediately, however, heat-resistant gloves should be worn, but even these can be penetrated by steam. If the heat-sensitive tape does not show the appropriate color change, the autoclave should be checked and the entire process should be repeated because sterility cannot be guaranteed.

Only general principles of equipment most frequently used in clinical laboratories have been discussed in this exercise. Almost without exception, every user must be familiar with the user's manual and user specifications for each piece of equipment. Equipment can also be contaminated with other hazards such as chemicals, radiation, and biohazards, so the reader should refer to those exercises for additional handling protocols.

Pressure gauge   Temperature gauge

Object to be sterilized — labeled with heat sensitive tape

Water reservoir

Steam sterilizer/autoclave

Figure 4-9

Summary Table: Equipment and Electrical Safety

Topic	Comments
Use of Electrical Equipment	1. Follow OSHA requirements: insulation, grounding, guarding, circuit protection, safe work practices
	2. Ground all equipment with 3-pronged plugs. Use surge protectors for delicate equipment
	3. Avoid extension cords. If absolutely necessary, make sure they are rated for the amount of current being used
	4. No "octopus" outlets or overloaded outlets
	5. Investigate blown fuses and tripped breakers. Use GFCI's in high-risk, wet areas.
	6. Consult user's manual for new or unfamiliar equipment
	7. Follow manual for cleaning, servicing and repair. Remove jewelry. When possible, unplug and use only 1 hand
	8. Use non-sparking and explosion-proof equipment
	9. *Never* plug a wet wire into a circuit. *Never* operate a wet motor. *Never* handle electrical equipment with wet hands or while standing in or near water
	10. Unplug and tag "DO NOT USE" any instrument which produces a tingle or is malfunctioning

Topic	Comments
	11. Follow lockout/tagout procedures when electrical systems and equipment are being serviced. Only person who placed lock/tag on a device can remove it
	12. Do not use frayed or broken wires. Do not compromise insulation; unplug equipment by pulling out plug, not by pulling on the cord
	13. Always maintain clear path to electric breaker box and a 3-foot clearance around it
	14. Replace fuses with those of identical ratings. If unavailable, uses fuses with HIGHER voltage or LOWER amperage
	15. Follow emergency power protocols; prevent generator backfeed
	16. Suspect electrical shock if victim frozen to equipment or burns present; separate victim with a non-conductor, not your hands
Glassware Safety	1. Discard cracked, chipped or flawed glassware
	2. Lubricate glassware connections; never force glass
	3. Handle glass from the bottom, not the "neck"
	4. Use gloves or tongs to handle heated glass
	5. Clean glassware after each use. Neutralize chemical or biological hazard before cleaning. Wear gloves to wash glass and line the sink with a rubber mat; let glassware air dry
	6. Sweep up broken glass with a broom and discard in puncture-resistant container
	7. Substitute plastic for glass whenever possible
Safety with Sharps	1. Discard sharps into a puncture-resistant container, don't overfill; discard when 3/4 full
	2. *Never* recap or shear a needle by hand
	3. Safety-engineered sharps required by Needlestick Safety and Prevention Act. If unavailable, cover with the "one-handed scoop" technique
	4. Incinerate or autoclave sharps to neutralize biohazards. Consult medical waste regulations to see if total destruction is necessary
	5. Keep sharps injuries log. Consult with employees on purchase of sharps devices Review injuries, devices, employee opinions and new technologies annually
Centrifuge Safety	1. Operate with covers closed and items/carriers balanced with regard to weight
	2. Cover or cap items in centrifuge to prevent aerosols; do not spin flawed objects
	3. Allow centrifuge to stop on its own or use brake; do not stop by hand
	4. When an item breaks in a centrifuge, allow the aerosols to settle before opening Flammables are the exception
	5. Clean centrifuges after breakage and on a routine basis following manufacturer's instructions
Steam Sterilizer/ Autoclave Safety	1. *Never* open an autoclave until pressure is back to ambient
	2. Open autoclaves while standing to one side with your face turned away
	3. Allow items to cool to room temperature or handle with gloves
	4. Loosely cap or cover all items in an autoclave to prevent explosion
	5. Do not autoclave oxidizers, bleach and flammables
	6. Follow manufacturer's directions for each autoclave
	7. Put heat-sensitive tape on items to be sure sterilization temperatures occurred
	8. Periodically autoclave heat-resistant organisms to verify that sterilization is complete

Abbreviations: GFCIs = ground fault circuit interrupters; OSHA = Occupational Safety and Health Administration

Exercise 4

Self-Evaluation Questions

1. ___ Instruments are "grounded" to:

  a. Disperse electrical charge
  b. Prevent them from moving while in use
  c. Calibrate them when no samples are present
  d. Calibrate them to sea-level specifications of air pressure
  e. Balance them with respect to weight, size and components

2. ___ Which of the following situations is acceptable?

  a. Operating a wet motor
  b. Using an instrument marked "broken" as long as the controls are within range
  c. Operating an instrument with a slight "tingle" as long as the controls are within range
  d. Washing an instrument with soap and water as directed by the manufacturer while the instrument is turned off but still plugged in
  e. None of the above

3. ___ All of the following statements are **TRUE EXCEPT**:

  a. Use the "one hand in pocket" rule when servicing equipment
  b. Use nonsparking equipment, especially in areas containing flammables
  c. Frayed electrical cords should not be used at any time, so instruments should be inspected periodically for damaged cords
  d. When you observe a victim frozen to an electrical source, you must pull him or her off forcefully with both hands without delay to prevent permanent damage
  e. Temporary extension cords are not acceptable unless they have been checked by an electrician to be sure they are large enough to carry the current used

4. ___ A centrifuge cover prevents all of the following **EXCEPT**:

  a. Electrical shock to the users
  b. Dispersal of aerosols from spinning liquids
  c. Jewelry, hair, and clothing getting tangled in the centrifuge
  d. Broken glass flying out when a tube in the centrifuge breaks
  e. Injury from interaction with centrifuge parts moving at high speed

5. ___ A centrifuge is making an odd noise. You should:

    a. Unplug it immediately
    b. Open the cover to see what is making the noise
    c. Turn it off, wait for it to stop, and check it for balance
    d. Turn it off, unplug it, and mark it "OUT OF SERVICE"
    e. Let it continue to run, but monitor its movement to be sure it is stable

6. ___ Choose the **CORRECT** statement:

    a. Flasks with minor chips that do not cause leaks are acceptable to use
    b. The safest way to wash glassware is to use gloves and let the glass air dry
    c. If broken glass is not contaminated with any hazard, it can be discarded with the regular trash
    d. A flask that held acquired immunodeficiency virus (AIDS) virus can be washed along the with other glassware as long as it is bleached afterward
    e. All of the above

7. ___ Safety-engineered sharps devices:

    a. Should never have the safety features bypassed
    b. Must not be purchased until employee input is given on the options available
    c. Are required at all times unless an employer can prove medical necessity for a traditional device
    d. Are acceptable to OSHA if they can easily be operated by one hand and the user's hand always remains behind the sharp
    e. All of the above

8. ___ Which of the following materials can be autoclaved?

    a. Ether
    b. Glass beaker
    c. Perchloric acid solution
    d. Needles soaking in a pan of bleach
    e. All of the above

9. ___ All of the following are correct practices for autoclaving materials **EXCEPT:**

    a. Objects in the autoclave are loosely covered or capped

    b. Heat-resistant organisms should be autoclaved weekly to demonstrate that the autoclave is sterilizing properly

    c. Heat-sensitive tape should be placed on the objects to ensure that the autoclave reached the correct temperature

    d. When timer indicates that the sterilization cycle is done, the autoclave should be immediately opened to give the contents time to cool

    e. The following should be excluded from autoclaving: flammable chemicals, radioactive materials, toxic chemicals, chemicals with hazardous heat decomposition products

10. Give an example of a conductor: _____

    Give an example of an insulator: _____

11. Electrical shock occurs when human beings accidentally become part of a:

    _____.

12. You must replace a 10 amp, 20 millivolt fuse.

    What is your first choice? _____

    What is your second choice? _____

13. Unplug an instrument by pulling on the _____

    not the _____.

14. ___ A circuit breaker has been turned off and a tagged with "Maintenance in progress. Do not turn circuit breaker back on." Who has authority to remove this tag and turn the circuit breaker back on?

    a. A qualified electrician

    b. The worker's supervisor

    c. The worker who placed the tag there

    d. The worker's partner on the maintenance project

    e. All of the above

Exercise 5

BIOLOGICAL HAZARDS

A biological hazard is one in which infectious organisms or products from organisms can cause illness or harm. The 5 categories of infectious organisms are bacteria, viruses, fungi, protozoa, and prions. Recombinant DNA/RNA sources are also typically categorized as biohazards.

THE BIOHAZARD SYMBOL

The symbol for biological hazard is shown in **Figure 5-1.** The biohazard symbol must be dark on a bright orange background to comply with the requirements of the Occupational Health and Safety Administration (OSHA). It must be displayed wherever any biohazards are present. This includes:

1. **Doors** Laboratory entrances, refrigerator doors, and incubator doors are examples.

2. **Trash cans and waste receptacles** OSHA does allow substitution of red bags for biohazard-labeled bags if staff members are fully informed and trained.

3. **Laundry bags**

4. **Specimens and/or specimen containers** OSHA does not require the symbol on every specimen if all specimens are in a single receptacle displaying the symbol or if a laboratory treats all specimens as biohazards.

BIOHAZARD

Figure 5-1

5. **Equipment** Centrifuges, analytical devices, and surgical equipment are examples. All equipment in a laboratory may be considered biohazardous, and the symbol on the door to the laboratory is sufficient. However, if a piece of equipment is sent out for repair, it must either be decontaminated or labeled with the biohazard symbol.

MICROBIAL SOURCES AND ROUTES OF INFECTION

The following are sources of microorganisms with which a laboratory worker may come in contact. Most of these potential sources are rarely, if ever, sterile and usually must be handled as biohazards.

1. Blood (whole blood, serum, plasma, or blood clot)

2. Culture specimens (swabs of various body sites)

3. Body fluids (such as spinal, peritoneal, amniotic, and pleural)

4. Unfixed microscopic smears

5. Fecal specimens

6. Urine

7. Body tissue and cadavers

8. Laboratory animals

9. People

The primary causes of laboratory infections are inhalation of airborne aerosols, accidental ingestion, direct inoculation (example: a needle puncture), mucous membrane splashes, and

insect transferral. Source handling will depend on the pathogen most likely to be present. OSHA does not have biosafety levels (BSLs) for microbes, so programs most frequently rely on the 4 BSL's recommended by the National Institutes of Health/ Centers for Disease Control and Prevention (NIH/ CDC). These levels specify physical containment and handling for microbes, specimens, and animals based on hazard level. The 4 BSL's are summarized in **Table 5-1**. The CDC and NIH publication *Biosafety in Microbiological and Biomedical Laboratories* lists specific organisms and the handling of each. It is an excellent resource for establishing procedures for each of the main components of a biosafety program (**Figure 5-2**). NIH categories for recombinant DNA and an alternative risk classification system used by the World Health Organization (WHO) is presented in **Table 5-2**.

Organisms that are almost always nonpathogens in normal human hosts are considered BSL-1. Academic laboratories using nonpathogens for teaching, water testing laboratories, and food quality control laboratories are examples of laboratories that might be classified as BSL-1. BSL-2 organisms cause disease in humans but are usually acquired

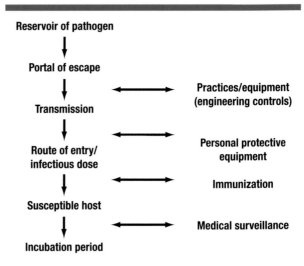

Critical components of a biosafety program (www.cdc.gov)

Figure 5-2

Table 5-1: Centers for Disease Control Biosafety Levels for Infectious Agents

Biosafety Level	Agents	Practices	Safety Equipment	Facilities (Secondary Barriers)
1	Not known to consistently cause disease in healthy adults	Standard microbiological practices (see **Table 5-4**)	None required	Easily cleaned, open bench top; sink required
2	Associated with human disease with direct contact: percutaneous injury, ingestion, mucous membrane exposure	BSL-1 practices plus: Limited access, bio-hazard warning signs, "sharps" precautions, biosafety manual defining waste decontamination or medical surveillance policies	Primary barriers = Class I or II Biological Safety Cabinets or containment devices for manipulations that cause splashes or aerosols of infectious material. Personal protective eqpt: lab coats, gloves, as needed face protection	BSL-1 plus: Autoclave available
3	Indigenous or exotic agents with potential for aerosol transmission; disease may have serious or lethal consequences	BSL-2 plus: Controlled access, decontamination of all waste, decontamination of lab clothing before laundering, baseline blood testing	Primary barriers = Class I or II Biological Safety Cabinets or containment devices for all open manipulations of agents Personal protective eqpt: protective lab clothing, gloves and as needed, respiratory protection	BSL-2 practices plus: Physical separation from access corridors, self- closing double door access, keep door closed, exhausted air (not recirculated), negative air flow into lab (lab at lower pressure)
4	Dangerous / exotic agents which pose high risk of life-threatening disease, aerosol -transmitted lab infections or related agents with unknown risk of transmission	BSL-3 plus: clothing change before entering, shower on exit, all material decontaminated on exit from facility	Primary barriers = All procedures conducted in Class III biological safety cabinet *in combination with* full-body air-supplied, positive-pressure personnel suit.	BSL-3 practices plus: Separate building or isolated zone, dedicated supply and exhaust, vacuum and decontamination systems, others in CDC text

Modified from Biosafety in Microbiological and Biomedical Laboratories, 5th edition. Washington, DC, US, Government Printing Office. February 2007. www.cdc.gov (January 18, 2008).

through direct contact, ingestion, or injection. Most clinical laboratories are BSL-2 because they work with specimens suspected to harbor pathogens transmitted by these routes. Specimens or cultures that may harbor organisms that are acquired by inhalation, such as *Mycobacterium tuberculosis*

many of the pathogenic spore-producing molds, should be handled at BSL-3. Some other high-risk organisms are also categorized as BSL-3. These include BSL-4 is typically reserved for handling highly pathogenic, extraordinary organisms (eg, Ebola virus, smallpox virus) and large amounts of

Table 5-2: NIH and WHO Biohazard Risk Classification

National Institutes of Health Guidelines for Research Involving Recombinant DNA Molecules (2002)		World Health OrganizationLaboratory Biosafety Manual (2004)	
		Description	Types of Agents
Risk Group 1	Agents not associated with disease in healthy humans	Low individual and community risk	Unlikely to cause human or animal disease
Risk Group 2	Agents associated with human disease that is rarely serious and for which preventative and therapeutic interventions are often available	Moderate individual risk and low community risk	Cause human or animal disease that is preventable/ treatable and transmission to laboratory workers, community, livestock and the environment unlikely
Risk Group 3	Agents associated with serious or lethal human disease and for which preventative and therapeutic interventions may be available	High individual risk and low community risk	Cause serious disease in humans or animals but infection usually self-limiting and treatment/prevention available
Risk Group 4	Agents associated with serious or lethal human disease and for which preventative and therapeutic interventions are not usually available	High individual and community risk	Cause serious disease in humans or animals that is transmitted between individuals and treatment/ prevention not usually available

Modified from Biosafety in Microbiological and Biomedical Laboratories, 5th edition. Washington, DC, US, Government Printing Office. February 2007. www.cdc.gov (January 18, 2008).

pathogens, as on an industrial scale. In uncertain situations, specimens should be handled conservatively using the most rigorous applicable safety level.

Risk assessment for biohazards requires evaluation of 2 main features, the inherent hazard of the biologic agent and the laboratory procedure(s) involved. The CDC/NIH BSL's are determined based on adult humans with normal immune systems. Staff members with special situations (like pregnancy) or compromised immune systems may require additional protection. Laboratory workers should also be familiar with the signs of the diseases caused by the microbes they encounter in their work (examples shown in **Table 5-3**). If they acquire an infection, it can then be treated immediately. Because the exact contents of clinical

specimens is unknown, initial handling and processing is recommended to be in a biological safety cabinet. Unless unusual pathogens are known or suspected, most workups on clinical specimens can be handled using BSL-2 conditions. Because BSL-2 procedures are so important for virtually all clinical specimens, the CDC recommendations for BSL-2 are reproduced here in their entirety (**Table 5-4**). All of the practices listed should be a routine part of biohazard manipulation.

Biosecurity

The CDC uses the term *biosecurity* to mean "protection of microbial agents from loss, theft, diversion, or intentional misuse." Global concern over bioterrorism has been increasing, and the CDC

Table 5-3: Signs and Symptoms of HIV, Hepatitis, TB

HIV	Hepatitis	TB
Initial infection: flu-like symptoms, lymphadenopathy	Jaundice, dark urine, malaise, nausea	Cough with thick, cloudy and/or bloody mucus lasting > 2 weeks Shortness of breath Fatigue, muscle weakness Loss of appetite, unexplained weight loss Fever, chills, night sweats
Later infection: lymphadenopathy, fever, diarrhea, skin/mouth lesions, yeast and viral infections		

has published several important security protocols for laboratories that handle biologic agents. Many relatively common organisms can be used as biological weapons, so one should not assume that security measures are only appropriate for those laboratories handling high BSL exotic organisms. The CDC/Department of Health and Human Services has developed "Select Agents and Toxins," a list of those organisms/toxins most desirable to terrorists, and the US Department of Agriculture has developed a list of restricted animal pathogens. This list is contained in Appendix 6, and information on the Select Agent Program can be found at http://www.cdc.gov/od/sap (accessed January 19, 2008). Laboratories handling these agents must register with the government and follow certain protocols established for security, including physical containment, inspections, and personnel clearances by the Department of Justice. Some agents cause human disease and/or would contaminate water supplies, while animal pathogens would disrupt food supplies. There is concern that some of these agents could be genetically altered to be resistant to the usual antibiotics, so if these organisms are encountered in specimens, prompt recognition, antibiotic sensitivity testing, and reporting are vital.

The CDC has established guidelines for microbiology laboratories to follow in the event of the detection of a critical agent or in an actual bioterrorism event. Each institution handling microorganisms should use these guidelines to establish bioterrorism protocols specific to the facility. National laboratories and regional reference laboratories receive referred specimens of suspected agents and are key elements in identifying those agents and helping coordinate emergency responses. Such laboratories should meticulously incorporate CDC guidelines. Most clinical laboratories, however, would be classified as sentinel laboratories that would encounter bioterrorist agents when a victim first seeks medical care. The CDC has transferred responsibility for sentinel laboratory guidelines to the American Society of Microbiology (ASM). Managers of sentinel laboratories should refer to the ASM Web site (http://www.asm.org/Policy/index.asp?bid=667, accessed January 19, 2008) for help in establishing protocols. Free bioterrorism training for sentinel laboratories can be obtained at www.bttrain.org (accessed 5/2008).

Some basic elements of a biosecurity plan articulated by the CDC include: (1) developing and managing a comprehensive program, (2) devising measures to secure the physical facility and information, (3) evaluating personnel for security risk and competency in security protocols and emergency response, and (4) managing inventory with complete accountability against theft/loss. Controlled access to laboratories is required for BSL-2 and -3 organism containment. According to the CDC, the security and access control required BSL-2 and -3 labs may be adequate for biosecurity at the sentinel lab level, but this should be evaluated. In addition, a particular concern about bioterrorism is the use of genetically modified

Table 5-4: Biosafety Level 2 Laboratory Practices

Biosafety Level 2 Criteria: Biosafety Level 2 builds upon Biosafety Level 1. BSL-2 is suitable for work involving agents that pose moderate potential hazard to personnel and the environment. It differs from BSL-1 in that (1) laboratory personnel have specific training in handling pathogenic agents and are supervised by scientists competent in handling infectious agents and associated procedures; (2) access to the laboratory is restricted when work is being conducted; and (3) all procedures in which infectious aerosols or splashes may be created are conducted in biological safety cabinets or other physical containment equipment. The following standard and special practices, safety equipment, and facility requirements apply to agents assigned to Biosafety Level 2:

A. Standard Microbiological Practices	
	1. The laboratory supervisor must enforce the institutional policies that control access to the laboratory
	2. Persons must wash their hands after working with potentially hazardous materials and before leaving the laboratory
	3. Eating, drinking, smoking, handling contact lenses, applying cosmetics and storing food for human consumption must not bepermitted in laboratory areas. Food must be stored outside the laboratory area in cabinets or refrigerators designated and used for this purpose
	4. Mouth pipetting is prohibited; mechanical pipetting devices must be used
	5. Policies for the safe handling of sharps, such as needles, scalpels, pipettes and broken glassware must be developed and implemented. Whenever practical, laboratory supervisors should adopt improved engineering and work practice controls that reduce risk of sharps injuries. Precautions, including those listed below, must always be taken with sharp items. These include:
	a. Careful management of needles and other sharps are of primary importance. Needles must not be bent, sheared, broken, recapped, removed from disposable syringes or otherwise manipulated by hand before disposal
	b. Used disposable needles and syringes must be carefully placed in conveniently located puncture-resistant containers used for sharps disposal
	c. Non-disposable sharps must be placed in a hard walled container for transport to a processing area for decontamination, preferably by autoclaving
	d. Broken glassware must not be handled directly. Instead, it must be removed using a brush and dustpan, tongs or forceps. Plasticware should be substituted for glassware whenever possible
	6. Perform all procedures to minimize the creation of splashes or aerosols
	7. Decontaminate work surfaces after completion of work and after any spill or splash of potentially infectious material with appropriate disinfectant
	8. Decontaminate all cultures, stocks, and other potentially infectious materials before disposal using an effective method. Depending on where the decontamination will be performed, the following methods should be used prior to transport:
	a. Materials to be decontaminated outside of the immediate laboratory are placed in a durable, leakproof container and secured for transport
	b. Materials to be removed from the facility for decontamination must be packed in accordance with applicable local, state, and federal regulations
	9. A sign incorporating the universal biohazard symbol must be posted at the entrance to the laboratory when infectious agents are present. Posted information must include: the laboratory's biosafety level, the supervisor's name (or other responsible personnel), telephone number and required procedures for entering and exiting the laboratory. Agent information should be posted in accordance with the institutional policy
	10. An effective integrated pest management system is required

Table 5-4: Biosafety Level 2 Laboratory Practices (continued)

	11. The laboratory supervisor must ensure that laboratory personnel receive appropriate training regarding their duties, the necessary precautions to prevent exposures and exposure evaluation procedures. Personnel must receive annual updates or additional training when procedural or policy changes occur. Personal health status may affect an individual's susceptibility to infection, ability to receive immunizations or prophylactic interventions. Therefore, all laboratory personnel and particularly women of child-bearing age should be provided with information regarding immune competence and conditions that may predispose them to infection. Individuals having these conditions should be encouraged to self-identify to the institution's healthcare provider for appropriate counseling and guidance
B. Special Practices	1. All persons entering the laboratory must be advised of the potential hazards and meet specific entry/exit requirements
	2. Laboratory personnel must be provided medical surveillance and offered appropriate immunizations for agents handled or potentially present in the laboratory.
	3. Each institution must establish policies and procedures describing the collection and storage of serum samples from at-risk personnel
	4. A laboratory-specific biosafety manual must be prepared and adopted as policy. The biosafety manual must be available and accessible
	5. The laboratory supervisor must ensures that laboratory personnel demonstrate proficiency in standard and special microbiological practices before working with BSL-2 agents
	6. Potentially infectious materials must be placed in a durable, leak-proof continter during collection, handling, processing, storage or transport within a facility.
	7. Laboratory equipment should be decontaminated routinely as well as after spills, splashes, or other potential contamination
	a. Spills involving infectious materials must be contained, decontaminated and cleaned up by staff properly trained and equipped to work with infectious material
	b. Equipment must be decontaminated before repair, maintenance or removal from the laboratory
	8. Incidents that may result in exposure to infectious materials must be immediately evaluated and treated according to procedures described in the laboratory biosafety manual. All such incidents must be reported to the laboratory supervisor. Medical evaluation, surveillance, and treatment are provided and appropriate records maintained
	9. Animals and plants not associated with the work being performed must not be permitted in the laboratory
	10. All procedures involving the manipulation of infectious materials that may generate an aerosol should be conducted within a biological safety cabinet or other physical containment devices

Biological Hazards

Table 5-4: Biosafety Level 2 Laboratory Practices (continued)

C. Safety Equipment (Primary Barriers and Personal Protective Equipment)	1. Properly maintained biological safety cabinets (preferably Class II) or other appropriate personal protective equipment or other physical containment devices must be used whenever:
	
	   a. Procedures with a potential for creating infectious aerosols or splashes are conducted. These may include pipetting, centrifuging, grinding, blending, shaking, mixing, sonicating, opening containers of infectious materials, inoculating animals intranasally, and harvesting infected tissues from animals or eggs
	   b. High concentrations or large volumes of infectious agents are used. Such materials may be centrifuged in the open laboratory using sealed rotor heads or centrifuge safety cups
	
	2. Protective laboratory coats, gowns, smocks, or uniforms designated for laboratory use must be worn while working with hazardous materials. Remove protective clothing before leaving for non-laboratory areas (eg, cafeteria, library, administrative offices). Dispose of protective clothing appropriately or deposit it for laundering by the institution. It is recommended that laboratory clothing not be taken home
	
	3. Eye and face protection (goggles, mask, face shield or other splatter guard) is used for anticipated splashes or sprays of infectious or other hazardous materials to the face when the microorganisms must be manipulated outside the biological safety cabinet or containment device. Eye and face protection must be disposed of with other contaminated laboratory waste or decontaminated before reuse. Persons who wear contact lenses in laboratories should also wear eye protection
	
	4. Gloves must be worn to protect hands from exposure to hazardous materials. Glove selection should be based on an appropriate risk assessment. Alternatives to latex gloves should be available. Gloves must not be worn outside the laboratory. In addition, BSL-2 laboratory workers should:
	
	   a. Change gloves when contaminated, integrity has been compromised or when otherwise necessary. Wear two pairs of gloves when appropriate.
	   b. Remove gloves and wash hands when work with hazardous materials has been completed and before leaving the laboratory.
	   c. Do not wash or reuse disposable gloves. Dispose of used gloves with other contaminated laboratory waste. Hand-washing protocols must be rigorously followed
	
	5. Eye, face and respiratory protection should be used in rooms containing infected animals as determined by the risk assessment

D. Laboratory Facilities (Secondary Barriers)	1. Laboratory doors should be self-closing and have locks in accordance with institutional policies
	2. Laboratories must have a sink for hand washing. This sink may be manually, hands-free or automatically operated. It should be located near the exit door
	3. The laboratory should be designed so that it can be easily cleaned and decontaminated. Carpets and rugs in laboratories are not permitted
	4. Laboratory furniture must be capable of supporting anticipated loads and uses. Spaces between benches, cabinets and equipment should be accessible for cleaning
	
	   a. Bench tops must be impervious to water and resistant to heat, organic solvents, acids, alkalis, and other chemicals
	   b. Chairs used in laboratory work must be covered with a nonporous material that can be easily cleaned and decontaminated with the appropriate disinfectant

Table 5-4: Biosafety Level 2 Laboratory Practices (continued)

5. Laboratory windows that open to the exterior are not recommended. However, if a laboratory does have windows that open to the exterior they must be fitted with screens

6. Biological safety cabinets must be Installed so that fluctuations of the room air supply and exhaust do not interfere with proper operations. Biological safety cabinets should be located away from doors, windows that can be opened, heavily traveled laboratory areas, and possible airflow disruptions

7. Vacuum lines should be protected with High Efficiency Particulate Air (HEPA) filters or their equivalent. Filters must be replaced as needed. Liquid disinfectant traps may be required

8. An eyewash station must be readily available.

9. There are no specific requirements on ventilation systems. However, planning of new facilities should consider mechanical ventilation systems that provide an inward flow of air without recirculation to spaces outside the laboratory

10. HEPA-filtered exhaust air from a Class II biological safety cabinet can safely be re-circulated back into the laboratory environment if the cabinet is tested and certified at least annually and operated according to the manufacturer's recommendations. Biological safety cabinets can also be connected to the laboratory exhaust system by either a thimble (canopy) connection or a direct (hard) connection. Provisions to assure proper safety cabinet performance and air system operation must be verified

11. A method for decontaminating all laboratory wastes should be available in the facility (eg, autoclave, chemical disinfection, incineration or other validated decontamination method)

* From Biosafety in Microbiological and Biomedical Laboratories, 5th ed. Washington, DC: US Government Printing Office; February 2007. www.cdc.gov (accessed January 18, 2008).

agents. Organisms that have been altered to be more dangerous may no longer fit the BSL to which they are traditionally assigned. Bioterrorism events may necessitate changes in organism manipulation based on the situation.

Infectious Agents of Note

Infectious agents usually of greatest concern to clinical laboratory workers are *M tuberculosis* and three bloodborne pathogens: hepatitis B virus (HBV), hepatitis C virus (HCV), and the human immunodeficiency virus (HIV or the virus that leads to acquired immunodeficiency syndrome [AIDS]). By far the easiest virus to contract from infected blood is HBV. (Seroconversion after parenteral exposure to HIV is 0.3%, to HCV is 1.8%, and to HBV is 6%-30%.)

Vaccination against the HBV is highly recommended for persons at risk, and this includes most clinical laboratory workers. By law, employers must offer the HBV vaccine free of charge to all staff members who may be exposed to blood and body fluids. There is, unfortunately, no similar vaccine for HCV or HIV, and both are currently incurable. Therefore, protocols to prevent exposure to blood and body fluids must be followed meticulously (see CDC Precautions Guidelines below). The Bacillus-Calmette-Guerin (BCG) vaccine for tuberculosis is not currently recommended routinely for laboratory workers. However, vaccinations for this and other agents should be evaluated on a case-by-case basis in laboratories with special situations or with workers who are particularly at risk such as those who are pregnant or immunocompromised.

The advent of several antiretroviral drugs to treat AIDS has allowed researchers to establish prophylactic protocols for workers inadvertently exposed to HIV. Many of these protocols are quite effective in preventing HIV infection. Prophylactic protocols for HBV infection are also available. Appendix 7 lists current recommendations for postexposure programs. The actual drugs or vaccines used for postexposure prophylaxis are not included because they change regularly; consult current CDC recommendations.

Tuberculosis infection has historically been curable with antibiotics, but in recent years dangerous strains of this bacterium have been isolated which are resistant to multiple antibiotics. Because this organism is almost always spread through inhalation of aerosols, it is far too easily acquired in the laboratory and in the community. Therefore, increased attention has been paid to surveillance and prevention of this disease. The success of prevention efforts in the workplace became apparent when on December 31, 2003, OSHA withdrew its own tuberculosis standard and instead now refers employers to the CDC guidelines.

The most recent recommendations at publication time regarding tuberculosis are "Guidelines for Preventing Transmission of *Mycobacterium tuberculosis* in Health Care Settings" (*Morbidity and Mortality Weekly Report.* volume 54, number RR-17, pages 1-141. December 30, 2005.). This document contains the following recommendations regarding tuberculosis: (1) who should be tested for tuberculosis and how often, (2) isolation and management procedures for tuberculosis patients, (3) treatment protocols for workers who test positive, (4) ventilation and safety equipment (including N95 masks), and (5) laboratory and decontamination procedures.

An important development in tuberculosis control is that in addition to the traditional skin test and x-rays, immune cytokine reaction–based blood tests have been developed. These tests have improved detection of active tuberculosis with less interference from other mycobacteria and BCG vaccination. The CDC indicates that the blood test can be used instead of the traditional skin test in all situations and has published guidelines for its use ("Guidelines for Using the QuantiFERON-TB Gold Test for Detecting *Mycobacterium tuberculosis* Infection, United States." *Morbidity and Mortality Weekly Report.* volume 54, number RR15, pages 49-55. December 16, 2005). Immunocompromised patients, especially those with HIV, have limited immune responses and may show false-negative results to either skin or blood tests.

Baseline 2-step skin testing is now recommended for health care workers. 2 tests are administered 1 to 3 weeks apart; if results of both tests are negative, nothing more is required. If the result of the first test is positive or negative and the second test is positive, the worker must be evaluated as a candidate for latent tuberculosis infection therapy. (A positive result following a negative one is believed to be due to immune boosting, allowing better detection of a low-level immune response.) Employees still must be monitored annually, and staff conversions from negative to positive tuberculosis tests must be monitored and followed up. Careful adherence to CDC guidelines is necessary to distinguish conversions from boosted reactions to previous skin tests or vaccination. Cytokine-based blood tests for tuberculosis do not need to be done in 2 steps and do not suffer from the boosted reaction problem.

Characteristics that increase infectiousness in a tuberculosis patient include: (1) presence of cough, cavitary disease, and/or acid-fast bacilli in the sputum, (2) involvement of the larynx or pleura in the infection, (3) inadequate antibiotic treatment, and

(4) aerosol generation to include uncovered cough and medical procedures. Environmental factors that support transmission of tuberculosis include: (1) small enclosed spaces with air recirculation and/or inadequate ventilation, (2) inadequate cleaning and disinfection, and (3) improper specimen handling. When suspected tuberculosis cases are admitted, airborne precaution protocols are generally initiated. However, because isolation facilities are limited and extra precautions can be costly, the ability to discontinue the precautions must be prompt. Given that *M tuberculosis* grows slowly in culture, the CDC recommends that 3 negative sputum smears collected at 8- to 24-hour intervals is sufficient to discontinue airborne precautions. Positive smears and other tuberculosis test results must be reported equally promptly, generally within 24 hours. Because making and staining smears is generally considered non–aerosol producing, smaller laboratories operating at BSL-2 can usually provide this service to rapidly categorize patients. All other activities with this organism should be conducted in a biological safety cabinet and/or using BSL-3 protocols.

One class of unusual infectious agents is the prion (**pro**teinaceous **in**fectious particle). These particles are incompletely characterized and not well understood, but they appear to be composed of only protein. (All other infectious organisms possess either DNA or RNA.) There has recently been much media attention to "mad cow disease" (bovine spongiform encephalitis or BSE) potentially being transmitted to humans and causing a condition similar to Creutzfeldt-Jakob disease (CJD). Both BSE and CJD are rare, fatal neurodegenerative diseases believed to be transmitted by prions. Chronic wasting disease, which is seen in deer and elk in parts of the central United States, also is caused by a prion. This may be an emerging problem for humans who handle deer and elk carcasses and/or consume the meat.

Current CDC literature states that BSL-2 or -3 is adequate for handling human prions, depending on the procedure. The blood and body fluids of patients with CJD have a low risk of being infectious. However, contact with neurologic tissue (brain, spinal cord, and adjacent structures) is associated with a very high risk. This category of tissue specimens is relatively rare in most laboratories because it is not lightly removed, but exposure during autopsy can be significant and special protocols are required. Prions are resistant to many of the standard decontamination procedures, including standard formalin-fixation of tissues; additional sterilizing measures are necessary.

Universal, Standard, and Transmission-Based Precautions

In the 1980s when AIDS was becoming a concern, the CDC issued recommendations that "Universal Precautions" must be observed when handling blood and other potentially infectious materials. In essence, every specimen is considered to be infectious, regardless of the source or the known infectious status. Recently the CDC replaced the term "Universal Precautions" with "Standard Precautions" and "Transmission-Based Precautions" for health care workers. The differences between the 3 terms are summarized below.

CDC Precautions Comparison

Universal Precautions for fluids likely to have blood or visibly bloody

Standard Precautions for all body substances except sweat

Transmission-Based Precautions specific for known microbe

Biological Hazards

Universal Precautions apply to blood, any fluid visibly contaminated with blood, semen, vaginal secretions, tissues, cerebrospinal fluid, synovial fluid, vitreous fluid, wound exudates, pleural fluid, peritoneal fluid, pericardial fluid, and amniotic fluid. Generally, sweat, tears, sputum, saliva, nasal secretions, feces, urine, vomitus, and breast milk do not require Universal Precautions unless they are visibly contaminated with blood. Because the exact source of the many fluids encountered in the clinical setting may not be known, many health care facilities practiced what was called "body substance isolation" and treated virtually every body substance as if it were infectious. This prevented staff members from having to judge if blood is "visible" or if an unusual fluid requires protection. Currently, the CDC has synthesized Universal Precautions and body substance isolation into a new recommendation entitled Standard Precautions. Standard Precautions are taken with all people and specimens to include: blood, all body fluids, secretions, and excretions except sweat (absence of visible blood no longer matters), nonintact skin and mucous membranes. Transmission-based Precautions are used in addition to standard precautions when a specific pathogen that has strong person-to-person transmission has been confirmed. The use of the term Universal Precautions in the literature and in infectious disease training materials is so pervasive that the reader can expect to continue to encounter it. In addition, there are non–health care settings in which Universal Precautions are more appropriate. For example, if Standard Precautions were used in a day care center with healthy children, merely changing a child's diaper would necessitate personal protective apparel, and this may not be reasonable.

Standard or Universal Precautions for handling human specimens virtually always requires gloves. This includes specimen procurement activities such as drawing blood. Gloves should be changed between patients. Hand decontamination after glove removal is mandatory to guard against contamination from any undetected leaks in the gloves. If there is a likelihood that specimens could splash or spill, fluid-proof gowns and face protection are also required. The Exposure Control Plan must include a task assessment for every job class. In this assessment, the types of exposure for each job are determined and the appropriate protective measures established. Task assessments in the exposure control plan are based on normal, healthy workers, but not every worker falls into this category. Staff members who are immunocompromised, pregnant, sick, or unvaccinated against certain illnesses may be at higher risk for certain agents. Work with microbes such as rubella and cytomegalovirus, known to cause fetal damage, may not be advisable for susceptible pregnant women. Workers with suppressed immune systems may require additional personal protective equipment. Supervisors should counsel these individuals on a case-by-case basis and should normally provide too much protection rather than not enough.

The *2007 Guidelines for Isolation Precautions: Preventing Transmission of Infectious Agents in Healthcare Settings* from the CDC added the following 3 new elements to standard precautions to protect patients as much as health care workers: Respiratory Hygiene/Cough Etiquette, Safe Injection Practices, and Special Lumbar Procedures. Patients and visitors must be educated to minimize transmission of respiratory pathogens and provided tissues and/or masks as needed. Single-use needles must be used in all cases even if there is ostensibly no potential for contamination (ie, when injecting medication into an intravenous line), and masks must be worn when accessing the spinal or epidural space.

Guidelines for patient contact vary with the type of illness (transmission-based precautions). Contact precautions are initiated when direct/indirect contact is required for organism transmission so gloves and gowns may be adequate. Droplet precautions are initiated when the organism is spread by droplets (>5 μm), but droplets travel less than 3 feet, so protective equipment is generally required when within a 6 to 10 feet of the patient. Organisms in this category include SARS-associated corona virus, group A Streptococcus, *Bordetella pertussis, Mycoplasma pneumoniae, Neisseria meningitidis,* influenza virus, adenovirus, and rhinovirus. Organisms in aerosols (<5 μm) that are suspended in the air and remain infectious over long distances require airborne precautions including isolation rooms, special ventilation, masks/N95 respirators for providers, and in some circumstances, patients. *Aspergillus* spores and *M tuberculosis* fall into this category. Recommendations for other organisms are located in Appendix A of the 2007 CDC Guidelines for Isolation Precautions: Preventing Transmission of Infectious Agents in Healthcare Settings (http://www.cdc.gov/ncidod/dhqp/gl_isolation_standard.html, accessed January 19, 2008). Additional measures may be required to prevent the worker from infecting an immunocompromised patient. In general, special precautions should be posted at a patient's door and should be checked before entering the room. Staff who are handling a particular patient should be consulted if there are any questions.

Specimens should be transported in a plastic bag or other container so that the specimens would be confined in the event of a leak. If specimens are being shipped, they should be placed in unbreakable containers and packed with enough absorbent material to contain a leak and triple packed. The outermost container should display the biohazard symbol or comply with regulations for hazard identification (see Exercise 1).

Histology Laboratories and Autopsy Suites

Many activities in histology laboratories and autopsy suites are inherently high risk. Once tissues are in fixed in alcohol, formalin, or paraffin they are usually considered a low biohazard risk. However, a considerable amount of cutting and dissection of unfixed bodies, organs, and tissues occurs in these laboratory areas, so staff members are at considerable risk for not only severe cuts but also infection. It is important to note that normal tissue fixation and embalming methods do not inactivate infectious prions; additional protocols may have to be used if these agents are suspected. The reader should refer to the CDC guidelines because these protocols are beyond the scope of this text.

In general, tissue specimens should be fixed as soon as possible and manipulation of unfixed specimens with sharps should be minimized. In many cases, double gloves, gowns, aprons, and face protection are required because aerosol formation may be difficult to prevent. To some degree double gloves reduce the risks associated with puncture because of the extra barrier.

The use of tissue grinders, blenders, and bone saws are particularly problematic. Microtomes that cut tissue embedded in paraffin are less biohazardous than cryostats which cut unfixed, rapidly frozen tissue (freezing does not inactivate infectious agents). Both have exceptionally sharp blades that must be cleaned, changed, and disposed with great care. Decontaminating agents for cryostats may vary from 100% alcohol for daily cleaning, to mycobacteriocidal agents for weekly cleaning, to sodium hydroxide for specimens from patients with undiagnosed encephalopathy, and/or known Creutzfeldt-Jakob agent. Bleach, a popular decontaminating chemical elsewhere in the laboratory, cannot come in contact with formaldehyde, so its use is generally restricted in histology. In addition, bleach is corrosive and can be damaging to many metal surfaces and instruments, so glutaraldehyde is often substituted in autopsy suites.

Autopsies are very high-risk procedures, and the Clinical Laboratory Standards Institute (CLSI) recommends constructing autopsy suites using BSL-3 standards (anteroom, cleanable surfaces, negative room pressure). Incoming bodies may have embedded sharps (intravenous lines, broken bones) and may be leaking fluids and body waste. Bodies should be transported in plastic bags and removed onto the prosection table with great care to minimize aerosols. When reasonable, staff members should wear heavy duty or metal mesh gloves to protect against sharps injury. There must be a source of running water and adequate drainage for autopsy tables as well as ventilation units positioned to minimize exposure to fumes.

The protocols to minimize autopsy risk include: (1) only 1 prosector with 1 sharp at a time is allowed to work on a body, (2) scissors with blunt tips should be substituted for scalpels when possible, (3) instruments should be placed on a tray to be picked up rather than passed hand to hand, (4) an uncontaminated assistant (the circulator or the diener) should be available to answer the phone, take notes, and fetch supplies while the prosector is performing the autopsy, (5) foot-operated dictation machines should be used, and (6) bone saws should be wet before use and should be attached to vacuums to minimize airborne bone dust. More detailed recommendations for autopsies can be found in publication M29-A3: "Protection of Laboratory Workers from Occupationally Acquired Infections" from CLSI.

Work with Laboratory Animals

All laboratories should have an insect and rodent control program in effect to prevent the spread of microbes. Some research laboratories use animals for experiments, and these animals are equally capable of spreading disease if handled improperly. Only healthy animals purchased from reputable sources should be brought into the laboratory. The reader should note that Animal Biosafety Levels (ABSL) 1 to 4 have been established by the CDC/NIH and that very specific requirements for each level are in place regarding facilities, air circulation, and waste management. Some very basic guidelines for working with animals are:

1. Autoclave the entire animal cage with its contents left inside before cleaning and disposal.

2. Quarantine new animals and assume all animals, even the controls, are infectious.

3. Check cages daily and at feeding time for dead animals, and remove any dead animals in biohazard bags immediately.

4. Wear *heavy* gloves at all times when handling animals.

5. Inoculate animals using a press cage or sedation. Handle sharps with extreme care.

6. House cages in specially designed rooms that will contain aerosols and waste and allow for hosing down and decontamination.

7. Perform animal necropsies in biological safety cabinets. Autoclave or disinfect all dead animals, waste, instruments, gloves, and gowns as any other biohazardous waste.

8. Animal pathogens are associated with an additional risk of disease. When possible, get vaccinated for any likely zoonoses. Medical monitoring for some zoonoses may be necessary.

Research with certain animals and/or specific pathogens may require additional restrictive procedures. In all cases, the animals must be treated humanely to reduce their pain and distress and to keep them in the best of health.

Aerosols and Droplets

Aerosols are fine mists of particles of up to 5 µm in size forced into the air. They can require up to 1 hour to settle. Splashing can cause airborne droplets which settle faster. Both may not be seen or smelled, but they may be inhaled and contain suspensions of pathogens. Aerosols or droplets may result from many common laboratory activities, examples of which are listed below:

1. **Activity** "Popping" open the stoppers of blood collection containers.

    Solution Open tops with a cover over the opening or open tops behind a work shield.

2. **Activity** Pouring liquid samples such as blood and serum from 1 tube to another.

    Solution Use automatic pipetting devices or Pasteur pipettes and deliver sample gently.

3. **Activity** Centrifuging uncapped liquids or overfilled liquid containers.

    Solution Centrifuge capped liquids no more than 90% full, and use covered centrifuges.

4. **Activity** Placing hot inoculating microbiological loop in broth or on media.

    Solution Allow loop to cool first.

5. **Activity** Forcibly delivering liquids when pipetting and/or blowing out the last drop.

    Solution Deliver liquids gently, allowing them to run down the sides of the container. Never blow into a pipette to expel the last drop or to mix the fluid. Never pipette by mouth.

6. **Activity** Flaming microbiological inoculation loop in open flame.

    Solution Obtain closed heat source for sterilizing loops such as the Bacticinerator®.

7. **Activity** Opening centrifuge immediately after breakage of specimen.

    Solution Allow the centrifuge to sit for 30 minutes before opening.

8. **Activity** Operating blenders uncovered or vortexing uncovered samples.

    Solution Only blend, mix, shake, or vortex covered samples. Let the aerosols inside settle before opening.

9. **Activity** Using bone saws in autopsies.

    Solution Wet bone saws before cutting and use vacuum attachments.

10. **Activity** Evisceration in autopsies.

    Solution Use single organ (Virchow) evisceration rather than blind evisceration (Rokitansky).

11. **Activity** Operating a cryostat to cut tissue without closing window.

    Solution Always operate any laboratory instrument with its cover closed.

It may be difficult to eliminate aerosols entirely. If aerosols are likely, even BSL-2 organisms, like

Class I Biological Safety Cabinet

Class I Biological Safety Cabinet

A. front opening; B. sash;
C. exhaust HEPA filter; D. exhaust plenum

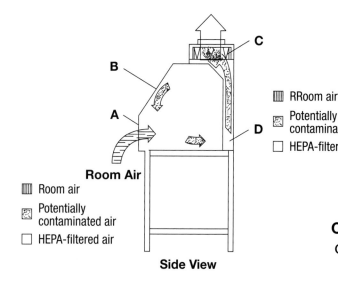

▥ Room air

▤ Potentially
contaminated air

☐ HEPA-filtered air

Room Air

▥ Room air

▤ Potentially
contaminated air

☐ HEPA-filtered air

Side View

Class II Biological Safety Cabinet

Connection to building exhaust system required.

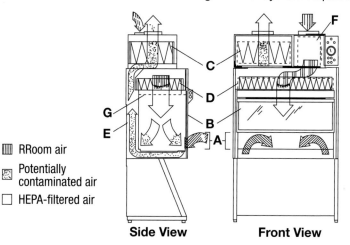

Side View   **Front View**

Class III Biological Safety Cabinet

Connection to building exhaust system required.

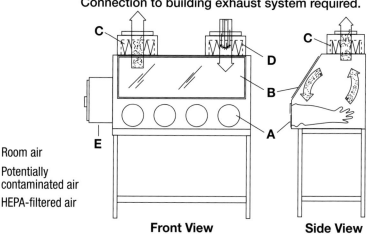

▥ Room air

▤ Potentially
contaminated air

☐ HEPA-filtered air

Front View   **Side View**

From "Biosafety in Microbiological and Biomedical Laboratories," US Department of Health and Human Services Publication No. (CDC)93-8395

Figure 5-3

BSL-3 organisms, must be handled in biological safety cabinets.

Biological Safety Cabinets and Air Circulation

Biosafety cabinets have air flowing upward away from the operator to confine microbes and aerosols in the cabinet. Air from the cabinets is filtered by a high-efficiency particulate air (HEPA) filter to prevent microbes from being expelled into the exhaust. Schematics of the major types of cabinets are shown in **Figure 5-3**. Class I cabinets protect the worker, but the contents of the cabinet can be contaminated from the influx of air. Class II cabinets protect both the work and the worker. They are suitable for BSL-2 and -3. Among the subcategories of class II hoods (A, B1, B2, and B3), class II B2 is recommended for manipulating tuberculosis cultures because it does not recirculate air and vents 100% to the outside. Class III cabinets (sometimes called glove boxes) are airtight, and specimens can only be manipulated by gloves at the front of the cabinet. These are used for BSL-4. Laminar flow hoods that are used to make sterile preparations protect only the product in the hood and not the worker, so they are unacceptable for use with biohazards.

Biological safety cabinets must be on a maintenance schedule to verify that the face velocity of air flow is adequate (usually 75-100 linear feet per minute) and to replace the particulate filters at appropriate intervals. Chemical fume hoods do not have filters and are designed differently, so they cannot be used interchangeably with biological safety cabinets.

Personnel must be trained in the appropriate use of each type of cabinet in a laboratory. This means that the sash opening must be in the correct position for proper air flow (usually open no more than 12 inches) and that cabinets are placed in areas of low air turbulence (low-traffic areas) so that air flow is at maximal efficiency. Supplies should be kept at least 4 to 8 inches away from the air intake at the face of the cabinet, and nothing should be placed in the cabinet that restricts air flow. A small object such a piece of yarn can be taped to the sash for visual determination of good air flow while staff members are using the cabinet. Cabinets should not be overloaded and should not be used to store things that are easily kept elsewhere. Air turbulence disrupts air flow, so devices that will disturb the air such as blenders and centrifuges should be placed at the back of the cabinet. Flames also disrupt the air and the heat could damage filters, so closed heat sources should be used. Workers should also attempt to reduce the effects of turbulence by (1) turning cabinets on for about 5 minutes before starting work, (2) inserting arms gently into the cabinet and allowing them to remain still for 1 minute to purge organisms before starting work, and (3) removing arms gently at the completion of work.

About 2.5 linear feet of workspace is recommended by OSHA for each worker using a cabinet to prevent overcrowding. Workers may need removable sleeve protectors or long-sleeved rather than wrist length gloves for better control of contamination after they remove their hands from the cabinet work space. Great care must also be taken with objects that have been in the cabinet. When possible, objects should be sealed or disinfected before removal. Horizontal, not vertical, disinfection pans should be used because they are easier to remove. Some cabinets are equipped with ultraviolet lights that can be turned on to decontaminate the contents inside before removal. A "clean to dirty" directional workflow should be established.

Even if biosafety cabinets are in use, proper air ventilation (at least 6-12 air changes per hour) and appropriate recirculation must be in place. For good containment, the laboratory should be at a negative air pressure; air flow should be directed into the laboratory and out an exhaust such that no air would leave the laboratory into surrounding spaces. Air recirculation can only occur among nonhazardous areas. Most designs require that laboratory doors remain shut at all times, and some designs require that biological safety cabinets remain on at all times.

Fomites

A fomite is an inanimate object such as a pencil, test tube, or book, that is not inherently biohazardous but has been exposed to microorganisms and it may be capable of transmitting infection. The list of potential fomites in the laboratory is almost endless, and the potential for harm is serious. Although

Biological Hazards

to date, no environmental transmission of HIV, HCV, or HBV has been documented, HBV has been recovered alive from dried blood spots up to a week old.

Clothing such as laboratory coats must be considered potentially infectious and should not be worn outside the laboratory, especially not to meals. Contaminated laboratory coats should be hung on separate pegs from coats and other clothing intended for wear outside the laboratory. Grossly soiled laboratory coats and other clothing should be removed from the laboratory in leak-proof biohazard bags and laundered in hot water and bleach. Ideally, all decontamination should be performed on site. Workers should not take home contaminated clothing, and furthermore, OSHA requires that employers provide laundering of contaminated clothing to employees at no cost.

There should be no hand-to-mouth, hand-to-nose, or hand-to-eye contact in the laboratory. Eating, drinking, chewing gum, putting on makeup, taking medication, inserting contact lenses, and smoking in the laboratory are strictly forbidden. Foods should *never* be placed in refrigerators or freezers used to store reagents or patient samples.

All laboratory equipment that is exposed in any way to infectious aerosols or handled by gloved personnel should be considered potentially hazardous. This includes items such as telephones, computer keyboards, benchtop supplies, and cabinet fronts in addition to those pieces of equipment that directly contact microbes such as petri dishes, pipettes, glassware, and needles. Some laboratories not only require that access to the area be strictly limited, but, also that all persons who enter the area wear gloves. Contamination of items such as telephones and computer keyboards is not usually visually apparent, and staff must be aware of which items are designated for gloved or bare-handed personnel to prevent unnecessary exposure. The use of speaker phones is highly encouraged. Some

laboratories label certain areas and equipment as "clean" areas to remind staff not to use gloves. This is important because some electronic devices may be impossible to decontaminate without being destroyed by the disinfecting agents.

Disposable items such as gloves and paper towels should be placed in orange biohazard bags for disposal. Items that are not technically "sharp" but which may puncture bags, such as capillary tubes and Pasteur pipettes, should be disposed of into puncture-resistant receptacles. Reusable items must be disinfected or autoclaved *before* cleaning. It is essential that these items not be put in ordinary trash or in routine cleaning units.

Spills and Decontamination

Many porous surfaces cannot be adequately decontaminated, so all surfaces possible, particularly countertops and flooring, must be impervious to chemicals/fluids. Carpets are not permitted, and floors should have as few seams as possible with coved edges.

A spill in a biological safety cabinet is not particularly hazardous as long as the cabinet is left on. Gloves must be worn to clean out the inside of the cabinet with the appropriate disinfectant. A spill in the open laboratory is much more dangerous. Universal absorbents such as sand and kitty litter can be used to contain large spills by placing them around the perimeter of the spill (creating a "dike" around the spill). Aerosols generated by the spill may require immediate evacuation and cessation of air ventilation. Contaminated clothing should be immediately removed, and any residue should be washed off in the shower. Personnel who clean up the spill must wear respiratory protection and gloves at a minimum. They may also need gowns, goggles, and footwear covers when cleaning a large spill. Whenever possible, reentry into the area should be delayed for about 30 minutes to allow the aerosols to settle, but BSL-3 spills in the open laboratory require evacuation for 60 minutes. A disinfectant of sufficient strength to kill the pathogen(s) spilled must be selected. However, penetration of large spills with high protein content and organism load may be poor with any disinfectant. Disinfection should be repeated after the bulk of the spill has been removed.

There are 3 broad classes of decontamination methods listed herein. The reader should note that disinfectants, antiseptics, and sterilants are not the same things. Sterilization procedures are by definition supposed to kill all microorganisms, whereas disinfectants and antiseptics may leave some organisms behind. Sterility is often not necessary, and the removal of the important human pathogens may be sufficient. Disinfectants are agents meant to be used on objects while antiseptics are meant to be used on human skin. They are not interchangeable. The Food and Drug Administration (FDA) regulates sterilants and antiseptics used for medical purposes, and the EPA regulates disinfectants used for environmental decontamination.

The choice of the following methods is based on the goal that needs to be achieved.

1. **Heat** Boiling, incineration, dry heat (ovens), or autoclaving (steam sterilization under pressure) are effective means to kill microbes, but objects must be heat-stable to be used.

2. **Radiation** Ultraviolet light or ionizing radiation can sterilize, but these techniques can be cumbersome, especially because exposure of humans to radiation is dangerous.

3. **Chemical** Certain gases can be used to sterilize equipment (ethylene oxide, for example). There are numerous low-, medium-, and high-level liquid disinfectants on the market

may be suitable for clinical laboratories. Low-level disinfectants are effective against a wide variety of organisms, but *M tuberculosis,* bacterial spores, and many viruses are resistant. Mid-level disinfectants kill *M tuberculosis,* most viruses, and fungi but not spores. High-level disinfectants kill virtually everything except high numbers of bacterial spores. Thus, laboratories must know which microbes are likely to be present and select the disinfectant accordingly.

Laboratories will most frequently be decontaminated with liquid chemicals. When possible, the disinfectant should be allowed to act for as long as possible (about 10-15 minutes) before removal to ensure adequate exposure of the microbes to the agent. Disinfectant may not penetrate large loads adequately, so it may be necessary to disinfect both before and after cleaning.

A simple and easily obtained chemical disinfectant is a fresh 1:10 solution of household bleach. Free chlorine in bleach kills microorganisms, but it escapes as a gas from squirt bottles. For this reason, the 1:10 bleach solution should be made fresh every 24 hours. Alternately, Association of Professionals in Infection Control (APIC) guidelines indicate that a 1:5 bleach solution can be made and used for up to 30 days, and disinfection efficiency will be as good or better than a 1:10 fresh solution. Although this is inexpensive and effective (activity against many spores), bleach is corrosive to some materials and creates toxic products when mixed with ammonia, acid, or formaldehyde. For these reasons, some laboratories may choose to use a mid-level disinfectant. Certain organisms such as rotavirus, norovirus, and *Clostridium difficile* may resist some hospital disinfectants, so commercial products should be evaluated carefully. In fact, exposure of *C difficile* to nonchlorine disinfectants has been shown to increase its spore formation and further increase its resistance to chemical disinfection.

Work surfaces and the interiors of biosafety cabinets should be decontaminated as needed or at least at the completion of work each day. A mid-level disinfectant or 1:10 household bleach will kill almost every organism of concern in a BSL-2 laboratory. Tissues preserved in 10% formalin in excess of 10 volumes of the tissue also have most important organisms deactivated. An important exception to both of these techniques is infectious prions. Some additional steps to take if you suspect prions are using a 1 to 2.5 dilution of household bleach or 1 N sodium hydroxide (NaOH) for 1 hour and then autoclaving. Incineration is also a method of choice for disposal of materials containing prions. The CDC has other useful recommendations for prion decontamination which should be consulted for particular situations.

There may be occasions when high-level disinfectants are required to decontaminate environmental surfaces, but this would be rare. Many high-level disinfectants and sterilants contain glutaraldehyde, a chemical which poses several health hazards. Exercise 3 has additional information on the proper handling of glutaraldehyde.

Accidental Exposures

Needlesticks, glassware punctures, and injuries involving any piece of equipment that is potentially contaminated should be immediately treated and reported. If a particular patient specimen was involved, that patient may be tested if state law permits. (In some states, patient permission must be obtained before testing can take place.) With their consent, accident victims may also be tested for infectious agents to establish a baseline against which seroconversion may be detected. Treatment protocols depend on the source and any organisms suspected to be present and could include administration of antibiotics, a tetanus vaccine, hepatitis B vaccine, hepatitis B immune globulin, and HIV

prophylaxis. Procedures should be established at each facility based on current standards of medical care and results of testing. Examples of current CDC recommendations are contained in Appendix 7. In all cases, OSHA requires that all related medical care at the time of the incident and subsequent to the incident be provided free of charge and documented in workers' records.

Puncture wounds are not the only means by which pathogens can be acquired. Laboratory coats and gloves should be worn at all times, and goggles should be available if production of large aerosols or splashing is unavoidable. Personnel should always cover any open cuts or wounds and wear gloves in the laboratory. In the event of intact skin exposure to infectious prions, the CDC recommends 1 minute of exposure to 1 N NaOH or a 1:10 dilution of bleach. These protocols are not recommended for other exposures.

To reduce the possibility of self-inoculation, hands should be kept away from any mucous membranes, such as the eyes, mouth, and nose. Frequent hand washing or decontamination is very important in reducing infections, even when gloves are worn. Exercise 10 contains additional information on hand decontamination.

Disposal

All biohazards must be disposed of in a clearly marked container, usually an orange biohazard bag. Many other types of containers are acceptable as long as the hazardous nature of the waste is clearly indicated. Containers with a lid are preferred so that the waste can be covered when work at the station has been completed. Sharp objects should never be placed in biohazard bags, and double bagging may sometimes be necessary to prevent leaks. Microbes in the waste must be destroyed before final disposal. This may be accomplished by chemical or radiation disinfection, autoclaving or incineration. Biohazard labeling should be removed or defaced after trash has been sterilized. Waste that is infectious must *never* be handled as ordinary trash.

Risk Assessment

Taking all of the aforementioned information into consideration, the CDC recommends a 5-step approach to assessing risk and implementing the proper protocols:

1. Identify the biologic agents present or most likely to be present and assign an initial risk category based on the BSL assigned to that agent. Unknown agents in clinical specimens are assigned a BSL-2 at minimum.

2. Review the hazards of the laboratory procedures being conducted. Take steps to minimize dangerous steps in the procedures themselves.

For example, potential aerosol generation is unacceptable at any risk category.

3. Make a final determination of BSL by considering the inherent hazards of the procedure and those of the agent(s) involved.

4. Train all staff in appropriate safety protocols and document their proficiency. Inspect and document that all safety equipment is functioning properly.

5. Review the final risk assessment and established protocols with a knowledgeable professional.

The steps above should be reviewed periodically, but especially as information about various organisms evolves.

Summary Table: Biological Hazards

Topic	Comments
Biohazard symbol	1. Put on doors, waste, laundry, equipment and specimens and/or containers 2. Must be dark on orange background 3. If staff is trained, red bags can substitute for symbol on waste
Microbial sources	1. Use Universal/Standard Precautions and CDC/NIH Biosafety Level guidelines 2. Wear gloves and lab coat to handle biohazards. Use fluid-proof lab coat and face protection and work in a biosafety cabinet if splashing likely 3. Assume all lab animals are infectious. Handle using animal Biosafety Levels 4. Segregate biohazards and decontaminate for disposal 5. Evaluate staff with compromised immune systems or special situations 6. Follow Transmission-Based Precautions posted on patient doors for specific diseases 7. Conduct risk assessment based on microbes present and tasks. Assign BSL-2 at a minimum for unknown organisms in clinical specimens, but process specimens in biosafety cabinet
Biosecurity	1. Consult regulated microbial agents and toxins listed by CDC and USDA 2. Consult CDC bioterrorism guidelines for referral labs 3. Consult ASM sentinel lab guidelines for most clinical labs 4. Evaluate restricted access for BSL-2/3 labs to see if adequate in clinical lab 5. Maintain lab security to deter bioterrorism

Biological Hazards

Summary Table: Biological Hazards (continued)

Topic	Comments
Notable infectious agents	1. Know signs/symptoms of diseases caused by microbes in lab. Maintain medical surveillance 2. Get vaccinated against HBV 3. Consult CDC post-exposure protocols. Example: anti-retroviral drugs for HIV 4. Make sure TB screening is current- single blood test adequate, two-step skin test for initial screening 5. Treat CNS tissue as high risk for prions. Use special decontamination procedures for prions
Precautions categories	1. Universal Precautions - Use for blood and all body substances likely to have blood or visibly contaminated with blood 2. Standard Precautions - Use for all blood and body substances except sweat 3. Transmission-Based Precautions - Use special protocols based on presence of an infectious agent
Histology and autopsy	1. Histology and autopsy high risk from dissection of unfixed tissue. Follow protocols 2. Minimize risks from sharp objects (bone saws, scalpels, sharps associated with body, cyrostat/microtomes, etc.) with appropriate handling protocols 3. Minimize aerosols (operate cryostat closed, use wet bone saws with vacuum, transfer bodies with minimal splashing, etc) 4. Decontaminate appropriately with at least a mid-level disinfectant. Use special protocols for suspected prions. Don't mix bleach and formaldehyde
Aerosols and droplets	To avoid aerosols and droplets: 1. Open tubes with cover over the opening or work behind shield 2. Use automatic pipettors and deliver liquids gently, allowing them to run down the side 3. Operate all instruments with covers closed 4. Cap all liquids to be centrifuged and use covered centrifuges 5. Allow aerosols to settle 30 minutes before opening a centrifuge containing breakage 6. Use a closed heat source for sterilizing loops and allow loops to cool before inoculation 7. Only blend, mix or vortex covered samples. Allow aerosols to settle before opening 8. Use biological safety cabinets if aerosols cannot be avoided. Verify air flow and clean HEPA filters on schedule

Biosafety cabinets and air circulation	1. Verify air flow (75-100 lfpm) and clean HEPA filters on schedule for cabinets
	2. Don't use chemical fume or laminar flow hoods for biohazards
	3. Know cabinet capabilities. Use at least Class II in clinical labs
	    Class I - protects worker only
	    Class II - protects worker and experiment, but not sealed
	    Class III - protects worker and experiment, but sealed "glove box"
	4. Minimize air disturbance around cabinets and make sure air flow is unrestricted
	5. Allow 2.5 feet per worker and set up "clean to dirty" work flow in cabinets
	6. Make lab at negative pressure with 6-12 air changes per hour with no air recirculation from hazardous areas

Summary Table: Biological Hazards (continued)

Topic	Comments
Fomites	1. Any objects exposed to biohazards are fomites 2. Remove lab coats and wash hands when leaving lab 3. Do not eat, drink, smoke, apply cosmetics, insert contact lenses or chew gum in lab 4. Segregate equipment with regard to usage by gloved vs. bare-handed personnel
Spills	1. If inside biosafety cabinet, leave it on and wear gloves to disinfect spill 2. Outside cabinet, contain spill with absorbent and evacuate if necessary. BSL-3 spills require one hour to settle 3. Disinfection requires gloves and may require respiratory protection, gowns, goggles and/or footwear covers 4. Disinfect with right level of disinfectant. Let disinfectant contact spill 10 - 15 minutes for maximum effect. May need to disinfect again after bulk of large spills removed
Decontamination	1. Major categories - heat/pressure, radiation, chemical 2. Chemical disinfectants: low-level (kills some viruses and vegetative bacteria), mid level (kills almost all viruses, fungi and bacteria, including TB), high-level (kills everything except large numbers of spores) 3. Mid-level disinfectant - daily 1:10 solution of bleach or every 30 days 1:5 dilution 4. High-level disinfectant- may contain glutaraldehyde (see exercise 3) 5. More rigorous treatment required if prions known or suspected or if specimen is high risk (brain, spinal cord or central nervous system tissue)
Accidental Exposures	1. Report the accident and seek immediate medical attention 2. Exposure source and exposed individual may be tested for infections 3. Facilities must establish treatment protocols consistent with current medical practice. May include vaccination, antibiotics, anti-retrovirals, tetanus shots, immune globulin, etc 4. Encourage vaccination in workers when appropriate. Know disease signs and maintain medical surveillance (TB testing, for example)
Disposal	1. Use biohazard symbol or red bags. Remove symbol when waste decontaminated 2. Double bag to prevent leakage. Sharps must be placed in puncture-resistant container 3. Waste must be decontaminated before disposal by chemical agents, heat or radiation

Exercise 5

Self-Evaluation Questions

1. ___ The symbol below is for:

    a. Biohazards
    b. Electrical hazards
    c. Radiation hazards
    d. Chemical hazards
    e. Compressed gas hazards

2. ___ Clinical AIDS specimens should be handled at biosafety level (BSL-)

    a. 1
    b. 2
    c. 3
    d. 4
    e. 5

3. ___ For any manipulations other than making microscopic smears, *Mycobacterium tuberculosis* specimens should be handled at biosafety level (BSL-)

    a. 1
    b. 2
    c. 3
    d. 4
    e. 5

4. ___ What type of containment is necessary for handling nonpathogens in a teaching laboratory?

    a. Class II biological safety cabinet
    b. Gowns, goggles, masks, gloves, shoe covers
    c. Standard microbiological procedures: minimal aerosols, hand washing, no mouth pipetting, benchtop decontamination
    d. All of the above
    e. None of the above. Nonpathogenic organisms require no special handling

5. When you handle human materials that might contain blood or are visibly contaminated with blood, you must assume that each specimen is infectious and treat it accordingly. This philosophy is called

_____.

6. ___ The only body fluid exempt from Standard Precautions is:

    a. Urine
    b. Tears
    c. Sweat
    d. Vitreous humor
    e. Cerebrospinal fluid

7. ___ Which laboratory worker(s) below might require protection in excess of that recommended by the CDC/NIH biosafety levels?

    a. Pregnant worker
    b. Worker who is HIV positive
    c. Worker with a kidney transplant
    d. Cancer patient who recently completed chemotherapy
    e. All of the above

8. Matching

    ___ Hepatitis B virus

    ___ Hepatitis C virus

    ___ Human immunodeficiency virus

    ___ *Mycobacterium tuberculosis*

A. Recommended baseline screening is two-step skin test.

B. Workers exposed to this virus should begin anti-retroviral drug therapy prophylactically.

C. All workers who come in contact with blood and body fluids should get this vaccine.

D. No vaccine, no cure, no prophylactic drugs.

9. ___ True/False: Only rare, exotic and rapidly lethal organisms can be used as weapons by bioterrorists.

10. ___ The most dangerous specimens for exposure to infectious prions are

   a. Blood
   b. Liver tissues
   c. Lymph nodes
   d. Central nervous system tissues
   e. Bone marrow biopsies from patients with zoonoses

11. ___ Which protocol is correct for handling laboratory animals?

   a. Monitoring for zoonoses when the laboratory animals involved are primates
   b. You must only wear gloves when handling animals inoculated with pathogen
   c. Autoclave cages after their contents have been removed and the cages cleaned
   d. Animal autopsies may be conducted on stainless steel counters as long as the work
       surfaces are decontaminated afterward with 10% bleach
   e. None of the above

12. ___ All of the following procedures for minimizing aerosols are **CORRECT EXCEPT:**

   a. Opening a capped tube with a tissue over the cap
   b. Centrifuging capped tubes of blood from an AIDS patient
   c. Keeping a centrifuge closed for 30 minutes after breakage
   d. Delivering liquid to a flask by allowing it to run down the side
   e. Making sure that tubes are completely full of fluid before centrifugation

13. ___ A class III biological safety cabinet is most appropriate for biosafety level (BSL-)

   a. 1
   b. 2
   c. 3
   d. 4
   e. 5

14. ___ Which of the following is **NOT** a potential fomite?

   a. Pencil
   b. Purse
   c. Intercom
   d. Eyeglasses
   e. All of the above are potential fomites if exposed to microbiological aerosols

15. ___ If a microbiological spill occurs in a biological safety cabinet you should:

a. Leave the fans on while cleaning up the spill with gloves on
b. Turn off the fans immediately to prevent microbes from entering the exhaust
c. Scrub the inside of the cabinet well with the most convenient source of soap and water
d. a and c
e. b and c

16. ___ All of the following can be used to dispose of biohazardous waste **EXCEPT:**

a. Autoclaving
b. Incineration
c. Landfill burial
d. Chemical disinfection
e. Exposure to ionizing radiation

17. ___ Which of the following is a mid-level disinfectant appropriate for decontamination of a BSL-2 countertop?

a. 1:5 dilution (20%) of household bleach made 15 days ago
b. 1:10 dilution (10%) of household bleach made 5 days ago
c. Commercial product labeled as "tuberculocidal" (kills *Mycobacterium tuberculosis*)
d. a and c
e. a and b
f. a, b and c

18. ___ Which of the following inactivate infectious prions?

a. Formalin fixation
b. 10% household bleach
c. 30 minutes of autoclaving at 140°C
d. All of the above
e. None of the above

19. ___ Current bioterrorism guidelines for sentinel laboratories in the United States are published by:

    a. The National Institutes of Health
    b. The American Society of Microbiology
    c. The Department of Homeland Security
    d. The Centers for Disease Control and Prevention
    e. The Occupational Safety and Health Administration

20. ___ Regulated microbial agents and toxins with potential for bioterrorism are published by:

    a. The US Department of Agriculture
    b. The American Society of Microbiology
    c. The Department of Homeland Security
    d. The Centers for Disease Control and Prevention
    e. a and c
    f. c and d
    g. a and d

21. ___ A clinical lab scientist is examinging a culture from a wound that may be *Franciscella tularensis.* What should be done next?

    a. Notify a supervisor
    b. Verify how to follow up using the lab's bioterrorism protocols
    c. Move all materials associated with the culture to a biosafety cabinet
    d. All of the above

Exercise 6
COMPRESSED GASES

Compressed gases are gases that are confined under great pressure in metal cylinders. They are used for various instruments in the clinical laboratory such as flames, carbon dioxide incubators, and gas chromatographs. Types of gas frequently used are air, nitrogen, oxygen, carbon dioxide, helium and propane.

NATURE OF COMPRESSED GAS

Gases by their nature completely fill any object in which they exist and exert pressure on the container. The higher the temperature, the more pressure that is exerted (exhibited by a balloon that pops when it gets too close to a candle). Using high pressure allows more gas to be stored in a smaller container, but the gas will readily leak out of the smallest opening. Standard 55-inch gas cylinders can have internal pressures of more than 3000 pounds per square inch, so leaks will readily occur, often with great force. Leaks may be difficult to detect because they often cannot be seen or smelled. This is potentially very hazardous. For example, a flammable gas could leak out of its cylinder and create conditions in which a single spark could ignite the entire laboratory. Sudden release of pressure, as seen when a cylinder's valve is sheared off or if the contents are heated, can cause the cylinder to become a deadly "torpedo" as the gas is quickly released from its high pressure (similar in process to blowing up a balloon and letting go).

Figures 6-1 and **6-2** are schematics of representative compressed gas cylinders. Cylinders have a valve at the top which allows gas to exit when open. Regulators are devices that fit into the exit hole and allow users to monitor cylinder pressure and control gas flow from the cylinder. When a regulator is in use, the valve is usually left open and gas flow is controlled through the regulator. Therefore, the *valve* must be closed to ensure that no gas escapes the cylinder.

Compressed gases are also hazardous because of their chemical nature. Oxygen and hydrogen are extremely flammable. Nitrogen has been called "asphyxiating gas" because significant nitrogen leaks reduce the amount of oxygen in the room to fatal levels. This can also occur with carbon dioxide

113

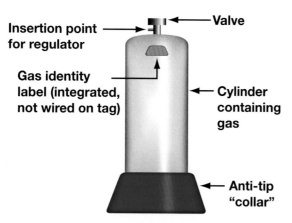

Schematic of a compressed gas cylinder ready to have a regulator applied

Figure 6-1

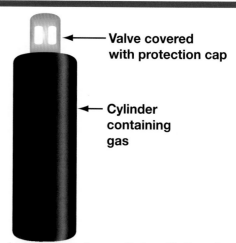

Schematic of a compressed gas cylinder with the valve covered

Figure 6-2

and other gases. Thus, no amount of leakage from a compressed gas tank is acceptable.

SAFE HANDLING OF COMPRESSED GAS

Compressed gases are hazardous because improper use and storage can result in fire, explosions, asphyxiation, or mechanical injury. General guidelines are as follows:

1. **Proper storage** Store and use *all* cylinders chained to the wall in a vertical position or secured in a "non-tip" or "anti-tip" base (collar) with valve covers on. Chains should be secure enough to prevent tipping and to hold the cylinder in place in the event of a sudden vertical release of pressure. Cylinders should be stored away from sources of heat and electricity. Ideally, gas cylinders should be stored in a separate room, especially if they are flammable. Good ventilation to disperse leaks and lack of moisture to prevent cylinder corrosion are essential in all areas in which gases are used or stored. Because some gases are heavier than air, consideration should be given

to where the storage is and where a leak would accumulate. For example, heavy gas storage in a basement could cause more accumulation of leaked vapors than a storage unit above ground with more windows and doors.

2. **Safety shut-off valves** If gas is being pumped in, shut-off valves should be clearly marked and unobstructed. All staff members in the vicinity should know where the valves are and how to use them.

3. **Inventory management** Use a "first in, first out" system of inventory management for the use of gas cylinders. Full cylinders should be stored such that the oldest cylinders are used first and those cylinders that have been in storage for too long are readily identified. Only keep the minimal amount of cylinders required for routine laboratory operation. A good rule of thumb is to store no more than the cylinder in use and one spare and/or no more than a week's supply. Different gas types should be stored separately to prevent incompatible mixtures.

4. **Safe transportation** Valve covers must be on cylinders during transportation. Cylinders should be moved using a hand truck or other appropriate transportation device. Improper transport of gases can result in a cylinder being dropped or damaged and a sudden, dangerous release of pressure.

5. **Minimal amounts** Use the smallest cylinder possible for any job. Larger cylinders present greater hazards.

6. **Labeling** Each cylinder should be marked as to the contents of that cylinder with a permanently affixed label, not a wired-on tag. Department of Transportation and Globally Harmonized System symbols are typically used as well, as shown in **Figure 6-3**. *Never* use an unmarked cylinder. Unmarked cylinders should be identified with a "DO NOT USE" tag and returned as soon as possible to the manufacturer.

7. **Valve protection** The weakest area of most cylinders is the valve area, so removable protection caps on cylinders should remain on until just before use.

8. **No defective cylinders** *Never* force or lubricate "frozen" or difficult cylinder valves.

GHS Flammable

GHS Compressed Gas

Examples of DOT Gas Hazard Symbols (top row)
Examples of Globally Harmonized Hazard Symbols (bottom row)

Figure 6-3

Compressed Gases

Use another cylinder, and return the defective cylinder to the manufacturer.

9. **Proper fittings** Use only those fittings made for the particular gas you are using. Cylinder fittings that connect a cylinder to a particular instrument are made to fit only on certain types of cylinders, thus preventing incompatible gases from mixing. Therefore, fittings should *never* be interchanged. Fittings should never be lubricated except according to manufacturer's instructions. Many regulators are used with washers to improve the seal of the fittings, and these should be visually inspected before use. It is important to distinguish between sealing washers that can be reused and crush gaskets that are designed for one-time use only. Serious oxygen fires have resulted from improper sealing of oxygen tanks because of the reuse of crush gaskets (Food and Drug Administration [FDA] and National Institute for Occupational Safety and Health Public Health Notification: Oxygen Regulator Fires Resulting from Incorrect Use of CGA 870 Seals, April 24, 2006).

10. **Regulators** Learn what the pressure gauges on regulators mean. **Figure 6-4** shows a typical regulator. In general, one gauge mea-

sures the amount of pressure within the tank, thus indicating how full it is. A second gauge monitors the pressure of the gas coming out. When the regulator valve is closed, it should read zero even when the tank is full.

11. **Safe installation** Make sure that the top cylinder valve is closed and that the exit pressure displayed on the regulator is zero *before* you remove a fitting from a used cylinder. When installing a new cylinder, briefly opening the top valve to allow the gas to expel any debris may be appropriate, especially with oxygen tanks. When placing a regulator on the new cylinder, secure all fittings as tightly as possible to prevent leaks. Stand to one side of the gauges (the gauge faces can blow out) and turn your face away. Open the top cylinder valve *slowly*, listening carefully for hissing sounds that would indicate leaks. Be prepared to shut the valve quickly if you hear a leak.

12. **No leaks** Check all connections to a gas cylinder for leaks with a soap solution, such as the commercial product Snoop® (Ohio Valley Specialty Company, Marietta, Ohio). A leak will cause bubbles in a soap solution to form over the leak. Since leaks can be difficult to locate,

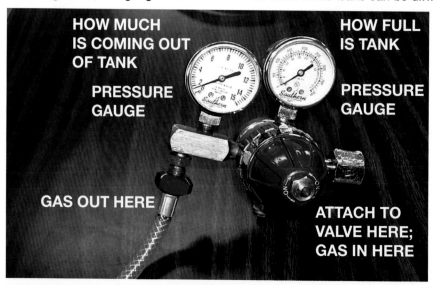

Figure 6-4

it is the idea that bubbles form directly over the leak that is important.

13. **Daily monitoring and shut-off** Check and record cylinder pressures daily when the gas is in use to detect leaks and cylinders approaching complete emptying. When the gas is not in use, close the cylinder at the valve to reduce pressure on parts.

14. **Empty tanks** Empty tanks should be labeled "EMPTY" and separated from full tanks. If an empty tank is accidentally hooked up to a pressurized system, foreign matter could enter into the empty cylinder and cause corrosion, explosion, or fire. Tanks should never be completely emptied because it could lead to negative pressure, and form a suction in the tank. Empty tanks are stored as if they were still full. Just as one always treats a gun as if it were loaded, one must assume that a gas cylinder labeled as empty could still contain gas.

The Compressed Gas Association (www.cganet.com) has a series of free posters displaying good practice with compressed gas cylinders. Other posters and information on medical gases are available from the FDA (http://www.fda.gov/cder/dmpq/gases.htm, accessed January 19, 2008) (Appendix 8).

Cryogenics

Temperatures below −100°F are usually considered cryogenic. Many applications in biological research and medical laboratory practice, such as "snap freezing" specimens use cryogenics. Low temperatures are generally achieved by liquefaction of gases. These gases have the high-pressure hazards discussed earlier, but they also are associated with flammability hazards. Some of the gases used are flammable, but extremely cold temperatures alone can also cause oxygen to condense into ordinary combustibles and increase their inherent flammability. For example, wood saturated with oxygen can be explosive. The materials used for cryogenic applications must be carefully chosen to not only withstand the cold but also avoid oxygen condensation. The work area must be kept exceptionally clean.

Damage to human skin and extremities at such temperatures can be catastrophic, so proper personnel protection for eyes, face, and body is essential at all times. Workers should not wear anything that could trap cryogenic fluids against the skin, so watches and jewelry are not permitted. Gloves, laboratory coats, aprons, and other apparel designed to protect against the cold should be worn.

Gases for Medical Use

The compressed gases used in laboratories usually differ from those gases used in patient care. Clinical laboratory staff, however, may have to comply with special procedures to prevent medical gas mix-ups. For example, in 2004, a patient died of nitrous oxide poisoning when an oxygen flow meter was forced into a nitrous oxide outlet (Institute of

Table 6-1: Standard Colors for Medical Gases

Gas Name	Standard Color
Medical air	Yellow
Medical carbon dioxide	Gray
Medical helium	Brown
Medical nitrogen	Black
Medical nitrous oxide	Blue
Medical oxygen	Green
Mixture or blend of medical gases	Standard colors for each component. Example: 95% oxygen and 5% carbon dioxide = green cylinder with gray band or shoulder

Table 6-2: Compressed Gases

Topic	Comments
Hazards	1. Contents under pressure. Likely to leak, and hazard worse if contents heated 2. Contents can be chemical hazards. (Oxygen and hydrogen are flammable, nitrogen and other gases can reduce room oxygen to fatal levels) 3. Valve area is usually weakest point of cylinder; protect it and use valve caps. 4. Gases used for cryogenics - severe physical hazard from cold and increased flammability of materials due to oxygen condensation
Storage	1. Chain all cylinders (even "empty" ones) to the wall in a vertical position or use "non-tip" base 2. Make sure all cylinders are permanently labeled (wired-on labels not acceptable). Return unlabeled cylinders to manufacturer 3. Learn GHS/DOT labels and FDA color codes 4. Store away from heat and electricity with good ventilation and lack of moisture 5. Segregate empty and full cylinders. Label empty tanks "EMPTY" 6. Use "first in, first out" inventory system. Maintain smallest inventory possible
Transport	1. Use hand truck or other transportation device, especially with heavy cylinders 2. Always transport with valve cover on
Usage	1. Keep shutoff valves to gas lines unobstructed and well-marked 2. Use the smallest cylinder possible for any job 3. Leave valve covers on until just before use 4. Never force or lubricate a valve. Return to manufacturer 5. Never interchange cylinder fittings 6. Close the top cylinder valve (not regulator valve) and make sure exit pressure is zero before removing a fitting 7. Learn function of gauges and valves on regulator 8. Learn locations of gas shut-off valves and how to use them 9. Use soap solution to detect leaks. Bubbles will form over leaks 10. Do not completely empty a tank. One of the regulator gauges monitors current pressure 11. Proper personal protection and no jewelry/watches for cryogenics 12. Scrupulously clean work area and proper materials for cryogenics

Safe Medication Practices Medication Safety Alert, 9(24), 2004). A portion of the flow meter designed to prevent insertion into an incompatible gas outlet was broken, and poor lighting in the room made it difficult to distinguish the oxygen tank (green) from the nitrous oxide tank (blue).

In April 2006, the FDA issued a proposed rule on medical gas containers and closures. The National Fire Protection Association has also revised its guidelines to include prevention of medical gas mix-ups. The FDA proposes a ban on converting industrial use cylinders to medical use, and outlines a set of standard colors (**Table 6-1**) and wraparound labels that would be required on all medical gases.

Additional measures include making gas-specific outlet fittings permanently attached or more difficult to remove or bypass. Although these measures are primarily designed to prevent patients from getting harmed from inappropriate gases, gas mix-ups in the laboratory are also potentially harmful to staff and laboratory equipment. Applying such requirements to laboratory gases could be very useful.

Certain gases or tanks of a particular size may require handling even more restrictive than that outlined herein. As with any equipment or chemical in a laboratory, the rules and regulations that apply to the particular compressed gas should be established before it is used.

Exercise 6

Self-Evaluation Questions

1. ___ Which of the following is a proper technique in the use of compressed gases?

    a. Store in a horizontal position
    b. Secure only full or partially full tanks
    c. Store all full cylinders in the same area
    d. Keep empty and full cylinders separated
    e. Completely empty tanks to be cost-effective

2. ___ A cylinder's tag has fallen off. You should:

    a. Open the valve to see what it is
    b. Label it "EMPTY" so no one will use it
    c. Ask around to see if someone knows what it is
    d. Not use that cylinder under any circumstances
    e. All of the above

3. ___ Cylinder fittings are:

    a. Checked for leaks using soapy solutions
    b. Best unfrozen with liberal use of lubricant
    c. Virtually impermeable to gases if installed properly
    d. Interchangeable if cleaned properly between different gases
    e. All of the above

4. ___ All of the following are characteristics of compressed gases that contribute to hazardous nature of gases **EXCEPT:**

    a. High pressure
    b. Biohazardous contents
    c. Flammability of certain kinds of gases
    d. Leaks that often cannot be seen or smelled
    e. Dropping a cylinder during transport can shear off the valve

5. ___ Before you remove a fitting on a gas cylinder, the most important thing to do is:

    a. First check the fitting with a soapy solution for leaks
    b. First lubricate the fitting so that it will come off easily
    c. Make sure the valve protector cap is nearby and ready to be placed back on the valve
    d. Make sure the cylinder valve is turned off and the exit pressure on the regulator is zero

6. ___ The symbol below indicates which hazard?

    a. Toxicity
    b. Reactivity
    c. Flammability
    d. Compressed gas
    e. Explosive hazard

7. ___ How are cryogenic gases hazardous?

    a. Gas under pressure
    b. Chemical nature of the gas
    c. Physically hazardous from extreme cold
    d. Increased flammability of materials from condensed oxygen
    e. All of the above

8. ___ If the cylinder valve is completely closed on a cylinder, which gauge(s) on the regulator should read zero?

    a. A
    b. B
    c. Both A and B
    d. Neither A nor B

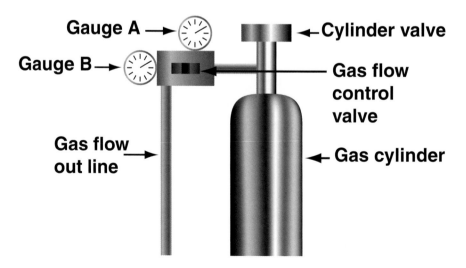

9. ___ Specifications for medical gases include all of the following **EXCEPT:**

    a. Standard colors for each gas type
    b. Labels that wrap entirely around the cylinder
    c. Standard color combinations for gas mixtures
    d. Prohibition on converting industrial gas cylinders for medical use
    e. The ability to bypass regulator fittings to deliver oxygen during a medical emergency

10. ___ A laboratory has an incubator in microbiology that uses approximately 1 CO_2 compressed gas cylinder a month. 5 spare CO_2 cylinders are stored in the corner of the room chained vertically to the wall with their valve covers on. Evaluate this situation.

    a. This situation illustrates proper storage and inventory of CO_2 compressed gas
    b. This situation is unacceptable because cylinders should not be stored vertically with chains
    c. This situation is unacceptable because an excessive number of cylinders are being stored in the laboratory
    d. This situation is unacceptable because valve covers should be removed when cylinders are placed in the laboratory
    e. This situation is unacceptable because carbon dioxide is heavier than air and these cylinders cannot be stored in the laboratory

Exercise 7

RADIOACTIVE MATERIALS

Radioactive materials are unstable isotopes of elements which alter (decay) in some way to form more stable isotopes. In the process of becoming more stable, these materials give off energy and/or particles that can be very harmful to living organisms.

TYPES OF RADIOACTIVE EMISSIONS

It is important to characterize the emissions of any particular radioactive isotope because the means of safely handling each type is different. The 3 types listed herein have laboratory applications. A 4th type, neutrons from fission reactions and other atom manipulations, is not used in laboratories and will not be discussed. **Figure 7-1** is a schematic of the three radiation types.

Alpha Particles

These are actually "naked" helium nuclei, 2 protons and 2 neutrons. Because they are particulate in nature, they are not able to penetrate any substance deeply, including human skin. They are usually associated with damage in localized areas, especially if they are ingested or inhaled. There are 3 things here that provide protection: gloves, plastic and Lucite. Gloves made of latex should provide adequate external protection, and good laboratory practice (such as minimal generation of aerosols, no hand-to-face contact) should provide adequate internal protection.

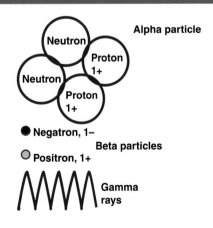

Categories of Ionizing Radiation

Figure 7-1

Radioactive Materials

Beta Particles

Beta particles can be negatrons (negative electrons) or positrons (positive electrons). Although these are also particles, they can penetrate more deeply than alpha particles because they are significantly smaller. Their greatest hazard is internal damage when they are ingested or inhaled. Again, there are 3 things here that provide protection: gloves, plastic and Lucite. Gloves made of latex provide adequate external protection for beta-emitters, and good laboratory practice provides adequate internal protection. Lead shielding should *not* be used for alpha and beta emitters because the interaction of high-energy beta particles with lead can *cause* additional radiation (Bremstrahlung radiation). The most common beta emitter which causes this problem is ^{32}P.

GAMMA RAYS

Gamma rays are a form of electromagnetic radiation with only energy and no mass. Because they are pure energy, they penetrate very deeply. (They are similar in nature to x-rays.) Only lead shields can absolutely block gamma rays. Gamma rays present both an internal and external hazard to humans.

Effects of Radiation

Particles and energy from radioactive decay interact with matter to ionize and excite it. This can be very damaging to the matter, particularly in biological systems. The damaging and/or destructive effects of radiation are cumulative and directly proportional to the intensity and length of exposure as well as the type of radiation. The lens of the eye is vulnerable to cataract formation under radiation exposure. Some cells destroyed by radiation (such as those in the bone marrow) cannot be replaced,

and some damaged cells become malignant cancer cells. Radiation has also been known to cause DNA mutations and damage developing embryos. Therefore, it is critical to monitor the exposure of personnel who work with high levels of radiation, with special monitoring and exposure limits applied to pregnant workers.

RADIATION EXPOSURE

The 3 basic means of reducing radiation exposure are time, distance, and shielding. Radioisotope work areas should be segregated from nonradioisotope work areas so that workers can put distance and shielding between them and the radioisotopes when they are not in use. Work stations should also be rotated so that no one worker has an excessive amount of time in the radioisotope area.

A rem (roentgen equivalent, man) is a unit of exposure that takes into account the biological effects of radiation on the person exposed. (Note: The SI unit for rem is the Sievert.) Radiation workers should have a means of monitoring exposure, such as wearing a thermoluminescent dosimetry device or a film badge. A commonly used isotope is ^{125}I, and the thyroid gland is the only organ which incorporates iodine to a high degree. Workers using this isotope may require thyroid monitoring.

In total, annual exposure for radiation workers must be less than 5 rem per year. However, the Nuclear Regulatory Commission (NRC) also specifies that the "ALARA" principle (see p. 125) be followed. This means exposure must be "as low as reasonably achievable." In other words, even in a work setting with an annual exposure of only 4 rems, if exposure can be reduced to 1 rem with the addition of a lead shield, then the shield must be applied. Exposure must be documented using a film badge or other device unless the total exposure in 1 year is unlikely to exceed 10% of the maximum allow-

Radiation Exposure:

"**ALARA**" - as low as reasonably achievable.
Minimize **TIME** with isotopes.
Maximize **DISTANCE** from isotopes.
Use proper **SHIELDING.**

able dose. Because the amount of radiation in many medical laboratories is very low, they are often exempt from monitoring requirements.

Safe Handling and Disposal of Radioactive Materials

All areas in which radioactive materials are used or stored must display the symbol for radioactive hazard (see **Figure 7-2**), and those areas should be restricted to essential personnel. Any laboratory using or possessing radioactive isotopes must be licensed by the NRC and/or by a state or local agency. Medical laboratories usually are categorized under "General License for Use of Byproduct Material for Certain In Vitro Clinical or Laboratory Testing (10 CFR 31.11)." At the time of this publication, the NRC recognized 36 "agreement states" (with an additional 4 pending) with licensing requirements acceptable to the NRC; in these states, the state license and regulations

prevail. Licenses are based on the amount, type, and usage of isotopes within a particular facility. Amounts of radiation are expressed as Curies (US) or Becquerels (SI units), and licenses will specify in these units the amount of radiation that is allowable at any one time. In US clinical laboratories, radiation is measured in microcuries (µCi).

The extent to which an isotope remains radioactive over time is expressed as the isotope's half-life. A half-life is the amount of time that it takes for 50% of an isotope's radioactivity to be lost. Some common isotopes with laboratory applications are presented in **Table 7-1**. Isotopes with longer half-lives remain radioactive longer and are therefore more hazardous to use in the laboratory. Procedures should be developed to use the smallest amount of isotope possible with the shortest half-life that is practical.

The safety protocol used by personnel for the handling, storage, and disposal of radioactive materials (**Table 7-2**) is very similar to the standard laboratory practices that apply to other kinds of materials. Additional requirements may be specified by NRC licensure, state licensure, local regulation or institutional policy to which staff must strictly adhere. The following list includes some general guidelines:

Symbol for radiation hazard

Figure 7-2

Table 7-1: Common Isotopes with Laboratory Applications

Isotope		Type of decay	Half-life
^{125}I	Iodine	Gamma emitter	60 days
^{57}Co	Cobalt	Gamma emitter	270 days
^{51}Cr	Chromium	Gamma emitter	27.8 days
^{3}H	Tritium	Beta-minus emitter	12.3 years
^{32}P	Phosphorus	Beta-minus emitter	14 days
^{14}C	Carbon	Beta-minus emitter	5730 years

1. **Protective gear** Wear protective clothing such as laboratory coats, safety glasses, and disposable gloves. Remove them before leaving the laboratory.

2. **Shielding** When working with large amounts of radioactive material, use protective shielding on the body or between the worker and the radioactive material. Because radiation occurs in all directions, in some cases 360° shields must be used around the isotope (in a box, for example). Use lead for gamma emitters and plastic or lucite for alpha and beta emitters. Lead *cannot* be used for some high-energy beta emitters because the particles will interact with the lead and *cause* radioactive emissions (Bremstrahlung radiation) from the lead. Because certain beta emitters (^{32}P, for example) will interact with silicon in glass, glass test tubes are not always acceptable. In the unusual (and generally undesirable) event that a beta emitter is mixed with a gamma emitter, the material should be placed first in the lucite box to block the beta radiation, and then the lucite box can be placed behind lead shielding.

3. **Exposure monitoring** Wear appropriate body and hand dosimeters (devices that detect and measure accumulated radiation exposure such as film badges) when working with enough radiation that exposure is likely to exceed 0.1 rem per year.

4. **Good laboratory practice** Never eat, drink, smoke, insert contact lenses, apply cosmetics, or refrigerate food and beverages in the laboratory. Inhalation and ingestion are particularly hazardous ways to be exposed to radioisotopes, so hand-to-face contact activities without proper handwashing can be very dangerous.

5. **Proper pipetting** Never pipette by mouth. Use appropriate pipetting devices or an automatic pipette.

6. **Spill confinement** When working with large amounts of radioactive liquid, you can confine a spill by working within trays lined with absorbent material. In the event of a spill, turn off fans, air conditioning, or air-circulating equipment to prevent contamination of other areas. Wash the affected areas with the appropriate decontaminating detergent, and verify that the area is indeed free of radioactive material by using a Geiger counter or other radiation detection device once the area has been cleaned.

7. **Aerosol and vapor confinement** If permitted by local air pollution laws, use a ventilated hood or glove box approved for radioactive materials when the materials are potentially volatile or airborne. Because radiation inhalation is so dangerous, aerosol generation should be minimized or eliminated.

8. **Proper disposal** Store or discard radioactive wastes in appropriately labeled containers. The licensing requirements and local regulations strictly define how many uCi of radioactive waste can be discarded and in what manner. Institutional policy should reflect these requirements and should be obeyed accordingly. Clinical laboratories usually handle very low levels of radioactivity, and typical protocols are as follows:

   a. Materials with short half-lives (for example, ^{125}I at 60 days) can be stored until no measurable radioactivity exists. After 10 half-lives, less than 0.01% of radioactivity remains, and most jurisdictions allow the labeling to be removed and the waste discarded in the customary manner. This means that storage vessels for radioactive trash ("decay pigs") must be accurately dated for monitoring and that mixing radioisotopes with different half-lives should be avoided.

b. Certain solid wastes with low radioactivity can be sent directly for incineration or landfill burial. Radioactive labeling should be removed or defaced.

c. Water-soluble liquid waste can be flushed down the sink with copious volumes of water. The NRC generally allows small amounts (<1 Ci) of short-lived radioactive waste to be disposed of into the sanitary sewer annually.

d. Human tissues implanted with radioactive sources may require special disposal depending on when the sources were implanted. A common example of this is brachytherapy for prostate cancer. Cancerous prostates can be implanted with pellets (most commonly ^{125}I or ^{103}Pd) to deliver sustained doses of radiation to the prostate over time. If these prostates must be subsequently removed and sent to the laboratory, the presence of these radioactive pellets must be considered in handling and disposal procedures.

9. **Labeled storage** Refrigerators, work areas, and storage areas containing radioactive materials should prominently display the radioactive hazard symbol, and access by nonauthorized personnel should be limited. Information on optimum storage conditions of reagents can be obtained from the manufacturer. The symbol for radioactive material hazards should be part of the reagent label. The symbol itself is bright purple on a yellow background.

10. **Secured storage** Certain radioactive materials are desirable to terrorists. Although clinical laboratories would seldom, if ever, have the amounts and types of radioisotopes that would be of interest to criminals and terrorists, radioisotopes should still be secured so that only authorized personnel can access them. Good inventory records of radioactive materials are essential, and the NRC takes very seriously the unexplained loss of radioisotopes.

11. **Decontamination** Work surfaces and items contacting radioisotopes should be decontaminated daily using the appropriate cleaning agents. It is important to work on nonporous counters because radiation spills into the pores of a material (wood, for example) are impossible to remove.

12. **Environmental monitoring** Regularly monitor and decontaminate laboratory equipment, glassware and work areas to ensure that the maximum permissible dose of radiation is not exceeded. This may be accomplished by means of a Geiger counter and/or a "wipe" test. A "wipe" test consists of taking a sample from a work surface or piece of equipment by wiping it with a detergent-soaked cotton swab. The swab is then inserted into the appropriate holder for counting in a radiation scintillation counter. A "wipe" test sample should be taken from all laboratory work surfaces that are exposed to radioactive materials. Institutional procedures may employ "maps" of the laboratory indicating all areas from which samples should be taken (**Figure 7-3**). In addition, acceptable levels of radiation for each area should be stated in each institution's policies. Every test for radioactivity should be documented in the appropriate institutional records along with the action(s) taken if the radioactive level was too high.

13. **Records** Complete record keeping is essential when handling radioisotopes. Reagent receipt and inventory, personnel dosimetry reports,

Radioactive Materials

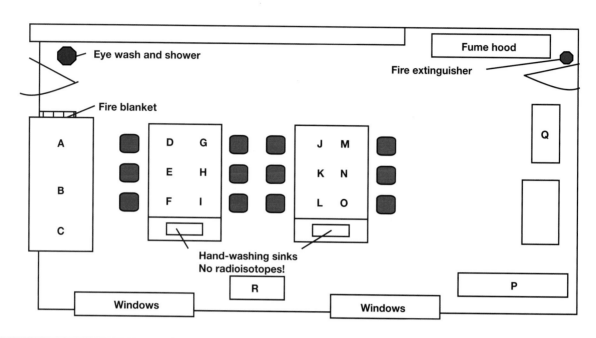

Sample Area	Geiger Counter Reading	cpm on ^{125}I Channel	cpm on ^{57}Co Channel
a. Contaminated sink			
b. Contaminated sink			
c. Contaminated sink			
d. Bench top			
e. Bench top			
f. Bench top			
g. Bench top			
h. Bench top			
I. Bench top			
j. Bench top			
k. Bench top			
l. Bench top			
m. Bench top			
n. Bench top			
o. Bench top			
p. Bench top			
q. Bench top			
r. Refrigerator			
s. Blank			

Actions taken if radioactivity too high in any area (counts may not exceed blank by more than 20 cpm)

Figure 7-3

environmental radiation monitoring, and waste disposal records are absolutely critical to document compliance with licensing requirements.

14. **Safety Officer/Committee** Each institution should have an appointed radiation safety officer who is responsible for the maintenance of records and the formation and implementation of policy. This officer should be consulted *before* procedures are initiated.

Table 7-2: Safety Protocols for Radioactive Materials

Topic	Comment
Wear protective clothing	Remove before leaving the laboratory
For large amounts of radioactivity, work behind shields	Lucite/plastic shields for alpha and beta emitters. Lead shields for gamma emitters only
Never eat, drink, smoke or apply cosmetics in the lab	Wash hands before leaving the laboratory and engaging in these or other hand-to-face contact activities
Do not store food or drink in laboratory refrigerators	Use storage designated for food
Never pipette by mouth	Always have automatic pipetting devices available
Contain spills	1. Work in trays lined with absorbent material 2. Turn off ventilation in the event of a spill, and wash affected areas with decontaminating detergent 3. Check with Geiger counter to insure no residual radiation
Use ventilated hood or glove box for airborne materials	Minimize aerosols and opportunities to inhale or ingest radioisotopes
Store and use in appropriately secured and labeled areas	1. Display the radiation hazard symbol wherever radioisotopes are in use or stored 2. Limit access and prevent theft of materials
Follow federal, state and local regulations for disposal	1. Waste "decay in storage" - after 10 half-lives, negligible radiation 2. Landfill disposal, as permitted 3. Incineration, as permitted 4. Flushing into sanitary sewer with generous water flow (<1 Ci per year), as permitted 5. Remove/deface radiation hazard symbol
Decontaminate exposed work areas and monitor for residual radiation	1. Use decontaminating detergent 2. Periodically check with "wipe" test and Geiger counter
Keep accurate records	1. Reagent receipt, inventory and disposal 2. Personnel dosimetry reports 3. Environmental radiation monitoring 4. Corrective actions taken
Appoint a radiation safety officer and/or committee	1. Formation of institutional policy 2. Maintenance of records 3. Source of information before new procedure is implemented
Get appropriate federal, state or local license	Follow most stringent applicable regulations

Radioactive Materials

Summary Table: Basic Information on Radioactive Materials

Topic		Comments
Types of decay	Alpha Particles	1. "Naked" helium nuclei 2. Cause local internal damage when ingested or inhaled 3. Gloves, plastic or lucite provide external protection 4. Minimize aerosols and no mouth pipetting
	Beta Particles	1. Negative or positive electrons 2. Smaller than alpha particles, so can penetrate more deeply 3. Cause local internal damage when ingested or inhaled 4. Gloves, plastic or Lucite provide external protection 5. Minimize aerosols and no mouth pipetting 6. Wear body and hand dosimeters 7. Some beta emitters interact with lead and cause Bremstrahlung radiation 8. Some beta emitters interact with silicon in glass so plastic must be used
	Gamma rays	1. Form of electromagnetic energy similar to an x-ray. No mass 2. Metallic lead only substance that can block penetration of gamma rays 3. Present internal and external hazard to humans 4. Wear body and hand dosimeters
Radiation Effects		Cataracts, mutations, malignancies, fetal damage/demise, death
Radiation Exposure		1. Measured in rems- 5 rems/y maximum permitted 2. Special restrictions possible on pregnant workers 3. Monitored by film badges or thermoluminescent detectors 4. Thyroid scans to monitor radioactive iodine 5. Follow the "ALARA" principle with time, distance, and shielding
Radiation Licenses		1. NRC general license for most laboratories with low radioisotope handling 2. US has 36 "agreement states" - follow state regulations that have been approved by NRC
Radiation terms		1. Rem - roentgen equivalent, man- unit of radiation exposure in US 2. Sievert - SI unit of exposure 3. Curie- unit of radiation amount in US 4. Becquerel - SI unit of radiation amount 5. Half-life - amount of time radioisotope reduces radiation by 50%
Radiation symbol		

Dark purple or black with yellow background

Abbreviations: ALARA=as low as reasonably achievable; NRC=Nuclear Regulatory Commission.

Exercise 7

Self-Evaluation Questions

1. ___ Which type of radiation is the most penetrating?

    a. Beta
    b. Alpha
    c. Gamma
    d. Delta
    e. All are equally penetrating

2. Matching. Only one answer is correct.

___ Rem	a. Time it takes for isotope's radioactivity to decrease 50%
	b. Only type of shield that prevents gamma penetration
___ Curie	c. Only type of shield that prevents alpha penetration
	d. Can shield beta penetration, but not gamma
___ Half-life	e. 50% of a reagent's shelf life
	f. Unit of amount of radioactivity
___ Lucite	g. Unit of exposure to radioactivity
	h. Unit of hazard for radioactivity
___ Lead	I. Inventor of the Geiger counter

3. ___ Which of the following is (are) a method to detect radiation exposure or contamination?

    a. Film badge
    b. "Wipe" test
    c. TLD dosimeter
    d. Geiger counter
    e. All of the above

4. ___ All of the following are responsible for granting radiation handling licenses or making legal requirements for the handling of radioactive isotopes and their waste **EXCEPT:**

    a. NRC
    b. EPA
    c. Radiation Safety Officer
    d. Local agencies (county health department, for example)
    e. State agencies (Department of the Environment, for example)

5. ___ Laboratory workers who use radioactive iodine may need monitoring of their ___ gland.

    a. Thyroid
    b. Adrenal
    c. Pituitary
    d. Prostate
    e. Lacrimal

6. ___ Which type of shielding can actually create additional radiation hazard if used to shield high-energy alpha and beta emitters?

    a. Lead
    b. Lucite
    c. Plastic
    d. Polystyrene
    e. Polyethylene

7. ___ When a laboratory uses a "decay in storage" program for its waste, it should seal and date the waste and discard it after ___ half-lives have passed.

    a. 1
    b. 5
    c. 10
    d. 20
    e. 100

8. What does "ALARA" stand for and what does it mean?

    _____

9. The 3 most important variables in minimizing radiation exposure are:

    _____, _____ and

    _____.

10. ___ The radiation hazard symbol

    a. Is purple with a yellow background
    b. Should be displayed on a refrigerator storing radioisotopes
    c. Should be displayed on the entrance door of a laboratory using radioisotopes
    d. Should be removed or defaced from waste that is no longer radioactive
    e. All of the above

Exercise 8

WASTE AND WASTE MANAGEMENT

The International Organization for Standardization standard ISO 15190 defines hazardous waste as "any waste that is potentially flammable, combustible, ignitable, corrosive, toxic, reactive, or injurious to people or the environment." This exercise will describe hazardous waste categories and some general principles of good waste management.

HAZARDOUS WASTE CATEGORIES

The Environmental Protection Agency (EPA) defines hazardous wastes in 2 ways: listed wastes and characteristic wastes. Listed wastes are those specifically named on lists published by the EPA and state/local jurisdictions as being hazardous, regulated wastes. However, the omission of a waste on these lists does *not* mean that it is unregulated or nonhazardous. Characteristic wastes are those that are regulated based on 1 or more of the following hazardous characteristics: ignitability, corrosivity, reactivity, or toxicity. It is up to the waste generator to determine if waste meets any of these characteristics. It is important to remember that drugs are chemicals too, and some pharmaceuticals, particularly the powerful antineoplastic drugs, would be classified as EPA toxic waste if discarded. The following also would generally be classified as characteristic hazardous waste:

1. Flammables with flash points lower than 140°F (60°C)

2. Corrosives with a pH less than 3.0 or greater than 10.0

3. Highly reactive chemicals

4. Toxic chemicals or those that generate hazardous or irritating fumes and vapors

5. Solids or viscous materials that can cause plumbing and drainage system blockages— many types of oil fall into this category

6. Materials with a high biological oxygen demand or which would kill significant numbers of microorganisms

7. Waste hotter than 104°F (39°C)

It is permissible to discard some chemicals as ordinary waste down the sink into the sanitary sewer or into landfills, but laboratories must be very, very cautious about this practice because stiff fines can be levied for introducing pollutants into the environment.

The EPA is primarily concerned with chemical waste and does not have separate waste categories for biohazardous, sharp, and radioactive wastes. This does not mean that the EPA doesn't retain authority to regulate other types of waste as it sees fit, only that other agencies often play a bigger role. Regulations for radioactive waste are generally handled by the Nuclear Regulatory Commission (NRC) while biohazardous and sharp waste are handled by the Occupational Safety and Health Administration (OSHA) Bloodborne Pathogens Standard, state regulations, and local mandates. Wastes with multiple hazards pose special problems because they may be subject to conflicting regulations from different organizations. For example, the NRC requires "decay in storage" for many radioisotopes so that they are not discarded until they are no longer radioactive. However, large waste generators cannot store waste any longer than 90 days, and this may not be long enough for the waste to decay 10 half-lives in storage. Another reason to avoid multihazardous waste is that licensed waste handlers often refuse to accept it.

Regulations in the OSHA Bloodborne Pathogens Standard do not address all categories of infectious waste. The major categories of infectious waste are as follows:

1. **Live infectious agents** Cultures, stocks, and live and attenuated vaccines

2. **Pathology waste** Body parts and fluids removed during surgery and biopsy (which may be multihazardous if preserved in chemicals such as formalin or if implanted with radioactive sources)

3. **Human blood** Blood products, and body fluids

4. **Contaminated sharps**

5. **Animals, animal waste, animal blood/body fluids/tissues**

6. **Isolation wastes** Tissues, blood, and body fluids from patients with highly communicable diseases

The guiding principle to handle biohazardous and sharp waste is to treat it and/or segregate it to prevent transmission of infectious disease. Sterilizing procedures, such as autoclaving or incinerating waste, are excellent ways to convert biohazards to nonbiohazards and permit routine disposal. A special problem of this waste category is the limited ability to store it. Many pathogens will continue to multiply in biohazardous waste, and much of it will decompose, producing dangerous organism loads, putrefaction products, and offensive odors.

HAZARDOUS WASTE REGULATIONS

Regulations of the EPA are based on the amount and type of hazardous waste generated, as shown in **Table 8-1**. Most medical laboratories would fall into the conditionally exempt small-quantity-generator status. Many institutions have a central storage area for waste accumulation, which can be quite dangerous. It is essential that waste accumulation storage areas be secured against unauthorized entry and the contents documented to ensure against theft of sensitive materials. Waste should be promptly removed from storage sites even though it may be more costly to do so. Fewer, more widely spaced pick-ups save money, but great care

Table 8-1: EPA Waste Generator Categories

EPA waste generator category	Amount of waste generated (Examples of acutely hazardous waste are arsenic and mercury.)	Waste storage limits
Large quantity generator	≥1000 kg per month ≥1 kg per month acutely hazardous waste	can accumulate waste up to 90 days
Small quantity generator	≥100 and <1000 kg per month <1 kg per month acutely hazardous waste	can accumulate up to 6000 kg in 180 days (270 days if transportation >200 miles)
Conditionally exempt small quantity generator	<100 kg per month < 1 kg per month acutely hazardous waste	can accumulate up to 1000 kg without time limits

must be taken not to exceed the amount of waste accumulation and time limits set by the EPA.

Air pollution from laboratories is usually small and not regulated by the EPA. However, in some jurisdictions, permits are required for emissions from chemical fume hoods; it cannot automatically be assumed that every laboratory is exempt. In addition, evaporation of hazardous materials through a chemical fume hood is not a legal disposal method.

Many EPA regulations are based on the 1976 Resource Conservation and Recovery Act (RCRA) which covers regulation of waste from the moment it is generated until its ultimate disposal ("cradle to grave"). Some of the provisions of this act require waste generators to:

1. Obtain an EPA identification number and EPA permits for on-site waste storage

2. Obtain EPA permits if they choose to treat their own waste

3. Use only EPA-licensed waste handlers for transportation of waste to an EPA-licensed disposal facility

4. Ship waste as follows:

a. Label waste according to Department of Transportation (DOT)/Globally Harmonized System (GHS) requirements (see Exercise 3)

b. Fill out a Hazardous Waste Manifest stating the contents of the shipment. The EPA requires this form to track all hazardous waste, and the DOT requires that the form accompany all waste on public roads. The EPA and DOT issued a new manifest form, (Appendix 3), that is required since September 5, 2006. The new base form is now identical for all 50 states, but each state can impose additional requirements. The reader should consult all local and state requirements before sending waste off site

5. Track ultimate disposal of waste:

a. The manifest must accompany the waste shipment at all times. When the waste is ultimately disposed, the disposer completes the form and a copy of the manifest is returned to the generator for records

b. Track all waste for which a manifest has not yet been received. Follow-up must be consistent and prompt to ensure that hazardous waste is not in the wrong place

c. Maintain records of manifests for at least 3 years to meet EPA requirements. There must be a documented "paper trail" between the generation of waste and its ultimate disposal. Most experts recommend that manifests be kept longer than 3 years because liability for the waste is permanent

6. Document a waste minimization program

The numerous state and local regulations are beyond the scope of this exercise. For example, some jurisdictions have strict controls on medical waste even though the EPA does not have a specific medical waste category.

A serious concern in waste management is that waste handlers with EPA licenses can sometimes be unscrupulous; waste generators are still responsible for the waste even if it was out of their direct control. It is important, therefore, to investigate waste disposal companies and only use reputable handlers. Payment to a waste handler should never be given until the final copy of the manifest has been received. The generator is liable forever for hazardous waste even if the documentation for final disposal is false.

Another problem in waste management is that manufacturers are not required to include chemicals on the material safety data sheet (MSDS) for a reagent if that chemical is less than 1% of the total. This means that laboratories are potentially discarding hazardous substances without knowing it. It may be necessary to request that a manufacturer certify that a particular reagent does not contain any of the hazardous chemicals listed in the regulations prior to disposal.

Biohazardous waste must be stored in red bags or in containers displaying the biohazard symbol. The best forms of disposal destroy infectious organisms and physically destroy sharps, but this varies

among jurisdictions. It is usually acceptable to flush human blood and body fluids into the sanitary sewer because pathogens in ordinary excreta are handled by this system. Many radioisotopes used in clinical laboratories also may be disposed in the sanitary sewer. Radioactive excreta from patients undergoing radiation treatments is exempt from regulation. However, human tissue specimens implanted with radioactive sources (for example, prostate glands implanted with radioactive pellets) are not automatically exempt and special disposal procedures may be required. For radioisotopes with half-lives less than 65 days, decay-in-storage programs also work quite well. Isotopes should be segregated by half-life and discarded as ordinary trash after 10 half-lives have passed and after all radioactive labels have been removed.

In general, no chemicals, radioisotopes, or organisms should be discarded into a septic tank that would introduce the waste directly into the natural ground water. If a laboratory plans to use the sanitary sewer for disposal, the manager should check with the local wastewater management authorities for proper permits and procedures for monitoring discharge.

ACCIDENTAL WASTE RELEASE

The preceding discussion relates to planning for waste generated under ordinary circumstances. Facilities must also plan for waste generated in emergencies such as chemical spills. Management of such waste is also covered by OSHA regulation 29 CFR 1910.120—Hazardous Waste Operations and Emergency Response, often referred to as "HAZWOPER." Clinical laboratories, which are usually conditionally exempt small quantity generators, would not typically have waste emergencies on a large enough scale to fall under the requirements of HAZWOPER . However, adequate emergency response procedures and plans for waste should be part of every laboratory's safety protocols to meet the OSHA requirements. Major requirements are:

1. Appointing an emergency response coordinator. Ideally this person has undergone HAZWOPER training and can direct staff and emergency responders to their appropriate duties.

2. Training staff at a "first responder awareness level." Full HAZWOPER training may not be necessary for all staff, but staff members should be trained in basic first responder emergency actions, the least of which are evacuation protocols and location of emergency phone numbers.

3. Prominent posting of emergency phone numbers. These include, but are not limited to, local emergency numbers such as 911, contact numbers for the emergency response coordinator and the EPA National Emergency Response Center (1-800-424-8802), which must be contacted when major accidental releases occur.

BASIC WASTE MANAGEMENT

Disposal of hazardous wastes is expensive. Licensed waste handlers often charge by the pound, and the management costs associated with the more restrictive EPA generator categories are usually higher. Minimizing hazardous wastes makes both economic and environmental sense. Some basic principles are:

1. **Planning** Only the minimum quantity required of a particular substance should be purchased. Chemicals frequently have a limited shelf-life, and the hazard is not considered reduced just because a chemical has expired. Accurate planning of chemical usage should minimize having to discard unused hazardous chemicals as waste.

2. **Labeling** All waste must be clearly marked, and hazardous waste must indicate the exact nature of the hazard.

3. **Storage** Waste containers must be closed and usually access doors should be locked. Storage areas must be clearly marked and provide good containment barriers and emergency equipment. They must be inspected at least weekly and emptied in a timely manner to comply with regulations. Contact information for personnel who should be contacted in case of emergency should be posted.

4. **Segregation** Hazardous wastes should always be segregated from nonhazardous wastes. If 1 mL of a hazard is mixed with 99 mL of water, the result is 100 mL of hazardous waste. Whenever possible, hazards should not be allowed to comingle with nonhazards. For example, a handwashing sink should have, in its vicinity, a biohazard disposal bag for contaminated gloves and a regular trash can for paper towels used to dry hands rather than one trash can for both.

5. **Reduce, reuse, recycle** There are 3 general ways to minimize hazardous wastes from procedures. The RCRA requires a waste minimization program, and any 1 of these 3 techniques is acceptable.

   a. Waste reduction: With careful planning, laboratories can avoid purchasing excess chemicals. Reducing the amount of chemical used in a procedure to its minimum (convert to microscale chemistry, for example) and substitution of a less harmful chemical are also useful. Radioactive substances can be held until they decay to a safe level. Biohazardous waste can be sterilized. Some chemicals can be neutralized (example: bases neutralize acids) or

Waste and Waste Management

Table 8-2: Waste and Waste Management

Topic	Comment
Identification of hazardous waste	1. EPA lists of specific chemicals 2. Wastes with specific characteristics: ignitibility, reactivity, corrosivity, toxicity 3. Medical waste/biohazards/sharps 4. Radioactive materials 5. Multihazardous: avoid!
Hazardous waste regulations	1. EPA chemical waste: requirements based on amount of waste generated and type of waste generated (acutely hazardous vs. hazardous) 2. Radioactive waste: NRC, decay-in-storage favored 3. Biohazardous waste: OSHA Bloodborne Pathogens Standard, attempt to neutralize infectious agents 4. State and local requirements can be added to above 5. EPA authority from by RCRA (Resource Recovery and Conservation Act) 6. EPA number and/or license to generate, store, transport, treat waste 7. OSHA "HAZWOPER" regulations for accidents
Sink disposal	1. Virtually never if sink empties into septic tank/natural ground water 2. Sanitary sewer permitted for some water soluble, minimally hazardous chemicals, some radioisotopes, human blood and body fluids if local authorities approve 3. Not permitted for: flammables, strong corrosives, viscous substances like oils, heated liquids, microbiocidals or toxic/noxious/fuming chemicals
Licensed waste handlers	1. Must have EPA license 2. Track waste by manifest: waste generators responsible for waste "cradle to grave" 3. Don't pay waste handler until completed manifest received 4. Keep completed manifests a minimum of 3 years
Basic waste management	1. Segregation and labeling: separate wastes by category and clearly label 2. Storage: don't exceed amount and time in storage permitted Keep sealed and door locked 3. Planning: order, store, use, discard least amount of chemical possible 4. Reduce, reuse and recycle

rendered less harmful (example: mercury treatment).

b. Waste reuse and recycling: Some procedures tolerate reuse of chemicals, which should be maximized. Procedures requiring very pure chemical can be paired with procedures requiring the same chemical at a lower level of purity. Some chemicals can be recycled either on site or at recycling facilities. For example, some facilities have found that on-site solvent distillation facilities are cost effective when compared with the cost of storing and disposing of hazardous waste. This process has been highly successful in the disposal of formalin and xylene, particularly in histology laboratories. Good training is essential, however, in the use of recycling instruments to ensure the safety of the operation and the quality of the product. For example, if formalin contains picric acid (in Bouin fixative) or colloidin (nitrocellulose) it cannot be distilled because these materials are explosive when heated.

Only the basic information on waste management has been reviewed in this exercise. For more detailed information, refer to EPA/state/local regulations, MSDS's, Centers for Disease Control and Prevention information on biohazards, and NRC regulations for radioactivity.

Exercise 8

Self-Evaluation Questions

1. ___ Concentrated hydrochloric acid (pH 1.2) does not appear on an EPA list as a hazardous regulated waste. Which of the following is true?

    a. EPA regulates it as a corrosive hazard
    b. It is acceptable to discard it into a landfill
    c. It is acceptable to flush it in the sanitary sewer
    d. It is acceptable to evaporate it in a chemical fume hood
    e. State and local regulations should be consulted prior to disposal

2. ___ A facility generates arsenic waste. Their responsibility for maintaining documentation on this waste ends when:

    a. They receive the completed disposal manifest from the disposal site
    b. The completed disposal manifest has been held for at least 3 years
    c. The waste is sealed into impermeable bags and labeled with DOT codes
    d. The waste and a completed manifest are given to a licensed waste handler
    e. 30 years after the staff who were exposed to the waste have completed employment

3. ___ A facility generates arsenic waste. Their responsibility for any harm that this waste causes:

    a. Never ends
    b. Ends when the disposal facility destroys the waste
    c. Ends when the waste is removed from the facility by a licensed waste handler
    d. Ends when the disposal facility sends the completed manifest documenting disposal
    e. Ends when the disposal facility completes the waste treatment process and the waste is at its final disposal site

4. ___ (True/False) The EPA regulates the following categories of hazardous waste:
chemical
radioactive
biohazard/medical

5. ___ Which of the following can usually be discarded in the sanitary sewer?

      a. Motor oil
      b. Human blood
      c. Cancer chemotherapeutic agent
      d. All of the above
      e. None of the above

6. ___ (True/False) The EPA allows all 50 states to develop and require their own hazardous waste manifest form.

7. State the three "R's" of minimizing waste.

    _____

    _____

    _____

8. When should a licensed waste handler receive payment?

    _____

9. ___The authority for regulating laboratory waste by the EPA comes primarily from the:

      a. Clean Air Act
      b. Medical Waste Tracking Act
      c. OSHA "Right to Know" Standard
      d. Resource Recovery and Conservation Act
      e. OSHA Hazard Chemicals in Laboratories Standard

10. The NRC prefers that radioactive waste is eliminated by a _____ program that

discards radioactive waste after it has been stored more than _____ half-lives.

11. ___ What happens if nonhazardous waste is mixed with hazardous waste?

    a. The whole mixture is classified as hazardous and disposed accordingly

    b. The 2 wastes should be separated and disposed of in the normal manner

    c. The MSDS's for both wastes should be consulted to see if disposal techniques for each are compatible

    d. The mixture should be taken to the safety officer for an assessment of how or if they can be separated

    e. The hazardous waste should be washed off the nonhazardous waste and then each disposed in the normal manner

Exercise 9

IDENTIFY HAZARDS

Identify the 20 hazards in these pictures. Give a reason or reasons why they are hazards (see next page).

Figure 9-1

Exercise 9

Self-Evaluation Questions

1. _____
2. _____
3. _____
4. _____
5. _____
6. _____
7. _____
8. _____
9. _____
10. _____
11. _____
12. _____
13. _____
14. _____
15. _____
16. _____
17. _____
18. _____
19. _____
20. _____

Exercise 10

SAFETY EQUIPMENT AND SAFE WORK PRACTICES

Various safety equipment is used in laboratories, and many types of equipment, referred to as "engineering controls" by the Occupational Safety and Health Administration (OSHA), have been discussed in previous exercises. All safety equipment must be on a regular inspection and maintenance schedule so that it is ready and able to function in the event of an emergency. In general, all such equipment should bear an inspection tag indicating the last time it was checked. This exercise also outlines some general concepts of safe laboratory behavior, referred to by OSHA as "work practice controls."

BASIC WORK PRACTICES

Although detailed safety rules are essential for specific tasks, some rules are basic to virtually any laboratory procedure. They are:

1. Smoking, eating, drinking, applying cosmetics, taking medication, inserting contact lenses, or any other activity involving hand-to-face contact are forbidden. This includes mouth pipetting.

2. The appropriate personal protective clothing and equipment must be worn properly and at all times during laboratory procedures. (See below for additional information.) At a minimum, all workers must wear long-sleeved, buttoned laboratory coats and sturdy closed-toe shoes. If personal protective clothing and equipment are grossly contaminated during a procedure, it should be replaced. Hair must be tied back and jewelry must not interfere with protective equipment or procedures. Contaminated clothing and equipment must never be worn outside the laboratory. Laboratory coats and protective equipment should be hung on designated hooks within the laboratory, and storage facilities outside the laboratory should be used for personal items such as hats, purses, coats, and medicines. Because long fingernails, particularly artificial nails, have been shown to harbor microorganisms, they are also forbidden in many workplaces. Increased contamination of the hands due to jewelry and chipped nail polish has also been documented, but a direct link to increased infection rates is still being explored.

3. Serious and professional behavior is required at all times. No one should work in the laboratory under the influence of drugs or alcohol, and evidence of such is cause for dismissal.

145

4. Work areas and laboratory equipment should be kept clean and uncluttered. Laboratory workers, not housekeepers, are responsible for cleaning and decontaminating their own materials and area at the end of the work session. Hazardous materials should not be left for laboratory assistants or janitorial staff unless they have been properly trained. Trash should not accumulate and should be picked up regularly.

5. All workers must wash their hands when they are contaminated, when gloves are removed, and at the end of a work session. While using cosmetics is forbidden, use of approved hand cream to prevent chapped hands from frequent hand washing is encouraged.

6. Working alone in the laboratory and unattended laboratory operations are to be avoided, and some procedures are sufficiently hazardous as to have such practices forbidden. If someone does work alone in the laboratory, a second person should be aware of it.

7. Workers should strictly adhere to established safety protocols and expect harsh disciplinary action when they do not. Rushing procedures or taking unsafe shortcuts is strictly forbidden.

8. Laboratory procedures should be planned carefully ahead of time to ensure that all equipment is in good working order and all safety requirements are met.

SIGNAGE

All pertinent hazard information and safety instructions must be clearly posted on entrance doors, storage units (including refrigerators), equipment, and laboratory walls. Signs should be positioned for view by both normal and handicapped individu-

als, including those who are sight-impaired. Some important items to post would include:

- Universal hazard symbols as appropriate: **Figures 10-1** to **10-3** show symbols for biohazard, radiation, and the National Fire Protection Association (NFPA) chemical hazard diamond.

- Laboratory area designations: "Clean area—no gloves," "Dirty sink—no hand washing"

- Refrigerator information: "For food only," "No food permitted," "Explosion-proof"

- Standard OSHA danger signs (black, red, and white) or caution signs (yellow and black)

- Safety instructions (green and white): Signs for eyewashes and showers—symbols shown in **Figures 10-4** and **10-5**

- Fire evacuation routes and exit signs

TELEPHONE

A laboratory should have a telephone or some other dependable means of communication. Emergency numbers should be clearly posted, especially if the laboratory is an area that does not have the "911" emergency system. Emergency numbers to consider posting include: fire department, ambulance, police, poison control, security, supervisor(s), and safety officer(s).

FIRE SAFETY EQUIPMENT

No laboratory should be without some means to extinguish fires. In general, 1 or more fire extin-

Universal biohazard symbol

Figure 10-1

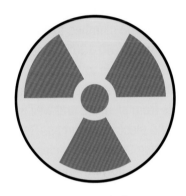

Universal radiation hazard symbol

Figure 10-2

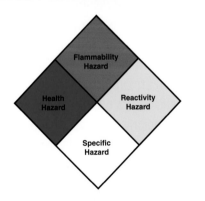

NFPA chemical hazard symbol

Figure 10-3

guishers, a fire blanket, a fire hose, a sand bucket, and a fire alarm system are required. Local fire codes outline amounts and types of fire equipment that must be on hand in any laboratory area. These codes take into account the type of work being

Eyewash symbol

Figure 10-4

Safety shower symbol

Figure 10-5

conducted in a specific area. (For more information on types and usage of fire safety equipment, see Exercise 2.)

SAFETY SHOWER

Safety showers are necessary to cleanse chemical, biohazardous, and radioactive body spills. They can also extinguish clothing fires. Showers should be well marked, centrally located, and have easy and unobstructed access because a person who has sustained a spill or is on fire may be disoriented and upset. The American National Standards Institute (ANSI) publication ANSI Z358.1 contains specifications for safety showers and eyewashes. Although this standard has not been adopted by OSHA, it contains many good suggestions.

Safety showers should be located less than 100 feet or at less than 10 seconds traveling time from the farthest point in the laboratory but still well away from instruments and electrical sources. Safety showers should be inspected and tagged at least once a month to verify that an uninterrupted flow of 30 gallons of temperate water per minute is available; ANSI, however, recommends weekly testing. Showers should not be connected solely to cold water because this could cause the victim to go into shock.

Safety showers are activated by pulling on the large handle ring to release the water. The ring must be low enough for a person in a wheelchair to reach. In addition, pull rings must not require undue force so that disabled users may be able to activate the shower. Many plumbing devices can be used to ensure appropriate accessibility, and laboratories should evaluate whether they should replace older equipment to comply with newer laws such as the Americans with Disabilities Act.

Spill victims should remain under the shower for 15 minutes until all the material is removed. Some showers remain activated for 15 minutes even if the ring is released, while others will turn off once the ring is released. Continuous water flow without operator intervention is considered superior. Victims of body fires and spills serious enough to warrant a deluge shower must always be given medical attention. Even if the victim appears to be suffering no ill effects, delayed reactions may occur and it is safer to obtain medical treatment.

Drains for safety showers are problematic. Because the showers are used infrequently, insects and debris can accumulate in them, thus necessitating periodic flushing. In addition, chemicals that should not enter the sanitary sewer system cannot be allowed to enter safety shower drains. If drain covers are used to minimize these problems, then

they need to be removed when the deluge shower is activated.

Deluge showers and eyewashes in combination units are often preferable to allow for less involved plumbing and the ability to flush eyes and body simultaneously.

EYEWASH

Squirt bottles and portable eyewashes are not permitted by OSHA except in field conditions. Eyewashes should be plumbed to a continuous source of tepid water (60-100°F according to ANSI) and should be accessible to the handicapped. Like safety showers, they should be less than 100 feet or 10 seconds from all users and well away from instruments and electrical sources. They should be inspected often to verify that clean, temperate, aerated water freely flows from the eyewash at a rate of at least 0.4 gallons per minute. According to ANSI Z358.1, eyewash plumbing should be flushed about 3 minutes each week to decrease bacterial growth in the lines and minimize possible infections from eyewash use. Eyewashes should require minimal effort to activate and should remain on for 15 minutes without intervention. 2 jet eyewashes (1 for each eye) are preferred over single-nozzle washes. Plastic covers over each jet, if used, should be bleached regularly. Eyewashes should flush both eyes simultaneously, ideally in a hands-free manner.

When chemicals, especially corrosives, are splashed into the eyes, they should be rinsed for 15 minutes in an eyewash or under a faucet if an eyewash is unavailable. To use an eyewash, the victim should place open eyes directly in the flow of water, and the victim should roll his/her eyeballs around to get all surfaces and under the eyelids covered. If contact lenses are in the injured eye, they should be removed as soon as possible. An eyewash is much less effective in the presence of contact lenses, and liquids that get trapped under the lenses can cause severe damage. If the eye is sufficiently damaged that the contact lens is "stuck," it should not be forced from the eye. Again, the victim should receive medical attention.

PROTECTIVE WEARING APPAREL

When personal protective equipment is necessary, it implies a reasonable chance that a worker could come in contact with a hazard. Therefore, minimizing or eliminating possible contact with a hazard by engineering and/or administrative controls must first be attempted. For example, if a chemical with hazardous fumes needs to be used, the first steps include good ventilation in the laboratory with functional fume hoods—not placing respirators on all workers. Protective wearing apparel, while certainly necessary in many situations, should be the "last resort" to be used when all other means to reduce a hazard have been exhausted.

Protective wearing apparel ranges from the common laboratory coat to the positive-pressure "space suit" worn in P4 biohazardous containment facilities. The correct apparel to be worn in any situation should be determined by:

1. **Type of procedure** Will it be difficult to minimize splashing? Will it be difficult to minimize aerosols? Will there be extreme heat or extreme cold? Are there sharp objects? Is electrical equipment involved?

2. **Degree of risk** Are the chemicals corrosive, flammable, toxic, explosive, radioactive or reactive compounds? What is the appropriate biosafety level for the organisms/animals/specimens used in the laboratory? Are compressed gases involved?

3. **Condition of the worker** Is the worker ill or immunocompromised? Does the worker have cuts, abrasions, or skin conditions that might make him or her more vulnerable to a hazard? Does the worker wear glasses or contact lenses? Is the worker pregnant?

Given these considerations, some broad categories of protective wearing apparel are commonly used. An important aspect of all personal protective equipment is that it should fit the user properly so that safety is not compromised. This may mean, for example, that employers have to purchase many sizes of laboratory coats and not a "one size fits all" model.

1. **Face/respiratory protection** This type of protection includes eye goggles, masks, face shields, and protective respiratory devices. Two types of eye protection are shown in **Figure 10-6**. Safety glasses should have side shields and be made of shatter-proof glass or plastic. However, safety glasses protect only against minimal aerosol formation as they do not make a seal around the eyes. This is why prescription eyeglasses are sometimes considered adequate protection in low-risk procedures. Any proce-

Safety glasses

Safety goggles with side shields

Figure 10-6

dure with a high risk of splashing, especially of corrosives, requires the use of eye goggles and a face shield. It should be noted that face shields are *not* considered adequate for eye protection, and goggles or glasses may have to be worn under the face shield. Also available are special goggles that protect the eyes from ultraviolet (UV) and laser light. Even with these goggles on, however, one should *never* look directly at UV and laser light sources. **Figure 10-7** shows hazard labeling for lasers.

Masks that fit over the nose and mouth are useful for respiratory protection from particulate hazards, such as spores from a mold, but are not very effective against harmful chemical fumes. Volatile chemicals should be used under a fume hood. In the event of a chemical spill outside a fume hood, a respirator would be necessary to prevent inhalation of the harmful vapors.

The National Institute for Occupational Safety and Health classifies masks worn for protection against bacteria such as *Mycobacterium tuberculosis* as particulate respirators. They are required to filter particles of 1 µM in size with more than 95% efficiency (N95 particulate masks). Categories of respirators can be

Laser hazard symbol

Figure 10-7

found at the Centers for Disease Control and Prevention (CDC) Web site (http://www.cdc.gov/niosh/npptl/topics/respirators/disp_part/, accessed April 24, 2008).

Facilities must conduct fit testing to verify that staff can don respiratory protection properly and use it appropriately. Beards or facial anomalies can prevent respirators from fitting properly, so some staff may not be eligible for tasks requiring full respiratory protection. Staff with compromised pulmonary function also may not be eligible to wear respirators because of the extra effort required to breath through filters; medical evaluation may be necessary.

2. **Hand protection** Hands are protected with various types of gloves. Insulated gloves should be used to handle hot objects such as items that have been autoclaved or cold items such as dry ice. Puncture-resistant gloves should be used for handling animals to protect against bites. Infectious materials require the use of latex, nitrile, or vinyl gloves. Correct glove composition (such as nitrile, neoprene, or rubber) for chemicals may require evaluation on a case-by-case basis because many chemicals dissolve latex and vinyl. In 1997, dimethyl-mercury penetrating a latex glove led to a fatality; it only takes about 10 minutes for 100% isopropanol to penetrate latex or vinyl. A chemical that can penetrate a glove will come in close contact with the hand, and is more likely to cause damage than not wearing any glove. Many material safety data sheets (MSDS's) will specify the optimal composition of gloves for a chemical, including toxic antineoplastic drugs. Thicker gloves can be used longer without chemical breakthrough, but they may impair grip and dexterity which is potentially hazardous. Therefore, evaluation of the task to be performed as well as the chemical involved influence glove selection.

Many gloves, particularly those made of latex, are intended to be single-use and they should never be washed and reused because cleaning chemicals can compromise the integrity of the glove. Heavy duty gloves resistant to chemicals may be intended for multiple uses, so staff should be trained to inspect reusable gloves before and after use and follow decontamination protocols carefully. Even highly resistant gloves may be penetrated after multiple uses, so it may be necessary to track when such gloves were put in service. Chemical resistance charts for gloves are typically provided by the manufacturers.

It is important to note that some people have serious allergic reactions to products that contain latex. Potential symptoms of latex allergy include skin rashes, hives, flushing, itching, nasal/eye/sinus symptoms, asthma, and shock. A latex barium enema retention ring has been associated with 1 death. Therefore people with severe allergies may wear a medic alert bracelet. Irritation and inflammation associated with glove use should always be investigated and corrected. Sometimes the reaction is caused by the powder in the gloves rather than the latex. In general, powdered latex gloves should be avoided because the powder can make latex particles airborne for up to 5 hours and can cause respiratory reactions in sensitized individuals. These airborne allergens can affect anyone in the room, even individuals not wearing the latex gloves, 1 reason why latex-related occupational asthma is being increasingly identified. Corrective options include the use of glove liners, powder-free gloves, and latex-free gloves. When unnecessary, latex use should simply be avoided. Because some hypoallergenic gloves are more expensive, it is usually financially smart to determine the exact cause of an allergy. Chronic skin inflammation, how-ever, is never acceptable because broken skin makes workers more vulnerable to hazards.

The choice of glove material is not simple. An excellent review of glove materials by *Ozanne is listed in the references,* and is summarized here. Vinyl gloves are more likely to leak than nitrile or latex gloves, and they generally show higher rates of penetration by biologic agents. Nitrile gloves are more resistant to perforation than latex gloves, but when they are perforated, the perforations enlarge faster. This could be beneficial only if it more quickly draws the attention of the user to the hole. All 3 materials have different profiles regarding chemical penetration, so the MSDS for a chemical should typically be checked for recommended glove type. In some cases, using double gloves may be recommended. Of the 3 materials, vinyl is generally least preferable in terms of barrier protection, but it is usually the least expensive. Regardless of material, jewelry and long fingernails are more likely to compromise gloves and should be avoided.

Because latex is so widely used, it is important to note ways in which latex is compromised. Latex becomes more porous upon exposure to ozone (generated by electrophoresis, for example), certain hand lotions, x-rays, UV light, temperatures higher than 33°C, and humidity greater than 40%. Therefore, latex gloves should be stored in cool, dry places away from electrical equipment and without exposure to light sources, including UV. Boxes should be dated when they are opened and remaining gloves discarded after 3 months; the only hand lotions permitted in the laboratory should be compatible with latex. Users should be trained to briefly inspect all gloves for imperfections when they are first worn and to change gloves after 30 minutes of work. Studies have shown that the combination of sweat and heat in a latex glove can make it permeable to the human immunodeficiency virus (HIV) and hepatitis B virus (HBV) after about 50 minutes.

Even when the correct type of glove has been selected, stored, and donned properly, users cannot assume that even new gloves are without defects. Until its new standards were published in 2006, the Food and Drug Administration (FDA) accepted defect rates of 4.0% and 2.5% for patient examination medical gloves and surgeons' gloves, respectively. Although they lowered the new acceptable defect rates to 2.5% and 1.5%, respectively; the expected defect rate is still not zero. The FDA estimates that at the old defect rates, 2.4 cases of HIV and 2.4 cases of HBV were transmitted annually because of faulty gloves alone. Therefore, although it will not guarantee the absence of a defect, users must be responsible for visually inspecting each glove they don before beginning work.

3. **Body protection** Laboratory coats come in various materials, including fluid-resistant and fluid-proof substances that minimize penetration of liquids and aerosols. Laboratory coats should be worn completely buttoned whenever laboratory work is being done. A laboratory coat is not much of a barrier if it is open and can easily snag various objects. The barrier provided by many fluid-resistant/fluid-proof laboratory coats make them hot to wear often creating static electricity, so tasks should be analyzed to be sure that such garments are absolutely necessary. Some manufacturers weave in a black static discharge carbon thread to minimize static electricity, and others provide barrier protection only in front, making the back more porous so as to make the user more comfortable. In addition, knit cuffs allow workers to pull gloves over the cuffs for additional protection. For more coverage, removable

sleeve protectors are useful for working inside contaminated hoods. It is often useful to examine products from various manufacturers to select the laboratory coat that best fits the needs of a particular laboratory.

For staff engaged in work with blood and body fluids, OSHA requires fluid-resistant laboratory coats that would not, under "normal conditions of use," permit the passage of infectious fluids. OSHA specifies the following qualities as tested by the American Society for Testing and Materials (ASTM): (1) spray rating of 90 or higher (water repellence), (2) air porosity rating of 10 or higher (for comfort), and (3) Suter resistance of 340 or more to fluid pressure. Because of the various laboratory coats available on the market, these criteria may be helpful in selecting what to purchase and understanding cost differences.

Plastic aprons are useful to prevent damage from liquid spills, but because plastic can collect static electricity, it may not be desirable when working with flammables. Bench top work shields are useful for upper body protection, but gloves and laboratory coats must still be worn because the arms must reach around the shield to perform the work. Significantly contaminated clothing must be removed immediately and bagged in leak-resistant material. Ideally decontamination is on site, but in any case workers should not take contaminated clothing home.

Proper footwear is essential to prevent damage from spills. Sturdy, fluid-impermeable shoes with nonslip soles that cover the entire foot are recommended. Additional disposal "bootie" foot covers can be worn over shoes, if necessary. Canvas shoes, open-toed shoes, and sandals are strictly forbidden.

Ear muffs or ear plugs may be required if the noise level exceeds the 85 dB specified by OSHA. Noise levels in excess of 100 dB require ear protection. Some laboratory equipment (tissue homogeneizers and sonicators, for example) should not be used without ear protection. Soft foam ear plugs are generally more than adequate. Users should wash their hands to avoid introducing contaminant into the ear canal, and then they should roll the foam into a narrow cylinder that is easily inserted and shaped to the ear canal. If the top of the ear is pulled up and back and the ear canal straightens, the rolled plug should be easy to insert. Proper fit can be verified by comparing muffling of sound when the hands are placed over the ears or when the ears are uncovered.

4. **Personal** Jewelry of all kinds should be avoided. Dangling jewelry can get caught in equipment, and hazardous substances can accumulate underneath rings. Many rings can also puncture gloves and eliminate the barrier that they provide. Long hair should be worn tied back away from the face, and beards should be neat and closely trimmed. For some types of sterile work, beard covers may be necessary. OSHA does not specifically regulate contact lens use in the personal protective equipment standard because of evidence that eye protection over contact lenses is sufficient. However, in many situations, contact lenses should be avoided because liquids and chemical fumes can be trapped under the lenses and greatly intensify the amount of hazardous material contacting the eye. In addition, some types of contact lenses are permeable to chemical vapors, so in some types of laboratory work, contact lenses are categorically forbidden.

HOODS

All chemicals that release harmful or combustible vapors must be handled under a chemical fume hood. Airborne biological hazards must be handled in biological safety cabinets. Class I, IIA, and IIB hoods are for organisms up to CDC biosafety level 3, and the sealed class III hoods are for BCL-4. Laboratories handling any of these hazards must use hoods. For more information on hoods, see exercises 3 and 5.

SHARPS

All sharp objects should be placed in puncture-resistant containers. Special receptacles for broken glass must also be used so that it is not put in ordinary trash. Brooms and dustpans should be available so that broken glass does not have to be picked up by hand. For more information see exercise 4.

FIRST AID AND SPILL CONTAINMENT SUPPLIES

Sand, kitty litter or vermiculite, spill pillows, or general absorbents can be used for almost any spill; a broom and dustpan would be useful to clear them away. Disinfectants for biohazards should be readily available. Barrier tape is helpful to prevent inadvertent traffic through the spill area. Personal protective equipment such as chemical-resistant gloves, goggles, and shoe covers should be available for spill cleanup. Other necessities will be based on the types of hazards present. Examples include acid/base neutralizing agents, mercury spill kits, and radiation decontaminating solution. See Exercise 12 for information on first aid and first aid supplies.

Safety Equipment and Safe Work Practices

HAND HYGIENE

Laboratory staff must wash their hands whenever they complete work and/or leave the laboratory. This is particularly important before hand-to-face contact and eating or drinking. Proper hand washing is absolutely critical for preventing the spread of infectious disease and eliminating chemical and radiation contamination from workers. Gloves are effective barriers, but they can easily get small tears and holes that cause hand contamination. Studies have also shown that a small percentage of new gloves also have small holes. Therefore, a thorough cleansing of the hands is vital on completion of any work, even if gloves are worn.

Gloves must be removed one at a time. The first glove can be pulled off by grabbing the fingers and pulling. The second glove cannot be removed this way, however, because the other hand is now bare and should not contact the contaminated surface. The correct procedure is to grab the first glove with the remaining gloved hand, slide the bare hand under the cuff where there is no contamination and roll the second glove off so that it becomes "inside out" and creates a noncontaminated surface around the 2 gloves. The gloves can then be discarded with bare hands because the contaminated surfaces are inside.

The hands must then be washed with soap in warm, not hot, water. Hand-washing sinks should be dedicated to noncontaminated processes only and should be separate from sinks with functions, such as waste disposal, instrument decontamination, and Gram staining. **Figure 10-8** shows sample labels for laboratory sinks. Hand-washing sinks accessible to the handicapped must be provided. Plenty of soap should be used and the hands should be washed in a downward motion for at least 1 full minute. Studies show that the average duration of hand washing in health care workers

Top: Label on sink used for biohazards

Bottom: Label on sink to be kept clean

Figure 10-8

is less than 15 seconds, so a sustained conscious effort is likely required to wash hands long enough. Particular attention should be given to the nails, between the fingers and under rings because these are frequent sites of contamination. A nail brush is useful to ensure that the areas under and around the nails are clean. The water should be left *on* while the hands are being dried, and the paper towel used to dry the hands should be used to turn off the water to prevent recontamination of the hands from the dirty faucets.

An antiseptic soap is helpful, but most of the decontamination occurs from the physical action of the scrubbing and rinse water. In addition, bacterial spores are highly resistant to most antiseptics. Laboratory workers may wash their hands many times during a work day, but repeated use of harsh

154

soaps may cause irritation and chapping, so these products must be used cautiously. When skin is irritated by loss of skin cells and/or lipids, its barrier function is reduced and only recovered by 50% to 60% after 6 hours. Full recovery can take up to 5 to 6 days, and often normal skin flora is deranged, which can promote colonization by undesirable organisms. Skin irritation is more likely if the water used is too hot, the humidity is low, the towels are too rough, and hand cream is not used after washing. Hand cream should not be petroleum-based because glove integrity could be compromised.

Many facilities have installed dispensers of alcohol-based hand gels for biohazard decontamination because they are equal or better germicides than plain or antimicrobial hand washing soaps. The addition of emollients to alcohol reduces skin irritation compared with normal hand washing with antimicrobial soaps, and fewer allergic reactions to alcohol have been reported. Use of alcohol gels does not preclude hand washing, which is still necessary when the hands are visibly soiled because alcohols poorly penetrate proteinaceous soil. In addition, alcohols have no residual antimicrobial activity on skin once they have evaporated, while many antiseptic products, such as chlorhexidine, remain on the skin and have residual activity.

Various alcohols (isopropanol, ethanol, n-propanol) alone and in combination at concentrations of about 70% have good germicidal activity against gram-positive and -negative vegetative bacteria (including multidrug-resistant forms), *Mycobacterium tuberculosis,* many fungi, and enveloped viruses (such as HIV, respiratory syncytial virus, herpes simplex virus, influenza, HBV, and hepatitis C virus). Infectivity of many nonenveloped viruses (such as rotavirus, adenovirus, rhinovirus, polio virus, and hepatitis A virus) is reduced by alcohols. It is important to note that prions and some organisms are *not* reliably killed by alcohol hand gels. According to

the CDC, some organisms not susceptible to alcohol gels include:

1. Spore-forming bacteria: *Bacillus anthracis, Bacillus cereus, Clostridium botulinum, Clostridium tetani, Clostridium perfringens, Clostridium difficile*

2. Certain parasites: cysts of amoebic dysentery, *Giardia lamblia, Cryptosporidium*

3. Certain viruses: Norovirus, Calicivirus, Picornavirus, Parvovirus

If the presence of these organisms is suspected, hand washing is absolutely essential, ideally with iodophors. Iodophor antiseptics are the most likely to be effective against spores, but they are generally too irritating to the skin to be used routinely.

Another problem with alcohol hand gels is that the alcohols used typically have flash points at approximately room temperature. Incidents have been documented in which residual gel on the hand has caught fire when exposed to a spark as small as that from a light switch or electrical outlet. This effect is worse in low-humidity situations. The simplest means to prevent fire is to apply the minimal amount of gel necessary to coat the hands and let it air dry before doing anything else.

Only alcohol hand gels containing emollients should be used. The correct amount of alcohol gel varies with the concentration of alcohol in a particular product, and many products have dispensers that provide the optimal amount of gel. Dispensers should be maintained regularly because over time they can develop blockages that prevent an adequate amount of gel from being dispensed. A rough guideline is that if the gel dose dries on the hands in less than 15 seconds, an adequate amount may not have been present.

Safety Equipment and Safe Work Practices

Studies have shown that some organisms, including methicillin-resistant *Staphylococcus aureus,* are developing resistance to antiseptics used in hand-washing products. There is currently no cause for alarm because the resistance is minimal compared with the concentrations of antiseptics currently in use. However, as soap dispensers are used, the bacterial load in the soap will increase, so it is a good practice to replace disposable dispensers rather than "topping them off" with additional soap.

The CDC recommends that for routine hand hygiene a worker should choose an alcohol gel or hand washing, but not both at the same time, to minimize skin irritation. For this reason, placement of alcohol gels near hand washing sinks is not recommended. If the hands are not visibly soiled, the use of alcohol is usually superior unless numerous (5-10) applications have resulted in a build up of emollient. The CDC also provides data to show that the increased cost of the gel products is easily justified with expected reductions in the rates of infections, particularly if gel dispensers are placed strategically at points of contact where hand-washing sinks are far away or inconvenient. Pocket-sized bottles of gel have also been shown to increase compliance with hand hygiene protocols. Further, because gels can be properly used in as little as 15 seconds, while correct hand-washing takes 60 seconds, decontamination is likely more effective with gels.

Many studies have shown increased bacterial burden with long nails (natural and artificial), chipped nail polish, and jewelry. Even with the use of gloves, bacteria colonizing patients have been detected in up to 30% of health care workers with long nails. Infection has been shown to be transmitted from long fingernails while actual infection events associated with jewelry and nail polish are still being studied. Current CDC recommendations are that workers with artificial nails should not be allowed around high-risk patients and that natural nails be 1/4 inch long or less. Data are insufficient to forbid jewelry and nail polish, but the aforementioned risk factors might be considered in outbreak situations when every possible avenue of transmission must be controlled. In addition, nails and jewelry could harbor chemical and radioactive contaminants, so workers should consider these factors carefully when engaging in any method of hand hygiene.

Summary Table: Safety Equipment and Safe Work Practices

Topic	Comments
Basic work practices	1. No hand-to-face activities permitted 2. Wash hands after removing gloves and when leaving lab 3. No jokes or horseplay. No alcohol or drugs. Discipline workers who ignore safety protocols 4. Avoid having personnel in the laboratory alone or unattended lab operations 5. Keep work areas clean and uncluttered. Decontaminate after procedures 6. Wear appropriate personal protective equipment (see below) 7. Plan procedures carefully so proper safety equipment is available
Signage	Appropriate signs on entrances, storage units, equipment and walls
Inspection & maintenance	1. All equipment should be on maintenance and inspection schedule 2. All equipment should bear tag stating latest inspection and/or maintenance
Telephone	1. All labs should have easy access to a reliable telephone 2. Post emergency numbers beside telephone
Fire safety	1. Know local fire codes and fire procedures for your laboratory 2. Fire equipment: extinguishers, blanket, hose, sand bucket, alarm system
Safety shower	1. Well-marked, easily located, unobstructed within 100 feet or 10 seconds of worker 2. 30 gallons per minute of temperate water 3. Drench victim 15 minutes and seek immediate medical attention 4. Position shower and pull ring for wheelchair access
Eyewash	1. Well-marked, easily located, wheel-chair accessible, unobstructed within 100 feet or 10 seconds 2. 0.4 gallons per minute of temperate, aerated water 3. If possible, remove contact lenses, rinse eyes 15 minutes and seek medical attention 4. Flush eyewashes weekly to minimize bacterial growth. Bleach jet covers

Protective apparel	1. Criteria for determining type needed: type of procedure; degree of risk; condition of worker
	2. Face/respiratory protection
	3. Gloves a. Latex, nitrile, vinyl or chemical resistant
	               b. Insulated for heat and cold
	               c. Puncture-resistant (animal handling)
	               d. Hypoallergenic/powderless gloves or glove liners for allergies
	               e. Compromised gloves - trying to re-use or decontaminate single-use glove, reusable gloves that are too old
	               f. Latex damage - heat, light, humidity, certain hand lotions, ozone
	4. Body protection a. Lab coats & fluid-resistant lab coats- buttoned; plastic aprons
	               b. Proper footwear. No open toes, sandals or canvas shoes
	               c. Ear muffs or ear plugs in high decibel areas
	5. Personal
	               a. Avoid jewelry of all kinds, especially dangling pieces
	               b. Hair pulled back. Beards may need beard covers
	               c. Avoid contact lenses

Hoods	1. Chemical fume hoods for chemicals with harmful or combustible vapors 2. Class I, IIA & IIB for BSL-1-3; Class III for BSL-4

Summary Table: Safety Equipment and Safe Work Practices (continued)

Topic	Comments
Sharps	1. Puncture-resistant containers and special needle boxes 2. Broken glass boxes 3. Brooms and dustpans to clean broken glass
Spill equipment and first aid supplies	1. General absorbents - sand, kitty litter, spill pillows, etc 2. Treatments for hazards present: neutralizing agents for acids and bases; radiation decontaminating solutions; mercury spill kits; disinfectants for biohazards 3. See exercise 12 for first aid supplies

Hand hygiene	1. Remove gloves without hand contamination (see text)
	2. Antiseptic soap for at least one minute. Check nails and between fingers
	3. Turn water off with paper towel, not the clean hand
	4. Minimize irritation with mild temp and gentle towels. Use non-petroleum hand cream
	5. Alcohol a. Disinfect most biohazards but not prions and spores
	              b. Let dry on hands to remove flammable hazard
	              c. Not a hand washing substitute. Wash hands when visibly soiled
	6. Designate dirty sinks and clean hand-washing sinks
	7. Sources of hand contamination: long nails (artificial and natural), jewelry, chipped nail polish

Exercise 10

Self-Evaluation Questions

1. ___ You are about to handle a chemical with toxic fumes. You should (choose the **BEST** answer):

    a. Wear a respirator
    b. Wear a face shield
    c. Work under a fume hood
    d. Wear a self-contained breathing apparatus
    e. Wear a mask that covers your mouth and nose

2. ___ You are about to perform a procedure which requires vigorous mixing of a hazardous microorganism and it is difficult to prevent splashing and aerosols. You should wear:

    a. Laboratory coat and gloves
    b. Laboratory coat, gloves, and face shield
    c. Laboratory coat only and work in a biological safety cabinet
    d. Laboratory coat, gloves, face shield, and mask and also work in a biological safety cabinet
    e. Laboratory coat with disposable sleeve protectors, gloves, face shield, and mask and also work in a biological safety cabinet

3. If a chemical is splashed into someone's eye it is important to be sure that _____

    _____ are removed from the eyes as soon as possible.

4. The safety equipment used to remove large spills from a person's body is:

    a _____.

5. Chemical spills on a person's body or in the eyes should be flushed with water for at least:

    _____ minutes.

159

6. ___ (True or False) If a corrosive chemical has been completely washed off a victim, and he or she is feeling well, it is not necessary to seek medical attention.

7. ___ Which of the following should be avoided when working in the laboratory?

    a. Unconfined long hair
    b. Wearing wedding rings
    c. Wearing contact lenses
    d. Canvas or open-toed shoes
    e. All of the above

8. ___ You come upon a spill in the laboratory and do not know what it is. However, it is important to confine the spill and begin cleaning it up as soon as possible. Which of the choices below is the **BEST** to use until the nature of the spill is known?

    a. Kitty litter alone
    b. Paper towels alone
    c. Bleach and paper towels
    d. Neutralizing agents and paper towels
    e. None of the above; no actions should be taken until the nature of the spill is known

9. ___ Which step in the following sequence is **INCORRECT?**
    i.   Remove first glove by tugging on contaminated surface
    ii. Remove second glove by inserting bare hand under cuff
    iii. Roll second glove off contaminated side out around first glove
    iv. Dispose of gloves
    v. Turn water on and wash with antiseptic soap for at least 1 minute
    vi. Inspect nails and between fingers, use nail brush if necessary
    vii. Leave water ON and dry hands
    viii. Turn water off with paper towel

    a. i
    b. iii
    c. v
    d. vii
    e. viii

10. ___ A worker develops a severe case of hives on her hands, and she is having some symptoms of asthma. What is the most likely concern to investigate first?

    a. Latex allergy
    b. Allergy to a chemical used in the laboratory
    c. Allergy to a microorganism being cultured in the laboratory
    d. Infection from a microorganism being cultured in the laboratory
    e. Infection from a microorganism contaminating the laboratory environment

11. ___ All of these substances may compromise latex gloves in a relatively short time period **EXCEPT:**

    a. Light
    b. Hand lotion
    c. Isopropanol
    d. Heat and sweat
    e. Radioactive isotopes

12. Safety showers and eyewashes must be located ___ feet or ___ seconds away from the worker.

Eyewashes should be flushed _____ to reduce microbial growth.

13. ___ Which situation below describes the correct use of alcohol hand gel?

    a. Gel is put on hands and work begins while gel is still wet
    b. Gel is used to wash off visible blood contamination from hands
    c. Gel used when gloves are removed and hands look clean
    d. Gel is used after doing venipuncture on a patient with *Clostridium difficile*
    e. All of the above

14. Matching

    ___ Chemical fume hood   A. OSHA administrative control
    ___ Pipetting liquids to minimize splashing   B. OSHA work practice control
    ___ Scheduling pregnant woman in nonradioisotope   C. OSHA engineering control
        laboratory rather than radioisotope laboratory

Exercise 11

LOCATING SAFETY EQUIPMENT AND DOCUMENTS

No piece of safety equipment or document can be used unless the laboratory worker knows its location.

The purpose of this exercise is to ensure that the reader:

1. knows what each piece of safety equipment looks like

2. knows the location of all of the safety equipment and documents in a laboratory in which s/he works

3. can correctly operate, when possible, the safety equipment available in a relevant laboratory

MATERIALS NEEDED

- Access to a laboratory (preferably a laboratory in which the reader will be working/ learning) and its safety equipment

- Accident report form

- Fire evacuation plan

- Instructions or procedures, as appropriate, for each piece of safety equipment

- Instructions or procedures, as appropriate, for safety in the laboratory

- Map of the laboratory, indicating exits and locations of all hazards and safety equipment, with which the reader should become familiar

- Material safety data sheets (MSDS) and chemical inventory

Locating Safety Equipment and Documents

INSTRUCTIONS

1. Attempt to locate the various pieces of equipment and/or documents in the list that follows. Similar equipment may be found in more than 1 laboratory area, and every piece listed herein may not be found in every laboratory. In addition, note the equipment that is available but not listed below.

    - Accident report forms

    - Biological safety cabinet

    - Broken glass containers

    - Brooms/dustpans/devices to clean broken glass

    - Bucket for carrying chemicals

    - Chemical aprons

    - Chemical fume hood

    - Chemical inventory

    - Chemical storage cabinets: acid, flammable, vented

    - Compressed gas storage collars, chains, hand trucks

    - Compressed gas regulators

    - Decontaminating solutions

    - Ear protection

    - Electricity breaker box

    - Escape route map

    - Eyewash

    - Fire alarm code

    - Fire alarms

    - Fire blankets

    - Fire evacuation route and posted instructions

    - Fire extinguishers

    - Fire hose

    - Flammable safety can

    - Foot covers

    - Fuse or breaker box

    - Gas shut-off valves

    - Gloves: latex, thermal, chemical-resistant

    - Goggles/face shields/work shields

    - MSDS's

    - Needle/sharps boxes

    - Pipetter bulbs and suction devices

    - Respiratory protection/masks

    - Safety-engineered sharps

    - Safety instructions/procedures

    - Safety shower

    - Safety apparel

- Sand bucket

- Spill containment materials (example: kitty litter)

- Special spill kits (example: mercury)

- Steam sterilizer/autoclave

- Telephone and emergency phone numbers

- Other materials available

2. Identify the location of each piece of equipment on the map of the laboratory.

3. When appropriate, read the instructions for the use of each piece of equipment to familiarize yourself with its operation and attempt to operate it correctly. For example:

- Apparel: Put on any goggles, masks, or laboratory aprons that you can and verify that you are wearing them correctly

- Eyewash: Activate the eyewash and verify the water is tepid

- Fire escape map: Exit the laboratory using the directions on the map so that you will evacuate correctly in case of a fire

- Fire hose: Locate the mechanism to activate the fire hose

- Fire extinguisher: Find the operating mechanism; note for which class(es) of fires it is used

- Fume hoods/biological safety cabinets: Be able to turn the air flow on and off, open and shut the sash; verify that air flow is adequate

- Gas and electricity: Make sure you understand how the gas and electricity could be completely cut from the laboratory

- Needle boxes: Practice discarding needles, particularly those that can be unscrewed into boxes with special tops

- Safety-engineered sharps: Make sure you can operate the mechanism correctly

- Safety shower: Locate the ring which activates the water flow

- *Do not* operate any piece of equipment with which you are unfamiliar

- *Do not* operate any piece of equipment without permission of the laboratory supervisor in the area

- *Do not* attempt to actually cut off gas and electrical supply to the laboratory

- *Do* notify laboratory personnel if you find that any piece of equipment is not operating correctly. If equipment is genuinely broken, it needs to be repaired. However, if you are operating it incorrectly, it may not be broken, and it is important that you learn the correct technique

4. Locate inspection tags to see if equipment has been recently serviced.

5. List any pieces of equipment which you did *not* find but which you feel should be included. Beside each item list the procedure(s) being performed that justifies the inclusion of a particular piece of equipment. If possible, speak with the supervisor of the area to find out why a specific item is not in use.

Locating Safety Equipment and Documents

166

Exercise 12

ACCIDENTS AND ACCIDENT PREVENTION

Laboratories should expend all possible effort toward accident prevention, but training in proper accident response should not be neglected in case prevention efforts fail. After the accident, the laboratory should learn from mistakes and take corrective action.

ACCIDENT REPORTS

Any accidents involving personal injuries, even minor ones, must be immediately reported to a supervisor. When an accident occurs on the job, the employer is required to make a written accident report and provide free medical care for the worker involved. While certain incidents seem minor at the time, serious repercussions could follow. For example, a piece of glass may cause a minor cut, but if the glass was later found to be contaminated with blood from a patient with acquired immunodeficiency syndrome (AIDS), the consequences could be enormous. Failure to report the initial incident delays appropriate treatment and may result in difficulty receiving worker's compensation. Therefore, accurate and detailed reports are always needed for proper medical care, insurance, worker's compensation, and other legal purposes.

Accident reports are also needed to prevent the accident from happening again. Documentation of "near misses" is not legally required, but analysis of these incidents can be valuable for prevention. Incident reports should document whether the correct procedure was being followed. Accident analysis is an excellent way to identify policy errors, areas in need of improvement, or the need for new policies. Safety protocols from OSHA and other bodies cannot cover every situation, and examination of specific incidents helps prevent accidents due to unique situations. Accident reports are also useful to determine if staff and/or equipment responded correctly to the emergency. For example, first aid may have been performed incorrectly, an emergency exhaust fan may not have worked, or a rescuer may have forgotten how to use the respirator. Employee retraining in emergency procedures and/or repair and replacement of equipment may be necessary.

Careful attention to detail on accident reports is critical. Follow-up medical care and accident analysis are more effective with complete, accurate information. Details can be easily forgotten over time. **Figure 12-1** is a schematic representation of the minimum amount of information required. In addition, all deaths and occupational injuries not considered "minor" must be reported to OSHA. Based on the OSHA Occupational Injury and Reporting regulation 29 CFR parts 1904 and 1952, minor injuries or illnesses "do not involve death, loss of consciousness, days away from work, restriction of work or motion, transfer to another job, medical treatment other than first aid, or diagnosis of a significant injury or illness by a physician or other licensed health care professional."

OSHA provides specific forms on which to record and track illnesses and injuries for all employers with more than 10 workers. OSHA Log Form 300 (formerly 200) is a list of all events occurring over the entire year at an institution. Employee names are not required on Form 300, only the incidents. OSHA Form 301: Supplementary Record of Occupational Injuries and Illnesses (formerly 101) is used to provide details on each particular illness/injury. Employers have 8 hours to report any employee deaths or accidents that hospitalize 3 or more people to OSHA. Other reporting requirements are contained in OSHA regulation 29 CFR parts 1904 and 1952.

Incident report for:				
Facility address:	Facility telephone:			
Name and title of person filling out report:	Date and time of report:			
Date and time of incident:	Exact location of incident:			
Person involved in incident- full name:				
Employee number:	Age:	Gender:	Job title:	Home address and telephone:
Description of incident (Provide enough detail so that the cause and manner of the incident is clear):				
Describe exact injury present, if any:				
Describe exact treatment given if injury present:				
Describe any other action taken, including emergency response measures:				
How could this incident have been prevented?				
Signature of Safety Officer:				
Title:	Time:	Date:	Print name:	

This completed form should be given to the Safety Officer for permanent storage.

Schematic of incident report form

Figure 12-1

GENERAL FIRST AID PRINCIPLES

First aid is temporary assistance given to a victim of a sudden illness or accident. It must be considered a stop-gap measure before professional assistance can be obtained. Every laboratory worker is strongly urged to take a basic first aid course and a cardiopulmonary resuscitation (CPR) course because of the serious potential for accidents in the laboratory environment. It is impossible in this exercise to cover anything except the most rudimentary elements of first aid.

So-called "Good Samaritan" laws in all 50 states protect the general public from legal prosecution over negative outcomes resulting from rendering first aid, provided that the rescuer took actions without financial compensation that were "reasonable and prudent." Fear of lawsuit should not typically stop rescuers from attempting to help in an emergency situation, but one should only render aid that is within one's skill level and try to "first, do no harm."

In the face of an emergency, one must stay calm. An accident victim will be prone to panicking, and rescuers must soothe the victim by being calm themselves. Time must be taken for accurate, albeit rapid, analysis of the situation so that the correct action is taken to save a life or prevent further injury. The American Red Cross outlines the 3 following basic steps of "Check, Call, Care":

1. **CHECK** A rapid assessment of the scene and the victim(s) is necessary to determine if the scene is unsafe or if the victim(s) can be left where they are. The nature of the accident and other people who can help must be determined as well as the victim's condition, including the presence of medical alert bracelets or necklaces. Victims should not be moved unless:

a. The immediate area presents a life-threatening hazard.

b. The rescuer needs to get to another person who is in worse condition.

c. The rescuer needs to position the victim so that proper care can be given.

If it is necessary to move an unconscious victim, he or she must be pulled by the long axis of the body. Victims can be grasped by both feet or beneath both shoulders with the arms supporting the head. A sharp pull on 1 side of the body can cause additional injuries. Conscious ambulatory victims should be escorted with the rescuer holding 1 of the victim's arms around his neck and placing the other arm around the victim's waist for support. If a wheeled chair is available, victims can be seated in the chair and wheeled out.

2. **CALL** A call should be placed to "911" or other appropriate emergency personel as rapidly as possible. Send someone for help if no phone is nearby. If the victim is an adult cardiac emergency, the call should be made before rendering any care. In breathing emergencies, brain damage begins 4 minutes after oxygen deprivation, so it may be necessary to delay the call to provide a few minutes of care. The exact timing of emergency response needs to be determined on a case-by-case basis.

3. **CARE** People without any knowledge of first aid can give comfort and reassurance to victims to help them remain calm. Beyond that, rescuers must always ask for permission to treat if the victim is conscious. (If the victim is a child and a parent is present, the parent must give permission unless the condition is life-threatening.) Implied consent under the law

is attributed to unresponsive or unconscious victims. Once care is begun, it must continue until professional medical help arrives, the scene becomes unsafe, or the rescuer is too exhausted to continue. Life-threatening conditions must be treated first to stabilize the victim until help arrives. When help comes or on arrival at a medical facility, the person(s) rendering first aid must give complete and detailed information to the medical professionals. This may include the type of chemical/organism/radiation involved, the symptoms observed, the type of equipment involved, the duration of any harmful contact, and the first aid measures already taken. Effective treatment will greatly depend on the information provided by witnesses of the accident, and it is important for those who provide first aid to ensure that any available information is conveyed to the medical professionals treating the victim.

First Aid Procedures

The classic first 3 steps of first aid can be remembered as "ABC":

1. **A** Airway. Make sure the airway is clear.

2. **B** Breathing. Make sure the victim is breathing or begin artificial respiration.

3. **C** Circulation. If the victim's heart is not beating, begin CPR or use an automated external defibrillator (AED).

Checking the "ABCs" is the first priority in treating any accident victim. If breathing and circulation are stable, the next 3 priorities are:

4. **Bleeding** Stop all bleeding.

5. **Shock** Treat for shock.

6. **Injury** Treat the injury.

The following is a more detailed explanation of each of the 6 major steps.

Clear the Airway

Coughing, choking, turning blue, or failure of the chest to rise and fall are signs of an obstructed airway. Conscious victims should be asked, "Can you speak?" Speech requires that some amount of air get into the lungs. Victims with a strong, forceful cough can probably clear obstructions on their own, and immediate intervention is not appropriate. If the victim cannot speak or if an unconscious victim's chest is not moving, clear the airway by:

1. Removing any foreign objects from the mouth.

2. Performing the "head tilt/chin lift" to open the airway. Place the victim flat on the back. Using your fingers, lift the chin upward while pushing gently on the forehead. For a victim who is not prone or who has a head injury, a jaw thrust maneuver can be used.

3. Performing abdominal thrusts (the "Heimlich maneuver") or back blows to remove deep obstructions. Get behind the victim. Place your fist, thumb side on the victim, just above the victim's navel and below the ribs. Place 1 of your legs between the victim's legs for support. Grab the fist with your other hand, and give a sharp upward jerk. This should force air out of the lungs and dislodge any objects blocking the airway. It may have to be repeated more than once or blows to the back should be attempted. If the victim is obese and abdominal thrusts are unlikely to be effective, chest compressions can be used.

4. Brain cell death begins about 4 minutes after the brain stops receiving oxygen. If an airway obstruction cannot be removed within about 2 minutes, the rescuer should not delay administering CPR. The chest compressions may help dislodge the obstruction.

Restore Breathing

Rescuers must "look, listen, and feel" for NORMAL breathing in an accident victim for no more than 10 seconds. Many heart attack victims will have intermittent gasps that are not normal breathing. Establish unresponsiveness by gently shaking the victim and shouting "Are you ok?" If no breathing is detected:

1. Clear the airway as described previously. Give 2 rescue breaths. If the chest is not rising, attempt to clear the airway again.

2. Pinch the victim's nostrils tightly shut, and place your mouth over the victim's mouth, making an airtight seal. Breathe in 2 slow rescue breaths in succession to determine if the airway is clear. Be sure the chest is rising and that you wait to let the air out. If it does not rise, the airway may be obstructed. Each breath should last 1 to 2 seconds to ensure that the lungs are inflated and not the stomach. Breathing too hard, too fast, or too long can cause excess air in the stomach which may cause vomiting. (Perform mouth-to-nose resuscitation similarly if necessary.) A visible chest rise is all that is necessary. Excessive ventilation also creates unfavorable pressures and diminishes cardiac output.

3. Check for a pulse on adults by placing 2 fingers beside the victim's voice box for no more than 10 seconds. (The pulse in the rescuer's thumb is more easily mistaken for the victim's pulse, so only the fingers should be used.) If a pulse is detected, continue breathing into the victim every 5 seconds. If no pulse is detected, initiate chest compressions and breathing.

Restore Circulation

If there is no pulse, an AED can be used if it is available (see "Heart Attacks, Strokes, and Sudden Illness"). If not, the essentials of CPR are as follows:

1. Compress the chest directly between the nipples using interlocked hands and straight arms at a 90° angle to the chest. This posture should allow the use of the rescuer's body weight for the compressions, making CPR less tiring. Deliver 100 compressions per minute on the lower half of the breastbone (sternum) to a depth of:

   a. 1.5 to 2.0 inches for adults

   b. 1.0 to 1.5 inches for adolescents

   c. 0.5-1.0 inches for children

   (Note a decrease of 0.5 inch per category)

   A good guideline to follow is that compressions should be about one-third to one-half the depth of the chest. Children may require only 1 hand for adequate compressions and infants only 2 fingers. The American Heart Association also suggests that rescuers "push hard and push fast" to estimate the 100 compressions per minute, taking care to allow the chest full recoil with each compression.

2. Every 30 compressions should be followed by 2 breaths if there is 1 rescuer. This is a universal ratio and does not need to be modified for age. If there are 2 rescuers, they should administer

1 breath to every 15 compressions. If there are 2 rescuers, the rescuer performing the breathing should be able to feel a pulse if the chest compressions are adequate. Rescuers can change places approximately every 2 minutes, keeping compressions continuous.

CPR should be studied and practiced under qualified instructors.

Discusssion of the ABC's and Changing CPR Guidelines

The increased availability of cell phones, AED's, and advanced cardiac life support have changed the way priorities can be set during emergency situations. The advice herein should be regarded as the most current available at the time of writing, but the reader should be aware of evolving changes.

The 2006 Red Cross CPR guidelines for community providers state that calling for help (such as dialing 911) should be done *before* starting any chest compressions on adults. This is because the majority of heart problems in adults require defibrillators and advanced cardiac life support to restore heartbeat, and delay can render CPR efforts useless. The Red Cross recommends giving care first to children and victims of drowning because they are more likely to face breathing emergencies, and in such cases, oxygen delivery to the brain is the primary need. Further, the Red Cross no longer recommends that members of the public take the time to check for a pulse in adults before initiating chest compressions because the collapse of adults usually involves heart dysfunction.

By contrast, the 2005 guidelines from the American Heart Association recommend 2 minutes of CPR *before* calling 911 and *before* using an AED. They have shown that early and aggressive chest compressions are associated with better survival and

less brain damage, and are even more important than giving rescue breaths. In addition, the 2 minutes of CPR provide a more oxygenated heart that responds better to AED stimulation.

The American Heart Association also recently published guidelines for "hands only" CPR for rescuers who are unable or unwilling to do conventional CPR. Convential CPR is still superior and is particularly preferred in infants, children, victims of drowning and/or breathing emergencies, and adults already unconscious with abnormal breathing. However, in the first few minutes after cardiac arrest, "hands only" CPR can be as effective as conventional CPR because immediately after arrest the blood still contains some oxygen. Rescuers need only "push hard and push fast" in the middle of the chest at a rate of 100 compressions/minute. Even this much CPR will be better than nothing.

Every emergency situation will be different, and the reader is left to simply make the best judgment for the occasion. The important message is that time matters. No one should take too long checking for breathing or a pulse. Calls for help and CPR must be done as soon as possible.

Stop Any Bleeding

The first action should be to apply direct pressure on the wound with the cleanest cloth available firmly over the bleeding. Additional dressings can be applied over the first dressings, but the first dressings should not be removed because bleeding may start again at their removal. If no other injury is present (like a broken bone), elevating the wound above the heart slows bleeding because the heart has to pump against gravity. Once a bandage has been applied, it is important to be sure that it is not too tight and is not cutting off circulation. There should be feeling, warmth, and color in the injured area if circulation has been maintained. Victims with nosebleeds should pinch their nostrils together and lean forward.

With training, rescuers can apply pressure directly on arteries between wounds and the heart at so-called pressure points. With the heel of the hand on femoral arteries or the fingers on brachial arteries, the vessels should be compressed against the bone. This should reduce the blood supply to the wounded area.

Only the most severe life-threatening emergencies, coupled with an extreme delay in the arrival of medical help, would ever justify the use of a tourniquet. As a last resort *only*, a tourniquet can be applied between the limb and the heart. It should be as close as possible to the wound but not over it, and it must be only tight enough to stop the bleeding. The decision to apply a tourniquet must be made with the knowledge that the victim will lose the limb to which the tourniquet has been applied. Therefore, apply a tourniquet only in cases of life-threatening bleeding, when the loss of the limb is less important than the loss of life. Once a tourniquet has been applied, it should not be removed except by medical professionals because blood clots from the tourniquet site could enter circulation. The exact time at which the tourniquet was applied should be written directly on the dressing, if possible.

There is no first aid for internal bleeding other than keeping the victim comfortable and warm. Immediate medical help is essential for internal bleeding. Signs of internal bleeding include:

1. Areas of the body that are swollen, hard, and sore

2. A faint rapid pulse

3. Skin that is pale, blue, clammy, or cold

4. Vomiting or coughing blood

5. Extreme thirst

6. Confusion, sleepiness, or loss of consciousness

If a body part has been severed, it should be wrapped in a clean rag or sterile gauze and put on ice. Lost teeth should be handled by their chewing edge, debris gently removed and the teeth placed back in their sockets, in saliva, or in milk.

Treat for Shock

Victims of virtually any serious injury may develop shock, but it is particularly associated with significant blood and/or fluid loss. In a serious injury, the body attempts to send blood to vital organs first (brain, heart, lungs) and diverts it from the limbs. When the limbs are oxygen-deprived and need blood, it is diverted from vital organs. If the body tissues cannot compensate for this compromised circulatory pattern or if medical intervention does not arrive, death can occur. Signs and symptoms of shock may include any or all of the following:

1. Shallow, rapid breathing

2. A rapid, weak pulse

3. Nausea and/or vomiting

4. Pale, cold, clammy skin

5. Thirst

6. Dilated pupils

7. Restlessness, irritability, or confusion

Shock is life-threatening, and victims of serious injury should be treated for shock even if signs and symptoms have not yet developed. Treatment is as follows:

1. Keep the victim flat. If there are no injuries that preclude it, elevate the feet 12 inches or less to maintain blood supply to the brain. Elevating the feet more than 12 inches may adversely affect breathing.

2. Do not give the victim anything to eat or drink. Victims who are vomiting should be placed on their sides.

3. Cover victims and keep them as warm and comfortable as possible until help arrives. Pain and anxiety can hasten the shock reaction.

In cases of electrical shock, separate the victim from the electrical source *with an insulator, not with your hand.* Suspect electrical shock if you see burns, and treat the victim as described before.

Treat the Injury

THERMAL AND CHEMICAL BURNS

First-degree thermal burns damage only the outer layer of skin and resemble the reddened skin of a sunburn. Second-degree burns are slightly more severe because underlying tissue is damaged, and blisters may be present. Jewelry and clothing should be removed from the burn area immediately because later swelling may make their removal difficult. First- and second-degree burns can be treated by immersing them in cool water or covering them with cool moist dressings. Treatment for shock may be necessary when severe second-degree burns are sustained. Blisters should not be disturbed, and ointments, butter, and other treatments should *not* be applied because they actually hold heat in.

In third-degree thermal burns, the underlying tissue is destroyed and the skin appears dark and charred. Loose clothing should be cut away from the burn, but any cloth embedded in the burn should be left because its removal may cause further damage. Third-degree burns should be covered with cool, moist dressings, and victims should always be treated for shock. Ointments or ice should never be used, and medical help must be summoned as soon as possible.

Chemical burns should be flushed with copious volumes of water, and the affected clothing should be removed as soon as possible. If affected clothing cannot be removed without contaminating other body sites, it must be cut off. Strong neutralizing agents should not be used because the neutralization reaction produces heat. Acids and caustic chemicals may be neutralized with weak solutions such as 2% bicarbonate for acids and 2% acetic acid for bases. Such solutions should be used only if they are immediately available in a burn station or kit, and rescuers must *not* take the time to prepare these solutions in the event of a burn. It is far more effective and important to use water on the burn as soon as possible than it is to use these solutions. Medical attention is always necessary, and severe cases may need treatment for shock. Medical personnel must always be informed of the *exact* chemical that caused the burn, because treatment can vary. For example, stating that "acid" caused the burn is not sufficient because hydrofluoric acid penetrates tissues deeply and can cause more damage even after flushing with water than other types of acids. If possible, provide rescue personnel with the material safety data sheet for the chemical.

Dry ice is extremely cold and can cause "burns" or frostbite. Damaged tissue should be treated with tepid, *not hot,* water.

BONE, MUSCLE, AND JOINT INJURIES

Signs of bone, muscle, and joint injuries include deformity or swelling of the area, inability to move or use the body part normally, and coldness and/or numbness of the body part. When possible, a good way to check for swelling and deformity is to compare the injured body part with the uninjured part.

The acronym "RICE" can be used to remember the basic steps in treating these injuries:

1. **REST** The victim should not attempt to move or use the injured body part.

2. **IMMOBILIZATION** The body part should be bandaged or splinted to prevent movement. Splints should extend above and below the injury, and the splint should be applied to the injury as it was found. No attempt should be made to restore a deformity to its original position. Anatomic splinting is a technique in which injured body parts are immobilized against uninjured parts of the body. For example, an injured leg can be tied to the uninjured leg, an arm can be bound to the chest, or 2 fingers can be bandaged together. If nothing else, the limb can be rested against the ground.

3. **COLD** Ice or cold packs can be placed against the injured area to reduce pain and swelling.

4. **ELEVATION** If elevating the injured body part does not cause more pain, this can be beneficial. Propping up an injured leg is a good example.

After bleeding is stopped, bone or joint injuries should be immobilized and the victim made as comfortable as possible until help arrives. Objects impaled into the injury should be left alone and the bandages applied around them. Injured areas should be checked for feeling, warmth, and color

to be sure that bandages have not been applied too tightly. Only professionals should attempt to set or treat broken bones, and victims should not be moved unless there is danger in the immediate area. If the injury and/or bleeding is severe, treatment for shock may be necessary.

Injuries of the head, back, and neck are special cases. Any damage to the spinal cord can cause permanent paralysis, so it is particularly important to immobilize anyone suspected of a head, neck, or back injury, especially if a deformity is observed. Important neurologic signs include seizures, nausea, visual disturbances, paralysis, numbness or tingling, loss of balance, confusion, or altered consciousness. Severe pain and fluids, both clear and bloody, coming from the nose and ears are also important signs. The head should be immobilized in line with the body, but if the victim cannot keep his head straight, it should never be forced.

EYE INJURIES

Chemicals should be flushed out of the eyes for at least 15 minutes with water. The victim should be encouraged to roll the eyes around to expose all areas to the flow. Every attempt should be made to remove any contact lenses while flushing the eyes, but treatment should never be delayed if the victim is not cooperative or if the contact lens is "stuck" to the eye by tissue damage. Contact lenses should never be forcibly removed from an eye injury at any time. Foreign objects should only be removed if it can be easily done with a wet (not dry) piece of sterile gauze. Objects that are difficult to remove or on which the eye is impaled should be covered and left alone until medical help arrives. Because the eyes move together, both eyes should be covered to prevent movement of the injured eye, and the victim should be prevented from rubbing the eye or attempting self-treatment. Eye injuries are very uncomfortable and frightening, and every effort

Accidents and Accident Prevention

must be made to keep the victim calm. Victims should never be left alone, and medical help must be obtained as soon as possible.

CUTS/PUNCTURES

Serious bleeding must be stopped as described before. If chemicals or biohazards are involved and the wound is not bleeding profusely, it is important to thoroughly flush the wound with water to neutralize the hazards. Medical attention may be necessary to remove any objects embedded in the wound and to administer a tetanus shot. In adults, tetanus booster vaccines confer immunity for 10 years, so if the wound is minor and the tetanus vaccine is current, the wound can be cleaned, dressed with antibiotic ointment, and bandaged with sterile gauze. Wounds greater than 1 inch or in which the skin will not touch should receive medical attention because they may require stitches.

HEART ATTACKS, STROKES, AND SUDDEN ILLNESS

Heart attacks, strokes, and sudden illness (such as diabetic emergency or seizure) can happen anywhere and anytime, including a laboratory. It will be important to distinguish such conditions from conditions caused by laboratory accidents so that appropriate treatment can be given. If staff members have conditions such as diabetes or seizure disorders, training in first aid for those conditions may be advisable.

The acronym "FAST" can be used to recognize a stroke:

1. **FACE** Weakness in the face, particularly if it is confined to 1 side, is a sign of stroke. Ask the victim to smile to see if the smile is asymmetrical.

2. **ARM** Weakness in the arms, particularly if it is confined to 1 side, is a sign of stroke. Ask the victim to raise both arms over his or her head and look for inability or asymmetry.

3. **SPEECH** Slurred or unintelligible speech is a sign of stroke. Ask the victim his or her name or simple questions.

4. **TIME** Note the time that any of the above occurs, and call 911.

Signs and symptoms of heart attacks are chest pain; arm, neck, or jaw pain; shortness of breath; nausea; and sweating. In recent years, emergency treatment for heart attacks in the form of AED's has become far more common, and in many cases, AED treatment is preferred to CPR. AEDs are being placed in public places, and the ability to use one is becoming more important. AED's have been designed to be intuitive even for untrained people. The diagrams for electrical pad placement are clear, and the instrument tells the user exactly what to do. The sequence is as follows:

1. The rescuer identifies a victim as possibly having heart trouble or a heart attack. The victim's skin on the upper torso is exposed. The skin must be bare and dry. It is dangerous to use an AED on wet skin. Skin patches such as nitroglycerin or nicotine should be removed.

2. The rescuer turns on the AED and applies 1 electrical pad to the victim's upper right torso and 1 pad to the lower left torso as indicated in the diagram attached to the AED and in **Figure 12-2**. The pads cannot touch. If the victim is small, like a child, 1 pad can be put on the chest and the other on the back, or pediatric pads can be used. (Victims under 55 pounds or 8 years of age are not candidates for adult AED treatment.)

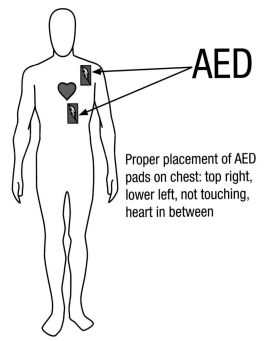

AED

Proper placement of AED pads on chest: top right, lower left, not touching, heart in between

Automated external defibrillator schematic placement

Figure 12-2

3. The rescuer stands back and does not touch the victim.

4. The AED will analyze the victim's heart rhythm to determine if a shock is necessary.

5. If a shock is necessary, the AED will advise the rescuer to stand clear and then delivers a shock.

6. The heart rhythm will be reanalyzed to see if additional shocks are necessary. CPR may eventually be necessary.

Because electricity is involved, AED's cannot be used around flammables or on wet or conductive surfaces. Cell phones and other devices should be moved at least 6 feet away.

Immediate aspirin administration has also been advocated for heart attacks. One *uncoated* adult aspirin can be given to a suspected heart attack victim unless the victim is allergic to aspirin, has stomach ulcers, is taking blood anticoagulants, or has been advised by a physician not to take aspirin.

FIRST AID KITS

Every laboratory should have a first aid kit with contents adequate for the types of emergencies anticipated. Obviously, the components of first aid kits will vary with the laboratory location and with the procedures performed in that laboratory. Laboratories located in hospitals are usually quite close to emergency medical treatment, and their first aid kits might contain only buffers for chemical spills, splints, antiseptics, gauze, and bandages. Blankets for shock treatment are advisable. Laboratories in more remote locations may have more varied supplies in greater quantities. First aid kits must be inspected periodically to ensure that their contents are adequate, and staff education should include training in the proper usage of each component.

Only the basics of first aid have been covered in this exercise. The reader is strongly encouraged to take both a CPR and a first aid course to practice the procedures outlined here and to learn the material in additional detail.

Accidents and Accident Prevention

Summary Table: Accidents and First Aid Principles

Topic	Comments
Accidents	1. Record details of all accidents, no matter how minor 2. Analyze accidents and "near misses" for causes, ways to improve policies and ways to prevent it from happening again 3. Fill out OSHA forms as required. Deaths and some serious injuries must be reported to OSHA within 8 hours
"Check, Call, Care"	1. Check the scene for safety, the nature of the incident, who can help, who should be treated first, who as a last resort should be moved 2. Call 911 or other emergency 3. Get victim's permission to render appropriate first aid. Unconsciousness is implied consent. Check for medic alert bracelets 4. Don't move victim unless in immediate danger or position not conducive to first aid 5. Move unconscious victims by pulling on long axis of body 6. Support ambulatory victims or place in wheeled chair to remove them

A: AIRWAY
Clear the airway
	1. Signs of airway obstruction - coughing, turning blue, choking, chest not rising
	2. Ask "Can you speak?" Victims who can speak are getting air
	3. Actions:
	    a. Remove foreign objects from mouth and throat
	    b. Perform abdominal thrusts (Heimlich maneuver)
	    c. "Chin lift, head tilt" - lift chin, press forehead gently
	4. Victims with strong cough can usually clear their own airway

B: BREATHING Restore breathing	1. Look, listen and feel for breathing no more than 10 seconds. Shake to establish unresponsiveness 2. Begin mouth-to-mouth resuscitation
C: CIRCULATION Restore circulation	1. Check for pulse with two fingers beside voice box 2. Begin CPR or use AED if available 3. Chest compressions at rate 100 per minute; 2 breaths per 30 compressions if alone and 2 breaths per 15 compressions if partnered
Stop bleeding	1. Apply direct pressure by covering wound with cleanest cloth available 2. Apply additional dressings as necessary, but leave original dressing in place. Check for feeling, warmth and color to be sure bandage not too tight 3. Elevate the wound above the heart if no other injuries exist 4. Apply pressure on the artery between the wound and the heart 5. ONLY IF BLEEDING IS LIFE THREATENING, apply a tourniquet between the wound and the heart, as close as possible to the wound. Use of a tourniquet almost guarantees loss of the limb 6. Internal bleeding - treat as shock, get immediate help
Treat for shock	1. Keep victim covered, warm & flat. Elevate feet ≤12 inches to maintain blood flow to brain 2. Do not give anything by mouth. Place vomiting victims on their sides 3. Burn marks - suspect electrical shock. Separate victim with insulator

Summary Table: Accidents and First Aid Principles (continued)

Topic	Comments	
Treat the injury	1. First-and second-degree-thermal burns	a. Remove jewelry and clothing b. Cover with cool water or cool moist dressings c. Treat for shock if burns severe
	2. Third-degree burns	a. Cut away loose clothing. Do not remove materials embedded in the burn thermal b. Cover with cool, moist dressing c. Treat for shock & get immediate medical attention
	3. Chemical burns	a. Flush with water for 15 minutes b. Remove affected clothing c. Do not use strong neutralizing agents d. Treat for shock & get medical attention
	4. Dry ice "burns"	a. Treat with tepid, not hot, water b. Get medical attention

	1. Bone and joint injuries- "RICE"
	    a. REST affected limb
	    b. IMMOBILIZE the affected limb. Bandage around any impaled objects
	    c. COLD to reduce pain and swelling
	    d. ELEVATE if no injuries.
	2. Treat for shock and get immediate medical attention
	3. Move victim only if in immediate danger. Move victims by pulling on long axis of body. (Under both shoulders or by both feet. Support head)
	4. Head/neck/spinal injuries - Immobilize victim with head "in line" with body	

	Cuts/punctures 1. Stop serious bleeding 2. Use water to flush out chemicals and biohazards. 3. Seek medical attention to remove embedded objects, to administer tetanus shots and to close wounds >1 inch or with skin that won't touch 4. Tetanus shots good for 10 years. If tetanus shot current, clean and dress minor wounds with antibiotic ointment and sterile gauze	
	Eye injuries 1. Flush eyes for 15 minutes with water. Roll eyes around to flush all 2. Remove contact lenses if possible. Do not force 3. If easily done, remove foreign objects with wet sterile gauze 4. If foreign objects cannot be removed, cover both eyes to prevent movement 5. Keep victim calm and get immediate medical attention	
Stroke	Evaluate "FAST": 1. FACE - Facial weakness, asymmetrical smile 2. ARMS - Arm weakness, asymmetrical lift of arms over head 3. SPEECH - Slurred or difficult speech 4. TIME - Note time symptoms started. Time to call 911	
Heart attacks	1. Give 1 adult uncoated aspirin, use AED and/or start CPR 2. AED - Follow directions from device. Don't use on wet victim, on wet surface or in presence of flammables and electrical devices within 6 feet	
First aid kits	Gauze, bandages, antibiotic ointments, splints, chemical buffers, blankets	

Exercise 12

Self-Evaluation Questions

1. ___ You believe that a victim of a laboratory accident is going into shock. You should:

   a. Lay the victim down and elevate his head
   b. Apply a cool cloth to the victim's forehead
   c. Gently give him as many sips of water as he will tolerate
   d. Cover the victim with a blanket or in some manner attempt to keep him warm
   e. All of the above

2. ___ You spilled concentrated sulfuric acid on your hand while making up a laboratory reagent. The correct sequence of actions to take is to:
   i.   Fill out an accident report
   ii. Report the injury to your supervisor
   iii. Neutralize the spill with 2% bicarbonate
   iv. Flush your hand with copious amounts of water

   a. i, ii, iii, iv
   b. iv, iii, ii, i
   c. iii, iv, i, ii
   d. iv, iii, i, ii
   e. ii, iii, iv, i

3. ___ Which of the following accidents would not require an accident report?

   a. Serum specimen splashed in eye
   b. First-degree burn to the arm less severe than a sunburn
   c. Acid spilled in lap and immediately flushed under shower
   d. Needle stick injury with current tetanus shot and no bleeding
   e. None of the above—all accidents, no matter how minor, must be reported

4. What are the "three C's" that should be done when an accident situation occurs?

   _____,

   _____,

   _____

5. List, in order, the 6 general steps for first aid.

1. _____
2. _____
3. _____
4. _____
5. _____
6. _____

6. ___ All of the following could be done to clear the victim's airway and restore breathing **EXCEPT:**

 a. Remove any foreign objects
 b. Perform the jaw thrust maneuver
 c. Tilt the head so that the chin is touching the chest
 d. Perform abdominal thrusts (the Heimlich maneuver)
 e. Perform mouth-to-mouth or mouth-to-nose resuscitation

7. ___ You must stop the bleeding of a cut to the arm. There are no broken bones, and the bleeding is not life-threatening. All of the following could be done **EXCEPT:**

 a. Elevate the arm
 b. Apply a pressure bandage
 c. Apply direct pressure with a clean cloth
 d. Apply pressure to the arm's pressure point
 e. Apply a tourniquet between the wound and the heart but not over the wound

8. ___ You must treat a third-degree burn. Which of the following should you do?
 i. Apply ice
 ii. Treat for shock
 iii. Apply a cool, moist dressing
 iv. Apply burn ointment

 a. i and iii
 b. ii and iv
 c. ii and iii
 d. i, ii and iii
 e. i, ii, iii and iv

9. Bone and joint injuries should be _____ until help arrives.

10. Foreign objects in the eye which are difficult to remove_____ (should, should

not) be left in the eye, and then the eye should be covered. When covering an eye injury, both eyes

should be covered to prevent _____

because _____.

Chemicals should be flushed from the eyes using large amounts of_____,

and if they are present, one should attempt to remove_____

from the eyes.

11. ___ Accident victims should be moved:

   a. If there is no visible injury
   b. If they are the most severely injured in a group
   c. If they are in immediate physical danger at the accident site
   d. If they can comfortably be moved by grasping 1 arm and 1 leg
   e. All of the above

12. Work injuries resulting in death or hospitalization of more than 3 people must be reported to

_____.

13. AED's must not be used in the presence of:

_____

14. ___ Each of the following is **CORRECT** regarding adult CPR technique **EXCEPT:**

   a. Compress chest 0.5-1.0 inches deep on the sternum
   b. Compress chest at a rate of 100 compressions per minute
   c. For 2 rescuers, give 2 breaths for every 15 compressions
   d. For single rescuers, give 2 breaths for every 30 compressions
   e. If a heart attack is suspected and an AED is available, give 2 minutes of CPR
      and then attempt to use the AED

Exercise 13

ACCIDENT SITUATIONS

SCENARIO A

During a toxicology extraction, Phillip was evaporating an organic solvent in a hood atop a hot plate purchased at a discount store. Suddenly, a spark from the hot plate ignited a burst of flames across the top of the beaker. Phillip immediately grabbed a carbon dioxide (CO_2) extinguisher and snuffed out the flames. Disgusted over the mishap that ruined his toxicology extraction, Phillip dropped the fire extinguisher on the floor and walked out of the laboratory for a coffee break. When he came back to his work station, Phillip found a fire squad actively fighting a large blaze coming from the hood.

1. What is the proper sequence of actions Phillip should have followed after the ignition of the first blaze?

    ___ Evacuate all other personnel
    ___ Put the fire out with the extinguisher
    ___ Pull the fire alarm and call the proper extension
    ___ Close the glass door of the hood and turn it off
    ___ Watch for rekindling of the blaze

2. ___ How could the first fire have been prevented?

    a. Run the procedure with the hood turned off
    b. Carry out the procedure in the sink rather than the hood
    c. Never use a procedure that requires the evaporation of an organic solvent
    d. Use nonsparking, explosion-proof electrical equipment designed for use with flammable solvents

3. ___ Was a CO_2 extinguisher acceptable to use in this situation?

   a. No, and that is why the fire started up again
   b. No, a water extinguisher should have been used
   c. No, a dry chemical extinguisher should have been used
   d. Yes, although a water extinguisher could also have been used
   e. Yes, although a dry chemical extinguisher could also have been used

4. ___ There is still some CO_2 left in the extinguisher Phillip used. What should be done?

   a. The CO_2 extinguisher should be refilled no matter how much CO_2 is left
   b. The CO_2 extinguisher should be refilled if less than half of the CO_2 is left
   c. The CO_2 extinguisher should be returned to its storage site and the
      remainder of the CO_2 can be used on the next fire

5. ___ Was this the type of fire that is appropriate for an extinguisher?

   a. Yes
   b. No, because of the size of the fire
   c. No, because of the location of the fire
   d. No, because of the hazardous gases produced by the fire

SCENARIO B

Lauren was becoming discouraged because her small volumetric flasks kept coming back unclean from the utility room. One day she decided to clean the flasks herself and proceeded to make up a cleaning solution of concentrated sulfuric acid and potassium dichromate at her work station in the Chemistry department. After Lauren had poured a small amount of cleaning solution in each of the small volumetric flasks, she set the beaker containing cleaning solution on a small shelf above the work bench. Because the shelf was too narrow to hold the beaker adequately, a slight jaring of the shelf caused the beaker to overturn and pour acid over the work bench, wetting Lauren from the waist down. Sizing up her situation, Lauren decided not to use the nearby safety shower but to go the restroom to remove her clothing. Another scientist, Kelly, saw her going to the restroom in a hurry and went to see what was wrong. She quickly rushed Lauren to the safety shower and then to the emergency department. Later in the emergency department, the physician evaluated the burns on Lauren's hip and thigh to be first- and second-degree burns.

1. ___ What action(s) should Lauren have taken to prevent this accident?

    a. Wear an acid-protective apron
    b. Prepare strong acid solutions over the sink
    c. Never put acid on a high shelf or in an open beaker
    d. All of the above

2. ___ What is the first thing Lauren should have done to minimize her injury?

    a. Report to the supervisor for help and advice
    b. Neutralize the acid with 20% sodium hydroxide
    c. Wash off in a safety shower and remove her contaminated clothing
    d. Go to immediately to the emergency department so that medical treatment could be initiated as soon as possible

3. ___ If you were the supervisor evaluating the report of this accident, what improvements would you make in your laboratory to prevent this from occurring again?

    a. Increase the number of safety showers and eyewashes
    b. Retrain laboratory personnel in safety procedures, particularly handling acids
    c. Set up burn stations with 20% sodium hydroxide and 20% hydrochloric acid
    d. Remove all strong acids from the laboratory and place them into locked storage

4. ___ How should the acid spill at Lauren's work station be cleaned?

    a. Use gloves and body protection to sweep up the waste
    b. Create a "dike" around the spill with kitty litter to prevent it from spreading
    c. Sprinkle it with a weak neutralizer such as sodium bicarbonate
    d. All of the above

5. ___ What else should Kelly have done when she realized what had happened?

    a. She should have notified a supervisor before she treated or transported Lauren anywhere
    b. She should have asked someone to check the scene to see if anyone else was hurt or in danger
    c. She should have checked the MSDS's for concentrated sulfuric acid and potassium dichromate to be sure they could be flushed down the safety shower before she put Lauren into it
    d. All of the above

Accident Situations

SCENARIO C

Andrew was setting up a suction flask. Using his bare hands, he attempted to put a piece of glass tubing through a rubber stopper. The tubing was very difficult to insert, so when Andrew increased the force on the tubing, the glass broke and caused a deep cut in his left palm.

1. ___ What steps should Andrew have taken to prevent the accident?
   i.   Heat the glass tube
   ii. Use a lubricant on the glass tubing
   iii. Never use rubber stoppers; instead use cork
   iv. Use a towel or some other protection for his hands

   a. iv only
   b. i and iii
   c. ii and iv
   d. i, ii and iii

2. ___ Andrew was able to stop the bleeding in his palm with no difficulty. His next course of action should be to:

   a. Fill out an incident report form and give it to the supervisor
   b. Go to the emergency department and ask for a tetanus shot and an antibiotic
   c. Report the accident to the supervisor immediately, and get medical attention
   d. Apply a waterproof bandage to the cut, finish his work, and report the accident to the supervisor later

3. ___ The laboratory has the following choices for disposal. Where should the glass that punctured Andrew's palm be disposed?

   a. Ordinary trash can
   b. Segregated chemical waste containers
   c. Needle disposal box, biohazardous waste
   d. Broken glass container, non-biohazardous waste

SCENARIO D

Lia needed to change the hydrogen tank of the gas chromatograph because the gauge indicated that the cylinder was almost empty, and she knew that it should never be emptied completely. She took a wrench and began to disconnect the fitting. When the fitting was slightly loose, there was a sudden, violent release of gas from the fitting. Lia was not hurt, so she proceeded to change the cylinders as usual. Within a few minutes, Rachel entered the room that housed the gas chromatograph to put some specimens for the gas chromatograph on an old rotator. When she turned on the rotator, a spark caused the entire room to burst into flames.

1. ___ How could this accident have been prevented?

    a. Only nonsparking equipment should have been used
    b. Lia should have turned off the valve of the hydrogen tank before removing the fitting
    c. Lia should have ventilated the laboratory and notified a supervisor that there had been a hydrogen gas leak
    d. All of the above

2.   If Lia had turned off the valve the hydrogen tank, how could she tell if it was safe to remove the fitting?

_____

SCENARIO E

Matthew needed McFarland 0.5 bacterial suspensions for antibiotic sensitivity testing and wanted to vortex mix them before deciding if the suspensions were of the correct turbidity. He turned the vortex mixer to "HIGH" and placed the first tube into the vortex. Because it was not covered, it splashed his entire face, including his eyes and mouth. Matthew grabbed a paper towel and wiped off his face with soap and water. Within a few days, Matthew had conjunctivitis in his eye and a positive blood culture.

1. ___ What action should Matthew have taken immediately after the accident?

    a. He should have flushed his entire face, eyes, and mouth for at least 15 minutes with the eye wash
    b. He should have washed his face and flushed his eyes with a disinfectant like iodine or phenol
    c. He should have reported to his supervisor so that they could advise him based on the organism he was handling
    d. He should have reported to the emergency department for prophylactic antibiotics and a vaccination against the organism he was handling

2. ___ How could this accident have been prevented?

    a. Suspensions should be mixed with a stir bar
    b. Only tightly covered samples should be vortexed
    c. Vortexing should only take place in a biological safety cabinet
    d. Antibiotic sensitivity testing with bacterial suspensions should be eliminated

SCENARIO F

Taryn plugged a vortex mixer in near the sink where she was working. When she spilled some water on the electrical cord, she noticed that a portion of the cord was frayed and that it was giving off sparks. She tried to unplug the cord and received a severe shock.

1. ___ To prevent the shock that she received, the best thing Taryn could have done is to:

    a. First turn the vortex off
    b. Put on latex gloves to pull out the plug
    c. Put on nitrile gloves to pull out the plug
    d. Turn off power to the outlet from the breaker box
    e. First create a dike around the water spill with kitty litter and then absorb all
        of it with paper towels

2. ___ What unsafe practice(s) contributed to Taryn's situation?

    a. Using a frayed electrical cord
    b. Using electrical equipment around a source of water
    c. Using an electrical receptacle near a source of water
    d. All of the above

3. ___ This scenario indicates that the electrical receptacle was probably not ___, and the laboratory should consider replacing it if proximity to water cannot be eliminated.

    a. Polarized
    b. Grounded
    c. A ground-fault circuit interrupt
    d. A surge-protected wet receptacle

SCENARIO G

Laurel had been processing blood specimens when she was told she had a phone call. She took the call in the laboratory and did not remove her gloves. Later another worker, Anna, washed her hands so that she could go to lunch. She used the same phone to let her supervisor know that she was going to lunch. Twelve weeks later, Anna had an acute case of hepatitis B.

1. ___ What policy would you recommend to this laboratory?

    a. Equipment should be designated for use by either gloved or nongloved personnel

    b. Staff should not receive phone calls while processing blood or performing other laboratory functions

    c. Equipment such as telephones and computer keyboards should be disinfected daily with a mid-level disinfectant

    d. Iodine hand scrubs capable of killing the hepatitis B virus should be used for routine handwashing

2. ___ Which of the following is true regarding Anna's case of hepatitis?

    a. Anna's employer is financially responsible for all medical care if Anna's infection is job-related

    b. It is Anna's fault for using a laboratory telephone without gloves, so she must pay for any medical costs

    c. Laurel is responsible for Anna's medical expenses because she is the one who contaminated the telephone

    d. If Anna had gotten the hepatitis B vaccine, she would not have hepatitis. Therefore, Anna is responsible for the medical costs

SCENARIO H

David carefully packed a dozen whole blood samples in a cardboard box and surrounded them with styrofoam "peanuts" to prevent breakage. He labeled the package with the name and address of the reference laboratory and took the package to the US Post Office. The next day, the upset post office supervisor called the laboratory. The package had leaked over a mail sorter, and he wanted to know the contents of the package.

1. ___ What did David do wrong?
    i. He did not use triple packaging
    ii. He used a cardboard box rather than plastic
    iii. He failed to use absorbent material in the package to contain any leakage
    iv. He sent the blood through the US mail, and federal mail sorters do not know how to properly handle blood

        a. iv only
        b. i and iii
        c. ii and iv
        d. i, ii, and iii

Accident Situations

2. ___ What else should David have put on the exterior of the package?

    a. A clear plastic bag
    b. Not more than 2 layers of plastic cling wrap so that package markings are still visible
    c. The appropriate biohazard/diagnostic specimen warning label designated by the US Postal Service
    d. The appropriate biohazard/diagnostic specimen warning label designated by the US Department of Transportation

SCENARIO I

For many months, Naomi had been disposing of a manufacturer's pre-prepared reagent mixture down the sink. When the sink got clogged, a plumber was called to examine the sink. The sink was an old one and the drain was composed of metal pipes. When the plumber tried to unscrew the pipes with a wrench, they exploded.

1. ___ What was in the pre-prepared mixture that most likely caused this problem?

    a. Mercury
    b. Picric acid
    c. Nitroglycerin
    d. Sodium azide
    e. Perchloric acid

2. ___ What could be done to prevent this from occurring again?

    a. Install plastic pipes
    b. Use a commercial drain cleaner such as Drano to unclog pipes
    c. Use a plunger to unclog pipes
    d. Use a plumber's "snake" to unclog pipes

3. ___ Where should Naomi have been able to find the information telling her about the disposal of this reagent?

    a. In the procedure for the test using that product
    b. In the chemical hygiene plan for the laboratory
    c. In the material safety data sheet for the product
    d. All of the above

SCENARIO J

Noah, a recent hire, has never worked in a laboratory before. He was given 7 tubes of blood to spin in a centrifuge. He placed the tubes in random carriers, closed the centrifuge, and turned it on. A few minutes later, he heard a spectacular crash and saw that the centrifuge had fallen off the edge of the bench and onto the floor.

1. ___ What probably caused the centrifuge to fall off the bench?

    a. There was a short circuit in the motor
    b. The suction cups on the bottom were defective
    c. The contents were unbalanced with regard to weight
    d. Someone knocked against it and normal motor vibrations caused it to fall off the edge

2. ___ What should Noah do first to respond to this incident?

    a. Notify a supervisor and fill out an incident report
    b. Evacuate the immediate vicinity because of potentially infectious aerosols
    c. Unplug the centrifuge and create a dike around the immediate area with kitty litter
        and spray it with 10% bleach
    d. Check the source patients of the blood and check to see if they are positive
        for infectious disease

SCENARIO K

Patrick notices that at the end of each work day, when he removes his gloves, his hands are itchy, and he seems to be developing a mild red rash. His wife loans him some of her hand cream and suggests that he use it during the day under his gloves. This does not improve the situation.

1. ___ What should Patrick do?

    a. Use latex-free gloves
    b. Use powderless gloves
    c. Use gloves that are both latex- and powder-free
    d. Wear glove liners underneath the gloves and wash with a more gentle soap
    e. Report the problem to his supervisor so that the exact cause of the rash can be investigated

2.   What else has Patrick done that has put him at additional risk?

Accident Situations

SCENARIO L

Nikka got a thermal burn on her arm from accidently leaning on a hot plate. She ran her arm under cold water and noticed several blisters. She used some aloe vera ointment on the burn and wrapped it in clean gauze and resumed her work. Within a few minutes, the pain in her arm was so intense that she felt woozy.

1. ___ What did Nikka do wrong?

    a. She used ointment on a burn
    b. She did not seek medical attention
    c. She did not report the incident to her supervisor
    d. All of the above

2. The blisters on the burn indicate that Nikka probably has _____ degree burns. Because she is

feeling "woozy," staff should treat her for _____.

SCENARIO M

Evan finished working on the laboratory computer, removed his gloves, and put some alcohol gel on his hands to decontaminate them. As he left the laboratory, he turned off the light switch on the wall. The light switch sparked and ignited the alcohol gel.

1. ___ What did Evan do wrong?

    a. He used alcohol gel instead of washing his hands
    b. He did not let the gel dry before touching anything else
    c. He turned off the light; laboratories must always be illuminated for safety
    d. All of the above

2. ___ Is alcohol hand gel ever appropriate to use after glove removal when working with biohazards?

    a. Yes, if hands are not visibly soiled
    b. Yes, if the laboratory is BSL-1
    c. Yes, if the laboratory is not BSL-4
    d. Yes, if the laboratory is BSL-1 or 2
    e. No

SCENARIO N

William was working on the third floor of the laboratory in the east wing. A "Code Red" was announced for the second floor east wing. William took the elevator in the east wing to evacuate. The elevator shaft is adjacent to the compressed gas storage room, so that when the compressed gas room exploded, it damaged the elevator mechanism and stopped the elevator. William was trapped in the elevator for 1 hour until the fire rescue team could release him.

1.____ Each of the following is an error that William made **EXCEPT:**

   a. He should have walked to the west wing first and then used the stairs
   b. He should not have evacuated using an elevator
   c. He should not have evacuated toward a high-risk area
   d. He should not have evacuated until a supervisor instructed him to do so

2.   If you were William's supervisor, what would you do?

_____

SCENARIO O

The explosion-proof refrigerator needed defrosting, so Benjamin loaded all the flammable chemicals from the refrigerator into the chemical fume hood. There were so many chemicals that the interior was crowded and the sash would not fit all the way down. When the supervisor entered the laboratory, she smelled a strong odor of organic solvent and immediately tried to identify the source before there was an explosion.

1. ___ What is the likely source of the odor?

   a. The chemical fume hood drawing air poorly
   b. The inside of the explosion-proof refrigerator releasing its fumes
   c. The frost inside the explosion-proof refrigerator releasing its fumes

2.   What should be done now?

_____

Accident Situations

SCENARIO P

A laboratory has an isolated room with controlled air flow to handle *Mycobacterium tuberculosis* cultures. Brad, the janitor for the building, had a compromised immune system. He acquired a fatal tuberculosis infection. Shortly thereafter, annual tuberculosis skin testing of all staff revealed that office workers down the hall had converted from negative to positive results. Workers in the laboratory were unaffected.

1. ___ What is the first thing that should be investigated in this situation?

   a. The community contacts of the office staff
   b. The air-handling system responsible for the exhaust from the tuberculosis laboratory
   c. Whether the tuberculosis laboratory is still at a positive pressure relative to the rest of the building
   d. Whether the tuberculosis laboratory is still at a negative pressure relative to the rest of the building

2. ___ Does this incident have to be reported to OSHA?

   a. No, OSHA no longer has a tuberculosis standard
   b. No, the worker's immune system was compromised
   c. Yes, it should be recorded and submitted in the annual OSHA report
   d. Yes, it should be reported immediately because an employee death occurred

APPENDIX

APPENDIX 1: ADDRESSES, PHONE NUMBERS AND WEBSITES FOR SAFETY AGENCIES

(Accessed 1/2008)

American National Standards Institute (ANSI)
1819 L Street, NW, 6th floor
Washington, DC 20036
(202)293-8020
www.ansi.org

Centers for Disease Control (CDC)
1600 Clifton Rd. NE
Atlanta, GA 30333
(800) 311-3435, (404) 4989-1515
www.cdc.gov

Clinical Laboratory Managers Association
989 Old Eagle School Road, Suite 815
Wayne, PA 19087
(610) 995-2640
www.clma.org

College of American Pathologists (CAP)
325 Waukegan Road
Northfield, IL 60093-2750
(404)639-3311
www.cap.org

Compressed Gas Association
4221 Walney Road, 5th floor,
Chantilly, VA 20151-2923
(703)788-2700
www.cganet.com

Clinical Laboratory Standards Institute (CLSI)
(formerly National Committee for Clinical Laboratory Standards, NCCLS)
940 West Valley Road, Suite 1400
Wayne, PA 19087-1898
(610)688-0100
www.clsi.org

National Fire Protection Agency (NPFA)
1 Batterymarch Park
Quincy, MA 02169-9101
(617) 770-3000
www.nfpa.org

National Institute for Occupational Safety and Health (NIOSH)
4676 Columbia Parkway
Cincinnati,
Ohio 45226
1-800-35-NIOSH (1-800-356-4674)
www.cdc.gov/niosh/homepage.html

National Institutes of Health (NIH)
9000 Rockville Pike
Bethesda, MD 20892
Telephone numbers for each division at:
http://www.nih.gov/health/infoline.htm
www.nih.gov

US Department of Homeland Security (DHS)
Washington, DC 20528
202-282-8000
www.dhs.gov

US Department of Labor
Occupational Safety and Health Administration (OSHA)
200 Constitution Ave. NW
Washington, DC 20210
Hotline: 1-800-321-OSHA(6742)
Telephone numbers for each division at:
www.osha.gov

US Department of Transportation (DOT)
U.S. Department of Transportation
1200 New Jersey Ave, SE
Washington, DC 20590
202-366-4000
www.dot.gov
hazmat.dot.gov/training/Transporting_Infectious_
Substances_Safely.pdf (accessed January 11, 2008)

US Environmental Protection Agency (EPA)
Ariel Rios Bldg, 1200 Pennsylvania Ave NW
Washington, DC 20460
www.epa.gov
Telephone numbers for each division at:
www.epa.gov/epahome/comments.htm

US Food and Drug Administration (FDA)
5600 Fishers Lane
Rockville MD 20857-0001
1-888-INFO-FDA (1-888-463-6332)
www.fda.gov

US Nuclear Regulatory Commission (NRC)
One White Flint North, 11555 Rockville Pike
Rockville, MD 20852-2738
1-800-368-5642, 301-415-7000
www.nrc.gov

US Postal Service General Information
http://www.usps.gov
Information on Hazardous, Restricted and Perishable Mail (Publication 52)
www.usps.com/cpim/ftp/pubs/pub52.pdf

APPENDIX 2: OSHA POSTER 3165

Source: www.osha.gov, accessed 1/2008

Source: http://www.epa.gov/epaoswer/hazwaste/gener/manifest, accessed 1/2008

Please print or type. (Form designed for use on elite (12-pitch) typewriter.) Form Approved. OMB No. 2050-0039

UNIFORM HAZARDOUS WASTE MANIFEST	1. Generator ID Number	2. Page 1 of	3. Emergency Response Phone	4. Manifest Tracking Number

5. Generator's Name and Mailing Address   Generator's Site Address (if different than mailing address)

Generator's Phone:

6. Transporter 1 Company Name	U.S. EPA ID Number

7. Transporter 2 Company Name	U.S. EPA ID Number

8. Designated Facility Name and Site Address	U.S. EPA ID Number

Facility's Phone:

9a. HM	9b. U.S. DOT Description (including Proper Shipping Name, Hazard Class, ID Number, and Packing Group (if any))	10. Containers No.	Type	11. Total Quantity	12. Unit Wt./Vol.	13. Waste Codes
	1.					
	2.					
	3.					
	4.					

14. Special Handling Instructions and Additional Information

15. **GENERATOR'S/OFFEROR'S CERTIFICATION:** I hereby declare that the contents of this consignment are fully and accurately described above by the proper shipping name, and are classified, packaged, marked and labeled/placarded, and are in all respects in proper condition for transport according to applicable international and national governmental regulations. If export shipment and I am the Primary Exporter, I certify that the contents of this consignment conform to the terms of the attached EPA Acknowledgment of Consent.
I certify that the waste minimization statement identified in 40 CFR 262.27(a) (if I am a large quantity generator) or (b) (if I am a small quantity generator) is true.

Generator's/Offeror's Printed/Typed Name	Signature	Month	Day	Year

16. International Shipments ☐ Import to U.S.   ☐ Export from U.S.   Port of entry/exit: _____
Transporter signature (for exports only):   Date leaving U.S.:

17. Transporter Acknowledgment of Receipt of Materials

Transporter 1 Printed/Typed Name	Signature	Month	Day	Year
Transporter 2 Printed/Typed Name	Signature	Month	Day	Year

18. Discrepancy

18a. Discrepancy Indication Space ☐ Quantity   ☐ Type   ☐ Residue   ☐ Partial Rejection   ☐ Full Rejection

Manifest Reference Number:

18b. Alternate Facility (or Generator)	U.S. EPA ID Number

Facility's Phone:

18c. Signature of Alternate Facility (or Generator)	Month	Day	Year

19. Hazardous Waste Report Management Method Codes (i.e., codes for hazardous waste treatment, disposal, and recycling systems)

1.	2.	3.	4.

20. Designated Facility Owner or Operator: Certification of receipt of hazardous materials covered by the manifest except as noted in Item 18a

Printed/Typed Name	Signature	Month	Day	Year

EPA Form 8700-22 (Rev. 3-05) Previous editions are obsolete.   DESIGNATED FACILITY TO DESTINATION STATE (IF REQUIRED)

APPENDIX 4: BOMB THREAT CHECKLIST

Source: www.dhs.gov, accessed 1/2008.

BOMB THREAT CALL PROCEDURES

Most bomb threats are received by phone. Bomb threats are serious until proven otherwise. Act quickly, but remain calm and obtain information with the checklist on the reverse of this card.

If a bomb threat is received by phone:

1. Remain calm. Keep the caller on the line for as long as possible. DO NOT HANG UP, even if the caller does.

2. Listen carefully. Be polite and show interest.

3. Try to keep the caller talking to learn more information.

4. If possible, write a note to a colleague to call the authorities or, as soon as the caller hangs up, immediately notify them yourself.

5. If your phone has a display, copy the number and/or letters on the window display.

6. Complete the Bomb Threat Checklist (reverse side) immediately. Write down as much detail as you can remember. Try to get exact words.

7. Immediately upon termination of the call, do not hang up, but from a different phone, contact FPS immediately with information and await instructions.

If a bomb threat is received by handwritten note:

- Call _____

- Handle note as minimally as possible.

If a bomb threat is received by e-mail:

- Call _____

- Do not delete the message.

Signs of a suspicious package:

- No return address
- Excessive postage
- Stains
- Strange odor
- Strange sounds
- Unexpected Delivery
- Poorly handwritten
- Misspelled Words
- Incorrect Titles
- Foreign Postage
- Restrictive Notes

DO NOT:

- Use two-way radios or cellular phone; radio signals have the potential to detonate a bomb.

- Evacuate the building until police arrive and evaluate the threat.

- Activate the fire alarm.

- Touch or move a suspicious package.

WHO TO CONTACT (select one)

- **Follow your local guidelines**

- **Federal Protective Service (FPS) Police**
  1-877-4-FPS-411 (1-877-437-7411)

- **911**

198

BOMB THREAT CHECKLIST

Date: _____   Time: _____

Time Caller Hung Up: _____   Phone Number where Call Received: _____

Ask Caller:

- Where is the bomb located?
  (Building, Floor, Room, etc.)
- When will it go off?
- What does it look like?
- What kind of bomb is it?
- What will make it explode?
- Did you place the bomb?   Yes   No
- Why?
- What is your name?

Exact Words of Threat:

Information About Caller:

- Where is the caller located? (Background and level of noise)

- Estimated age:
- Is voice familiar? If so, who does it sound like?

- Other points:

Caller's Voice	Background Sounds:	Threat Language:
☐ Accent	☐ Animal Noises	☐ Incoherent
☐ Angry	☐ House Noises	☐ Message read
☐ Calm	☐ Kitchen Noises	☐ Taped
☐ Clearing throat	☐ Street Noises	☐ Irrational
☐ Coughing	☐ Booth	☐ Profane
☐ Cracking voice	☐ PA system	☐ Well-spoken
☐ Crying	☐ Conversation	
☐ Deep	☐ Music	
☐ Deep breathing	☐ Motor	
☐ Disguised	☐ Clear	
☐ Distinct	☐ Static	
☐ Excited	☐ Office machinery	
☐ **Female**	☐ Factory machinery	
☐ Laughter	☐ Local	
☐ Lisp	☐ Long distance	
☐ Loud		
☐ **Male**	**Other Information:**	
☐ Nasal		
☐ Normal		
☐ Ragged		
☐ Rapid		
☐ Raspy		
☐ Slow		
☐ Slurred		
☐ Soft		
☐ Stutter		

Homeland Security

APPENDIX 5: TARGET ORGAN POSTER

Source: OSHA CFR 1910.1200, Appendix A

The following is a target organ categorization of effects which may occur, including examples of signs and symptoms and chemicals which have been found to cause such effects. These examples are presented to illustrate the range and diversity of effects and hazards found in the workplace, and the broad scope employers must consider in this area, but are not intended to be all-inclusive.

Hepatotoxins: Chemicals that produce liver damage

Signs & symptoms:	Jaundice; liver enlargement
Chemicals:	Carbon tetrachloride; nitrosamines

Nephrotoxins: Chemicals that produce kidney damage

Signs & symptoms:	Edema; proteinuria
Chemicals:	Halogenated hydrocarbons; uranium

Neurotoxins: Chemicals that produce their primary toxic effects on the nervous system

Signs & symptoms:	Narcosis; behavioral changes; decrease in motor functions
Chemicals:	Mercury; carbon disulfide

Agents that act on the blood or hematopoietic system: decrease hemoglobin function; & deprive the body tissues of oxygen

Signs & symptoms:	Cyanosis; loss of consciousness
Chemicals:	Carbon monoxide; cyanides

Agents which damage the lung: Chemicals which irritate or damage pulmonary tissue

Signs & symptoms:	Cough; tightness in chest; shortness of breath
Chemicals:	Silica; asbestos

Reproductive toxins: Chemicals that affect the reproductive capabilities, causing chromosomal damage (mutations) and effects on fetuses (teratogenesis)

Signs & symptoms:	Birth defects; sterility
Chemicals:	Lead; DBCP

Cutaneous hazards: Chemicals that affect the dermal layer of the body

Signs & symptoms:	Defatting of the skin; rashes; irritation
Chemicals:	Ketones; chlorinated compounds

Eye hazards: Chemicals that affect the eye or visual capacity

Signs & symptoms:	Conjunctivitis; corneal damage
Chemicals:	Organic solvents; acids

APPENDIX 6: HEALTH AND HUMAN SERVICES (HHS)/US DEPARTMENT OF AGRICULTURE (USDA)

Select Agent List. Source: www.cdc.gov, accessed 5/ 2008

HHS SELECT AGENTS AND TOXINS USDA SELECT AGENTS AND TOXINS (7 CFR Part 331, 9 CFR Part 121, and 42 CFR Part 73)

HHS SELECT AGENTS AND TOXINS

Abrin

Cercopithecine herpesvirus 1 (Herpes B virus)

Coccidioides posadasii

Conotoxins

Crimean-Congo haemorrhagic fever virus

Diacetoxyscirpenol

Ebola virus

Lassa fever virus

Marburg virus

Monkeypox virus

Reconstructed replication competent forms of the 1918 pandemic influenza virus containing any portion of the coding regions of all eight gene segments (Reconstructed 1918 Influenza virus)

Ricin

Rickettsia prowazekii

Rickettsia rickettsii

Saxitoxin

Shiga-like ribosome inactivating proteins

South American haemorrhagic fever viruses

Flexal

Guanarito

Junin

Machupo

Sabia

Tetrodotoxin

Tick-borne encephalitis complex (flavi) viruses

Central European tick-borne encephalitis

Far Eastern tick-borne encephalitis

Kyasanur forest disease

Omsk hemorrhagic fever

Russian spring and summer encephalitis

Variola major virus (Smallpox virus) and Variola minor virus (Alastrim)

Yersinia pestis

Venezuelan equine encephalitis virus

OVERLAP SELECT AGENTS AND TOXINS

Bacillus anthracis

Botulinum neurotoxins

Botulinum neurotoxin producing species of *Clostridium*

Brucella abortus

Brucella melitensis

Brucella suis

Burkholderia mallei (formerly *Pseudomonas mallei*)

Burkholderia pseudomallei (formerly *Pseudomonas pseudomallei*)

Clostridium perfringens epsilon toxin

Coccidioides immitis

Coxiella burnetii

Eastern equine encephalitis virus

Francisella tularensis

Hendra virus

Nipah virus

Rift Valley fever virus

Shigatoxin

Staphylococcal enterotoxins

T-2 toxin

Venezuelan equine encephalitis virus

USDA SELECT AGENTS AND TOXINS

African horse sickness virus

African swine fever virus

Akabane virus

Avian influenza virus (highly pathogenic)

Bluetongue virus (Exotic)

Bovine spongiform encephalopathy agent

Camel pox virus

Classical swine fever virus

Cowdria ruminantium (Heartwater)

Foot-and-mouth disease virus

Goat pox virus

Japanese encephalitis virus

Lumpy skin disease virus

Malignant catarrhal fever virus (Alcelaphine herpesvirus type 1)

Menangle virus

Mycoplasma capricolum/ M.F38/M mycoides Capri (contagious caprine pleuropneumonia)

Mycoplasma mycoides mycoides (contagious bovine pleuropneumonia)

Newcastle disease virus (velogenic)

Peste des petits ruminants virus

Rinderpest virus

Sheep pox virus

Swine vesicular disease virus

Vesicular stomatitis virus (Exotic)

USDA PLANT PROTECTION AND QUARANTINE (PPQ) SELECT AGENTS AND TOXINS

Candidatus Liberobacter africanus

Candidatus Liberobacter asiaticus

Peronosclerospora philippinensis

Ralstonia solanacearum race 3, biovar 2

Schlerophthora rayssiae var zeae

Synchytrium endobioticum

Xanthomonas oryzae pv. oryzicola

Xylella fastidiosa (citrus variegated chlorosis strain)

APPENDIX 7: POST-EXPOSURE PROTOCOLS FOR BLOODBORNE PATHOGENS

Appendix A and B modified from: Recommendations and Reports. Updated U.S. Public Health Service Guidelines for the Management of Occupational Exposures to HBV, HCV, and HIV and Recommendations for Postexposure Prophylaxis US Department of Health and Human Services Centers for Disease Control and Prevention (CDC) June 29, 2001 / Vol. 50 / No. RR-11 Vol. 50 / No. RR-11 MMWR APPENDIX A.
Practice Recommendations for HealthCare Facilities Implementing the U.S. Public Health Service Guidelines for Management of Occupational Exposures to Bloodborne Pathogens

Practice recommendation	Implementation checklist
Establish a bloodborne pathogen policy	• All institutions where healthcare personnel (HCP) might experience exposures should have a written policy for management of exposures • The policy should be based on the US Public Health Service (PHS) guidelines • The policy should be reviewed periodically to ensure that it is consistent with PHS recommendations
Implement management policies	• Healthcare facilities (HCF) should provide appropriate training to all personnel on the prevention of and response to occupational exposures • HCF should establish hepatitis B vaccination programs • HCF should establish exposure-reporting systems • HCF should have personnel who can manage an exposure readily available at all hours of the day • HCF should have ready access to postexposure prophylaxis (PEP) for use by exposed personnel as necessary
Establish lab capacity for bloodborne pathogen testing	• HCF should provide prompt processing of exposed person and source person specimens to guide management of occupational exposures • Testing should be performed with appropriate counseling and consent
Select and use appropriate PEP regimens	• HCF should develop a policy for the selection and use of PEP antiretroviral regimens for HIV exposures within their institution • Hepatitis B vaccine and HBIG should be available for timely administration • HCF should have access to resources with expertise in the selection and use of PEP
Provide access to counseling for exposed HCP	• HCF should provide counseling for HCP who might need help dealing with the emotional effect of an exposure • HCF should provide medication adherence counseling to assist HCP in completing HIV PEP as necessary
Monitor for adverse effects of PEP	• HCP taking antiretroviral PEP should be monitored periodically for adverse effects of PEP through baseline and testing (every 2 weeks) and clinical evaluation
Monitor for seroconversion	• HCF should develop a system to encourage exposed HCP to return for follow-up testing • Exposed HCP should be tested for HCV and HIV

Appendix 7 (continued)

Practice recommendation	Implementation checklist
Monitor exposure management programs	• HCF should develop a system to monitor reporting and management of occupational exposures to ensure timely and appropriate response **Evaluate** • exposure reports for completeness and accuracy • access to care (ie, the time of exposure to the time of evaluation) • laboratory result reporting time **Review** • exposures to ensure that HCP exposed to sources not infected with blood-borne pathogens do not receive PEP or that PEP is stopped **Monitor** • completion rates of HBV vaccination and HIV PEP • completion of exposure follow-up

Vol. 50 / No. RR-11 MMWR APPENDIX B.

Management of Occupational Blood Exposures

Provide immediate care to the exposure site

- Wash wounds and skin with soap and water
- Flush mucous membranes with water

Determine risk associated with exposure by

- type of fluid (eg, blood, visibly bloody fluid, other
  potentially infectious fluid or tissue, and concentrated virus) and
- type of exposure (ie, percutaneous injury, mucous membrane or nonintact skin exposure, and bites resulting in blood exposure)

Evaluate exposure source

- Assess the risk of infection using available information
- Test known sources for HBsAg, anti-HCV, and HIV antibody (consider using rapid testing)
- For unknown sources, assess risk of exposure to HBV, HCV, or HIV infection
- Do not test discarded needles or syringes for virus contamination

Evaluate the exposed person

- Assess immune status for HBV infection (ie, by history of hepatitis B vaccination and vaccine response)

Give PEP for exposures posing risk of infection transmission

- HBV: See current CDC recommendations
- HCV: PEP not recommended
- HIV: See current CDC recommendations
- — Initiate PEP as soon as possible, preferably within hours of exposure
- — Offer pregnancy testing to all women of childbearing age not known to be pregnant
- — Seek expert consultation if viral resistance is suspected
- — Administer PEP for 4 weeks if tolerated

Perform follow-up testing and provide counseling

- Advise exposed persons to seek medical evaluation for any acute illness occurring during follow-up

HBV exposures

- Perform follow-up anti-HBs testing in persons who receive hepatitis B vaccine
- — Test for anti-HBs 1–2 months after last dose of vaccine
- — Anti-HBs response to vaccine cannot be ascertained if HBIG was received in the previous 3–4 months

HCV exposures

- Perform baseline and follow-up testing for anti-HCV and alanine aminotransferase (ALT) 4–6 months after exposures
- Perform HCV RNA at 4–6 weeks if earlier diagnosis of HCV infection desired
- Confirm repeatedly reactive anti-HCV enzyme immunoassays (EIAs) with supplemental tests

HIV exposures

- Perform HIV-antibody testing for at least 6 months postexposure (eg, at baseline, 6 weeks, 3 months, and 6 months)
- Perform HIV antibody testing if illness compatible with an acute retroviral syndrome occurs
- Advise exposed persons to use precautions to prevent secondary transmission during the follow-up period
- Evaluate exposed persons taking PEP within 72 hours after exposure and monitor for drug toxicity for at least 2 weeks

APPENDIX 8: COMPRESSED GAS POSTER

Source: http://www.fda.gov/cder/dmpq/medgas_mixup/default.htm, accessed 1/2008

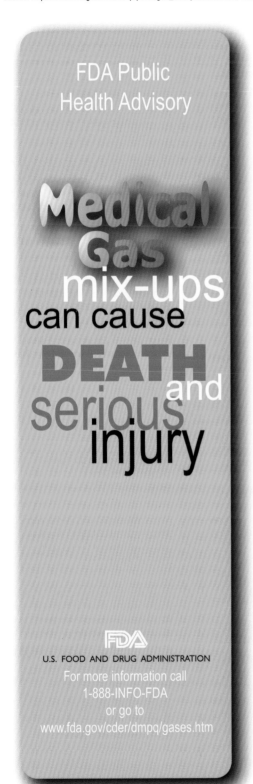

FDA Public
Health Advisory

Medical
Gas
mix-ups
can cause
DEATH
serious and
injury

FDA
U.S. FOOD AND DRUG ADMINISTRATION
For more information call
1-888-INFO-FDA
or go to
www.fda.gov/cder/dmpq/gases.htm

Gases for medical use are prescription drugs that must be carefully regulated and handled.

Adaptors should never be used and fittings never changed on medical gas containers. If a connection doesn't fit, it isn't supposed to fit. Contact the supplier immediately.

Store medical grade products separately from industrial grade products in well-defined areas.

Educate and train personnel who are directly responsible for handling medical gas to:

- recognize medical gas labels

- examine all labels carefully before hooking containers to the system.

Skilled and knowledgeable personnel should always check the container and connection prior to introducing the gas into the system.

Won't Connect?
Don't Connect!

Patients have been injured – and some have died – because of medical gas mix-ups. This usually occurs when the wrong gas is forcibly connected to the oxygen supply system. Please promote the importance of properly handling medical gases.

- Manufacturers who receive reports of death or serious injury associated with the use of medical gases are required by law to report those incidents to the FDA.

- Hospitals, nursing homes, and other health care facilities should submit reports of such mix-ups (whether or not they resulted in a serious injury) to FDA's voluntary reporting program, MedWatch:

    Phone - (800) FDA-1088

    Fax - (800) FDA-0178

    Mail - MedWatch, Food and Drug Administration
           5600 Fishers Lane
           Rockville, Maryland 20852-9787

References

1. American Heart Association. "Guidelines for Cardiopulmonary Resuscitation and Emergency Cardiovascular Care". *Circulation* 112: IV-1 - IV-5. 2005.

2. American Red Cross. *Community First Aid and Safety.* StayWell. Yardley, PA. 2002.

3. American Red Cross. *First Aid/CPR/AED for Schools and the Community.* StayWell. Yardley, PA. 2006.

4. Camiener, Gerald. "Laboratory Budget Reduction Through Hazardous Waste Minimization". *Laboratory Medicine,* 35(1), 9-12. January 2004.

5. Caskey, Cheryl. "Workplace Violence". *Clinical Laboratory Science,* 14(2), 95-100. Spring 2001.

6. Clinical Laboratory Standards Institute (CLSI, formerly NCCLS) documents to include:

   a. GP5-A. "Clinical Laboratory Waste Management". Approved Guideline. Clinical Laboratory Standards Institute Wayne, PA. 2002.

   b. GP17-A2. "Clinical Laboratory Safety". Approved Guideline. Clinical Laboratory Standards Institute. Wayne, PA. 2004.

   c. GP18-A2. "Laboratory Design". Approved Guideline. Clinical Laboratory Standards Institute. Wayne, PA. 2007.

   d. M29-A3. *"Protection of Laboratory Workers from Occupationally Acquired Infections".* Approved *Guideline*, Third edition. Clinical Laboratory Standards Institute. Wayne, PA.. 2005.

7. FDA and NIOSH Public Health Notification: Oxygen Regulator Fires Resulting from Incorrect Use of CGA 870 Seals. April 24, 2006.

8. Furr, A. K. (Ed.). *CRC Handbook of Laboratory Safety,* 5th Edition, CRC Press, 2000.

9. Gile, Terry Jo. *"Ergonomics in the Laboratory".* Laboratory Medicine, 32(5), 263-267. May 2001.

10. Henry, John B. editor. *Clinical Diagnosis and Management by Laboratory Methods,* 20th edition, Philadelphia, PA: W. B. Saunders, 2001.

11. Hoerl, Diane; Rostkowski, Christine; Ross, Sherril L. & Walsh, Thomas J. "Typhoid Fever Acquired in a Medical Technology Teaching Laboratory", *Laboratory Medicine,* 19(3), 166-168. March 1988.

12. Holmber, Daveda. "Laboratory Waste Legal Issues". *Laboratory Medicine,* 36(10), 604. October 2005.

13. *Infection Control Today.* www.infection-controltoday.com/articles/251portex.html. Accessed October 29, 2006.

14. Institute for Safe Medical Practices. "Fatal Gas Line Mix-Up Results in Nitrous Oxide Poisoning". ISMP Medication Safety Alert, 9(24), 2004.

15. Morse, Stephen A. "Bioterrorism: Laboratory Security". *Laboratory Medicine,* 6(32), 303-306. June 2001.

16. National Fire Protection Association. *Health Care Facilities* (ANSI/NFPA 99). NFPA. Quincy, MA. 1990.

17. Occupational Safety and Health Administration (U.S. Department of Labor), www.osha.gov. Material consulted includes:

    a. CPL 02-02-069 - CPL 2-2.69 - Enforcement Procedures for the *Occupational Exposure to Bloodborne Pathogens.* November 21, 2001.

    b. *Federal Register* 29 CPR Part CFR 1910.147. *Control of Hazardous Energy.* September 11, 1990.

    c. *Federal Register* 29 CPR Part CFR 1910.157. *Portable Fire Extinguishers.* November 7, 2002.

    d. *Federal Register,* 29 CFR Part 1910.1030. *Occupational Exposure to Blood-borne Pathogens.* Final Rule. December 6, 1991.

    e. *Federal Register,* 29 CFR Part 1910.1030. *Occupational Exposure to Bloodborne Pathogens;Needlestick and Other Sharps Injuries;* Final Rule. - 66:5317-5325. January 18, 2001.

    f. *Federal Register* 29 CPR Part 1910.1048 *Occupational Exposure to Formaldehyde.* May 27, 1992.

    g. *Federal Register* 29 CPR Part 1910.1450. *Occupational Exposure to Hazardous Chemicals in Laboratories.* January 31, 1990.

    h. "Use of Blunt-Tip Suture Needles to Decrease Percutaneous Injuries to Surgical Personnel." NIOSH publication No. 2007-132. March 23, 2007.

18. Ozanne, Gérard. "Latex, Vinyl or Nitrile? Characteristics of certain gloves used in the laboratory or in the field to reduce risk of skin exposure to biological agents". *Canadian Journal of Medical Laboratory Science,* 64: 29-35. 2002.

19. Parks, David G. "Legal Issues: OSHA's Personal Protective Equipment Standard". *Laboratory Medicine,* 27(2), 86-88 . February 1996.

20. Rose, Susan. *Clinical Laboratory Safety.* J.B. Lippincott. Philadelphia, PA. 1984.

21. Ruckert, Jenniger."In My Opinion". *Laboratory Medicine,* 27(5), 304. May 1996.

22. Rutala, William A. "APIC Guidelines for Infection Control Practice". American Journal for Infection Control, 24(4), 313-342. August 1996.

23. Sania, Amr and Bollinger, Mary E. "Latex Allergy and Occupational Asthma in Health Care Workers: Adverse Outcomes". From *Environmental Health Perspectives* and posted on www.medscape.com on March 18, 2004.

24. United States Department of Health and Human Services Centers for Disease Control and Prevention. www.cdc.gov. Material consulted includes:

a. *Biosafety in Microbiological and Biomedical Laboratories,* 5th edition. Washington, D.C. U.S. Government Printing Office. February 2007.

b. "Guidelines for Hand Hygiene in Health-Care Settings". *Morbidity and Mortality Weekly Report. volume* 51, number RR-16, pages 1 - 48. October 25, 2002.

c. "Guidelines for Isolation Precautions: Preventing Transmission of Infectious Agents in Healthcare Settings 2007."

d. "Guidelines for Preventing Transmission of Mycobacterium tuberculosis in Health Care Settings", *Morbidity and Mortality Weekly* Report. volume 54, number RR-17, pages 1 - 141. December 30, 2005.

e. "Guidelines for Using the QuantiFERON-TB Gold Test for Detecting Mycobacterium tuber-culosis Infection, United States". *Morbidity and Mortality Weekly Report.* volume 54, number RR15, pages 49-55. December 16, 2005.

f. Updated U.S. Public Health Service Guidelines for the Management of Occupational Exposures to HBV, HCV, and HIVand Recommendations for Postexposure Prophylaxis. *Morbidity and Mortality Weekly* Report. volume 50, number RR-11, pages 1 - 67. June 29, 2001.

25. United States Department of Health and Human Services Centers Food and Drug Administration. www.fda.gov. Material consulted includes:

a. *Federal Register* 21CFR Part 800 [Docket No. 2003N-0056(formerly 03N-0056)]. *Medical Devices; Patient Examination and Surgeons' Gloves; Test Procedures and Acceptance Criteria. Final Rule.* 71(243): 75865-75879. December 19, 2006.

26. United States Department of Homeland Security. www.dhs.gov. Material consulted includes:

a. Chemical Facility Anti-Terrorism Standards, http://a257.g.akamaite ch.t/7/257/2422/01jan20071800/ edocket.access.gpo.gov/2007/ E7-6363.htm, accessed July 19, 2007.

b. DHS Chemicals of Interest, http:// www.dhs.gov/xprevprot/laws/ gc_1175537180929.shtm, accessed July 19, 2007.

27. United States Department of Transportation (DOT). www.dot. gov. "Global Harmonization of Hazard Classification and Labeling Systems". Accessed November 14, 2006.

28. United States Environmental Protection Agency. www.epa.gov. Material consulted includes:

a. Resources for Small Quantity Generators. http://www.epa.gov/ osw/gen_trans/sqg_resources.htm. March 7, 2006.

b. Environmental Management Guide for Small Laboratories. Office of Small Business Ombudsman. http://www. epa.gov/sbo/.

29. U.S. Postal Service. 601 Mailability Standard. http://pe.usps.gov/text/ dmm300/601.htm#wp1064962. Accessed January 6, 2008.

30. Weinert, George. "Latex Antigen, Glutaraldehyde Trigger Complaints and Solutions". ADVANCE for Medical Laboratory Professionals. February 5, 1996.

31. Wagner, Kathryn D. and Leonard, K. Leigh. "The Power of Prevention". ADVANCE for Medical Laboratory Professionals. February 5, 2001.

32. Websites:

www.healthsafetyinfo.com

www.nrc.gov

www.paint.org/hmis/index.cfm

www.safetylady.com

www.hc-sc.gc.ca/whmis

References

POST-TEST

100 points possible. Multiple Choice, 1 point each. Others as indicated.

1. ___ Each organization below is paired **CORRECTLY** with one of its functions **EXCEPT:**

   a. CDC / standards for handling biohazards
   b. EPA / regulation of hazardous waste disposal
   c. OSHA / certifying personnel for laboratory work
   d. NRC / radiation and radioactive waste management
   e. DOT / regulation of hazardous material transportation

2. ___ Which OSHA standard below is primarily a performance standard?

   a. Formaldehyde
   b. Bloodborne Pathogens
   c. Hazard Communication
   d. Hazardous Chemicals in Laboratories

3. ___ In order to reduce biohazard contamination, workers must handle objects in the direction of "clean to dirty." In other words, once an clean object enters a contaminated zone, it never returns to the clean zone. OSHA would classify this as a(n)

   a. engineering control
   b. work practice control
   c. environmental control
   d. administrative control

4. ___ Which of the following is (are) always on an MSDS for a chemical?

   a. methods of disposal
   b. methods for safe use
   c. description of hazards
   d. all of the above

5. ___ Hazards should be shipped

   a. in properly labeled triple-packed containers
   b. in sturdy, unbreakable containers so that padding is not necessary
   c. with enough absorbent material so that containers that may leak can be shipped
   d. with enough padding to prevent breakage so that breakable containers can be shipped
   e. all of the above

6. ___ If the EPA has granted reciprocity or equivalency to a state department of the environment, then

    a. the state can have regulatory authority in place of the EPA
    b. the state's regulations are as strict or stricter than the EPA's
    c. facilities should follow state requirements rather than EPA requirements
    d. all of the above

7. Give 2 examples of disorders due to poor ergonomic conditions. (1 point)

_____

_____

8. ___ Which of the types of fire below could you use water on?

    a. Class A
    b. Class B
    c. Class C
    d. Class D
    e. All of the above
    f. It is never acceptable to use water on a fire in the laboratory

9.   Name the four components required to start a fire (the fire "quadrahedron"): (2 points)

    1. _____
    2. _____
    3. _____
    4. _____

10. ___ A hydrogen gas fire would be a ___ fire and correspond ___ shown below.

    a. Class A; symbol B
    b. Class B; symbol C
    c. Class C; symbol A
    d. Class D; symbol B
    e. Class E; symbol C

      a   b   c

11. ___ The first priority in the event of a fire is

    a. locating the nearest fire extinguisher
    b. turning off current and shutting the doors
    c. insuring the safety of all people by initiating an evacuation
    d. pulling the fire alarm and calling the appropriate extension

12. ___ The best way to evacuate a fire scene is to

    a. use the nearest stairway or elevator
    b. leave doorways open as you exit so that the fire is clearly visible
    c. cover your mouth and nose with a damp cloth as you run toward the door
    d. exit using a route that moves from areas of high danger to areas of low danger
    e. all of the above

13. ___ When using a CO_2 fire extinguisher you should

    a. aim at the top of the fire and work your way down
    b. hold the discharge horn firmly to direct the stream accurately
    c. activate the extinguisher by pulling out the locking pin and firmly squeezing the double handle
    d. all of the above

14. ___ Which sketch below represents a dry chemical extinguisher?

 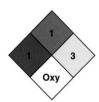 

    a. A
    b. B
    c. C

A   **B**   **C**

15. ___ The most significant hazard of a chemical with the NFPA label shown is

    a. health
    b. reactivity
    c. corrosivity
    d. flammability

16. Matching (4 points)

    ___ environmental hazard
    ___ health hazard
    ___ poison
    ___ flammable

A   **B**   **C**   **D**

17. ___ The HMIS label shown would be most appropriate for which chemical listed below?

| 3 |
| 2 |
| 3 |

Strong irritant and sensitizer.
Wear gloves, use in hood.

a. mercury
b. formaldehyde
c. hydrogen cyanide
d. compressed nitrogen gas

18. What information is missing from this chemical label? (1 point)

15% Hydochloric Acid
Strong corrosive
Use in the hood wearing gloves, face protection and goggles

_____

19. Matching. Match the hazard below to its correct method of storage, handling or disposal.
(4 points)

___ Combustibles

___ Cyanide compounds

___ Corrosives

___ Mercury

___ Oxidizers

___ Ether

___ Azides

___ Liquid radioactive waste

A. Do not flush in sinks with copper or lead plumbing
B. Isolate these from contact with hydrocarbons
C. Isolate these from contact with acids
D. Form explosive peroxides with oxygen
   Dispose after 1 year
E. Wear safety goggles & add these slowly to water to minimize splashing
F. Store in a vented safety cabinet
G. Flush with copious volumes of water down the sink if local regulations permit
H. Extreme health hazard. Clean spills with special kit and wear respiratory protection

20. ___ A properly installed and maintained chemical fume hood has

a. a clean HEPA filter
b. an air flow of 100 linear feet per minute
c. the hood exhaust pipe connected to the building's air handler
d. all of the above

21. ___ Formaldehyde exposure can be minimized by:

    a. using a backdraft hood since formaldehyde is heavier than air
    b. performing environmental monitoring to ensure PEL's are not exceeded
    c. requiring work practices that ensure that no odor of formaldehyde can be detected
    d. all of the above

22. ___ Which of the following should not be mixed with bleach or chlorine-containing compounds?

    a. xylene
    b. paraffin
    c. picric acid
    d. formaldehyde

23 ___ If a hazardous spill occurs, how should absorbent material be used?

    a. First in the middle of the spill, then working outward
    b. First at the largest part of the spill, then working outward
    c. First around the entire perimeter of the spill, then working inward
    d. Absorbent material should not be used for hazardous materials since it will then become hazardous too

24. ___ When is an electrical consumer product acceptable for lab use around hazardous chemicals?

    a. if it has a 3-prong plug
    b. if it has a polarized plug
    c. if it is certified, by Underwriters' Labs, for example
    d. all of the above
    e. none of the above. Electrical equipment that is safe to use around lab hazards is usually manufactured differently

25. ___ Which of the following are acceptable ways to use electrical equipment in the lab?

    a. using extension cords
    b. operating equipment with wet hands
    c. unplugging an instrument by pulling on the cord
    d. using 2 prong mating receptacles for 3 prong plugs
    e. marking malfunctioning equipment with "OUT OF SERVICE"
    f. all of the above

26. ___ Electrical shock occurs when

    a. the electricity has a high enough voltage
    b. the electricity has a high enough amperage
    c. a person contacts an electrical circuit with an insulator
    d. a person becomes part of a completed electrical circuit
    e. all of the above

27. ___ Emergency generators should not be connected directly to power lines because

    a. the generator could be damaged
    b. laboratory equipment connected to the generators could be damaged
    c. electrical "backfeed" from the generator could harm workers trying to restore power to the normal power lines
    d. electrical "backfeed" from the generator could harm the laboratory workers trying to use equipment connected to it

28.   OSHA requires five general categories of electrical hazard management. Name them and give an example of each (5 points)

    1. _____

    2. _____

    3. _____

    4. _____

    5. _____

29. ___ Each of the following is paired **CORRECTLY** with an accepted method of disposal **EXCEPT:**

    a. human blood / incineration
    b. broken glass / puncture-resistant container
    c. needles / recap and discard in Biohazard bag
    d. microbiological cultures, Biosafety Level II / autoclaving
    e. scalpels / discard entire thing into puncture-resistant container

30. ___ Identify which practice below is unsafe:

    a. carrying a volumetric flask by the "neck" at the top
    b. lubricating glass connections (if no oxidizers in use)
    c. operating centrifuge with a fixed cover over the moving parts
    d. leaving a biological safety cabinet on after a spill has occurred inside it
    e. opening an autoclave after the pressure and temperature have dropped to ambient
    f. all of the above

31. ___ Observe the centrifuge schematic below.

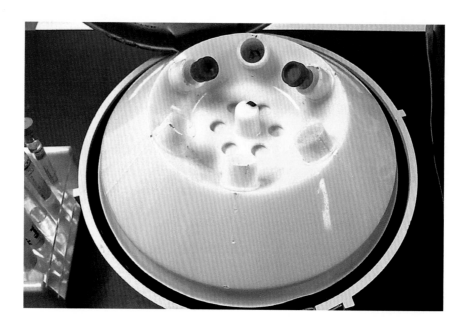

    a. this centrifuge is loaded incorrectly
    b. this centrifuge could make odd or excessive noise
    c. the centrifuge may "walk" (move across the bench) when it is turned on
    d. all of the above

32. ___ Each statement below is **CORRECT EXCEPT:**

    a. Mouth pipetting is never acceptable under any circumstances
    b. Biosafety Level 4 is for handling non-pathogens in a teaching laboratory
    c. The three broad classes of disinfectants are heat, chemicals and radiation
    d. Aerosols can form when a hot inoculating loop is placed in broth or when open tubes are centrifuged
    e. Objects contaminated with biohazards such as computer keyboards, telephones and pencils are called fomites

33. ___ Choose the **CORRECT** statement below:

    a. infectious molds should be handled at a BSL-1

    b. volatile organic solvents should be handled under a chemical fume hood.

    c. the minimum classification of biological safety cabinet for handling BSL-3 is Class 3

    d. you don't have to wear goggles if you are pouring less than 100 ml of concentrated acid in the sink

    e. centrifuges should be opened as soon as you hear breakage so that you can remove the broken glass and minimize damage to the centrifuge

34. ___ If no aerosols or splashing are expected, specimens from AIDS patients are handled at BSL-

    a. 1

    b. 2

    c. 3

    d. 4

35. ___ All of following are acceptable when handling animals in a laboratory **EXCEPT:**

    a. wear heavy, "bite-proof" gloves

    b. autopsy animals in biological safety cabinets

    c. inoculate animals using a press cage or sedation

    d. autoclave all cages after you have cleaned them out

    e. assume that even the control animals are infectious

36. List 6 standard microbiological practices at a BSL 2. (6 points)

    1. _____

    2. _____

    3. _____

    4. _____

    5. _____

    6. _____

37. ___ All of the following are components of an Exposure Control Plan **EXCEPT:**

    a. disposal protocol for chemicals

    b. provisions for hepatitis B vaccine

    c. treatment protocols for blood exposure

    d. task assessments for all staff who contact blood

38. ___ A mid-level disinfectant is the minimum requirement to chemically decontaminate the organism:

    a. Creutzfeldt-Jakob agent
    b. *Mycobacterium tuberculosis*
    c. *Bacillus anthracis* and *Clostridium difficile* spores
    d. all of the above

39. According to the CDC, all human blood and body should be handled using (1 point)

    _____. However if a particular disease is known to be

    present, the specimens must also be handled using _____.

40. ___ (True/False) Autoclaving procedures which inactivate Biosafety Level 4 organisms should deactivate infectious prions. (1 point)

41. ___ A 10% solution of household bleach made 30 days ago is considered a

    a. low-level disinfectant
    b. mid-level disinfectant
    c. high-level disinfectant
    d. none of the above

42. Compressed gas should be stored in a(n) _____ position

    and kept _____ to the wall at all times so that it will be confined

    if there is a sudden release of pressure. Gas cylinders should never be used until they

    are completely_____ or negative pressure could

    suction materials into the cylinder. Inventory management for cylinders should keep full

    and empty cylinders _____ and should ensure that the

    _____cylinders are the ones used up first. You should only use the

    _____ for the particular type of gas which you are using

    since they are designed to prevent incompatible chemicals from mixing. (3 points)

43. The most penetrating form of radiation is _____. The only way to prevent its penetration is with the metal _____. All laboratories that handle radiation must have a _____ from the NRC, state and/or local governments, which defines the amount and types of radiation that can be used and how waste can be disposed. The length of time that a material remains radioactive is expressed as the material's _____, whereas the quantity of radioactivity is expressed as _____. The unit of biological exposure is

_____.

A worker's exposure to radiation is monitored by a _____ that the worker wears. Personnel exposure as well as radioactive inventory, environmental monitoring and waste disposal must be very carefully _____ to verify that a laboratory is complying with regulations. (4 points)

44. What are the three main ways to keep radiation exposure "as low as reasonably achievable" ?
(3 points)

   1. _____

   2. _____

   3. _____

45. ___ Labs using a "decay in storage" disposal program for radioisotopes can discard isotopes as ordinary trash after ___ half-lives have passed.

   a. 10
   b. 100
   c. 1000
   d. none of the above—radioisotopes can never be discarded as ordinary trash

46. ___ One of the most critical documents for demonstrating compliance with EPA and RCRA regulations is the

    a. EPA license to treat waste
    b. EPA license to store waste
    c. EPA license to generate waste
    d. completed Hazardous Waste Manifest

47. ___ An EPA-regulated characteristic waste is defined as a waste that

    a. cannot be discarded in EPA-administered landfills
    b. appears on an EPA regulatory list because of its characteristics
    c. appears on an EPA, state or local regulatory list because of its characteristics
    d. does not appear on an EPA regulatory list but has one of the following characteristics: toxicity, reactivity, flammability or corrosivity.

48. ___ The Resource Recovery and Conservation Act says:

    a. facilities generating <1 Ci of radioactive waste don't need to recycle it
    b. facilities are responsible for their chemical waste until its ultimate disposal
    c. all chemical waste must be recycled by EPA methods that have low environmental impact
    d. chemical waste must be reduced by 10% annually in every facility until a 50% reduction has been achieved

49. What are the three main ways to minimize generating hazardous waste? (3 points)

    1. _____

    2. _____

    3. _____

50. ___ All of the following is **TRUE EXCEPT:**

    a. since chemical waste will no longer be used in the lab, labeling requirements are less stringent
    b. the EPA does not have an infectious waste/medical waste category, but most state and local governments do
    c. the EPA and DOT have developed a hazardous waste manifest that is the base form now required in all 50 states
    d. based on the issued permit, the EPA can fine labs for having either too much hazardous waste on site or holding it too long without disposal

51. ___ Each type of equipment below is paired **CORRECTLY** to one of its functions **EXCEPT:**

    a. heat resistant gloves / handling hot glassware
    b. face shields / protection against hazardous fumes
    c. goggles / eye protection against chemical splashes
    d. safety shower / wash off and dilute chemical spills on the body
    e. latex or vinyl gloves / protection against some chemicals and biohazards

52. ___ Which of the following may be permitted in some labs?

    a. smoking
    b. eating and drinking
    c. applying cosmetics
    d. using non-petroleum-based hand lotion
    e. replacing a contact lens which has fallen out

53. ___ Which of the following can cause increased carriage of microbes on the hands?

    a. chipped nail polish
    b. rings and other jewelry
    c. long natural nails and artificial nails
    d. all of the above

54. ___ Workers should be monitored carefully for reactions to gloves because:

    a. some people have latex allergies
    b. some people have allergies to certain powders
    c. broken and irritated skin puts workers at additional risk
    d. all of the above

55. ___ The barrier function of latex gloves can be compromised by all of the following **EXCEPT:**

    a. exposure to light
    b. exposure to ozone
    c. storage in an unheated room
    d. contact with certain hand lotions
    e. prolonged contact with sweaty hands

56. ___ All of the following is (are) important limitations of alcohol-based hand gels **EXCEPT:**

   a. the gels are flammable
   b. more gel must be used to kill spore-forming organisms
   c. some viruses are not killed by the action of the alcohol
   d. work cannot continue until the gel has dried on the hands

57. ___ All of the following are functions of accident reports **EXCEPT:**

   a. documenting worker's compensation claims
   b. documenting cause for employee termination
   c. documenting appropriateness of actions taken
   d. analyzing the incident to prevent similar ones from occurring

58. ___ The first step in first aid is to

   a. clear the airway
   b. restore breathing and heartbeat
   c. stop any bleeding
   d. treat for shock
   e. treat the wound

59. ___ Each condition below is paired **CORRECTLY** with its appropriate first aid treatment **EXCEPT:**

   a. bleeding from 2-inch cut / apply a tourniquet
   b. shock / keep victim warm and elevate the feet
   c. first-degree burn / cover with cool water or a cool, moist dressing
   d. object impaled in eye / cover both eyes and do not attempt to remove the object

60. ___ After an accident has occurred, the appropriate reason(s) that a victim could be moved is (are)

   a. the immediate area is life-threatening
   b. the rescuer needs access to a more seriously injured person
   c. the rescuer cannot give appropriate care with the victim in his current position
   d. all of the above

61. Matching (4 points)

___ Shock

___ Stroke

___ Electrical shock

___ Second degree burn

A. Skin is red like a sunburn
B. Skin is red and has blisters
C. Skin is black, charred and clothing is embedded in the burn
D. Skin shows evidence of a burn and victim has no breathing or heart beat
E. Victim cannot raise both arms overhead, speak or smile normally
F. Victim is pale, listless, thirsty with rapid breathing and heartbeat

62. Matching (9 points)

___ Explosive symbol

___ Eyewash symbol

___ Compressed gas symbol

___ Laser symbol

___ Fire blanket symbol

___ Radiation symbol

___ Deluge shower symbol

___ Biohazard symbol

___ No smoking symbol

A

B

C

D

E

F

G

H

I

63. ___ The safest laboratory is the one which

a. has all the recommended safety equipment
b. has trained all of its workers thoroughly in safety
c. has supervisors who are aware of all safety standards
d. has all written policies in compliance with OSHA standards

Answers

Q=Questions A=Answers S=Scenarios

Exercise 1

Q	A
1	a
2	a
3	a and d; c and f ; a and e
4	b
5	d
6	e
7	c
8	e, g, h, c, a, b, d, f; Legal enforcement: NRC, DOT, USPS, CLIA '88, EPA Voluntary: CDC, NIH, NFPA, CAP, JCAH
9	d

Exercise 2

Q	A
1	g and j; h and i; a and f; c and d; b and e
2	d
3	a
4	e
5	c
6	d
7	b
8	a
9	b, c, a
10	d
11	a
12	a

Exercise 3

Q	A
1	c
2	e
3	a
4	e
5	b, d, a, c
6	d
7	minimize chemical amounts; rotate stock so oldest used first ("first in, first out"); separate incompatible chemicals; maintain cool temperature and good ventilation; minimize heat and electrical sources; secure against theft, no toxic/flammable fumes in refrigerators
8	a
9	e
10	d
11	e
12	d,c,a,e,b,f
13	explosive peroxides, white deposits
14	e
15	picric
16	sodium azide
17	reducers or hydrocarbons, for example grease, oil, gas and certain metals
18	cold water
19	landfill, incineration, sanitary sewer and licensed waste handler
20	d
21	c
22	e
23	e
24	xylene, formaldehyde
25	hepatotoxin

Exercise 4

Q	A
1	a
2	e
3	d
4	a
5	c
6	b
7	e
8	b
9	d
10	Water with ions, metals; Plastic, rubber, glass, wood, ceramic
11	Completed electrical circuit
12	10 amp, 20 millivolt; higher voltage, lower amperage
13	plug, cord
14	c

Exercise 5

Q	A
1	a
2	b
3	c
4	c
5	Universal Precautions
6	c
7	e
8	c, d, b, a
9	false
10	d
11	e
12	e
13	d
14	e
15	a
16	c
17	d
18	e
19	b
20	g
21	d

Exercise 6

Q	A
1	d
2	d
3	a
4	b
5	d
6	d
7	e
8	c
9	e
10	c

Exercise 7

Q	A
1	c
2	g, f, a, d, b
3	e
4	c
5	a
6	a
7	c
8	As low as reasonably achievable- Radiation exposure should be the smallest that it practically can be
9	time, distance, shielding
10	e

Exercise 8

Q	A
1	a
2	b
3	a
4	False
5	b
6	False
7	Reduce, reuse, recycle
8	When the completed manifest is received by the site generating the waste
9	d
10	decay in storage, 10
11	a

Exercise 9

Q	A
1.	Fire extinguisher hung too high with laboratory coat hanging over it
2.	Person carrying acid without acid bucket and holding the bottle by the neck rather than the bottom
3.	Person has a cigarette in his hand and "NO SMOKING" sign is prominent
4.	Exit blocked
5.	Sand bucket with cigarettes in it
6.	Coffee cup or food on counter with specimens
7.	Person picking up broken glass with fingers
8.	Person pipetting by mouth
9.	Person recapping a needle

10.	Spider web in a corner makes insect and rodent control programs suspect
11.	Person vortexing uncovered specimens
12.	Electric cord plugged in over sink
13.	Two-pronged plug. There should be a third grounding pin
14.	Person slowing down centrifuge of specimens with hand
15.	Unstoppered specimens in centrifuge
16.	Person handling specimens without gloves
17.	Person pouring liquid without goggles. Should use automatic pipetting device to avoid splashing
18.	Chemical spill on shelf
19.	Can of ether out on counter
20.	Gas cylinder unchained and unidentified

Exercise 10

Q	A
1	c
2	e
3	contact lenses
4	safety or deluge shower
5	15
6	False
7	e
8	a
9	b
10	a
11	e
12	100 feet, 10 seconds, weekly
13	c
14	c, b, a

Exercise 12

Q	A
1	d
2	b
3	e
4	check, call, care
5	Clear the airway. Restore breathing. Restore circulation. Stop any bleeding. Treat for shock. Treat the injury.
6	c
7	e
8	c

9	immobilized
10	should, movement, both eyes move together, water, contact lenses
11	c
12	OSHA
13	flammables, cell phones/electrical equipment within 6 feet, wet or conductive surfaces
14	a

Exercise 13

S	Q	A
A	1	1, 4, 2, 3, 5
	2	d
	3	e
	4	a
	5	a
B	1	d
	2	c
	3	b
	4	d
	5	b
C	1	c
	2	c
	3	c
D	1	d
	2	Pressures would read zero on regulator
E	1	a
	2	b
F	1	d
	2	d
	3	c
G	1	a
	2	a
H	1	b
	2	c
I	1	d
	2	a
	3	d
J	1	c
	2	b

K	1	e
	2	Some hand creams can dissolve glove material leaving small holes
L	1	d
	2	Second, shock
M	1	b
	2	a
N	1	d
	2	Review fire evacuation routes with all employees and hold fire drills at least annually
O	1	a
	2	Ventilate the room immediately and place chemicals in an alternate storage site such as a vented flammable cabinet
P	1	b
	2	d

POST-TEST ANSWERS

Q	A
1	c
2	b
3	b
4	d
5	a
6	d
7	Any two of the following: eye strain such as excessive computer use, cumulative trauma disorders from repetitive motion such as carpel tunnel syndrome, hearing loss, skeletomuscular disorders such as a strained back
8	a
9	fuel, heat, oxygen, a sustainable chain reaction
10	b
11	c
12	d
13	c
14	b
15	b
16	c, b, d, a
17	b
18	Dates that acid was made and/or received. Initials of responsible person.
19	f, c, e, h, b, d, a, g
20	b
21	d
22	d
23	c

24	e
25	e
26	d
27	c
28	Categories are: insulation; non-conductors surrounding sources of electricity such as plastic covers guarding; separation of electrical sources from the public such as locked doors grounding; low resistance connection of electrical device to earth to disperse charge circuit protection devices; devices that protect against surges of current such as fuses, circuit breakers, GFCI Safe work practices; techniques that reduce electrical hazard such as separation of equipment from water, not using extension cords, following maintenance procedures See text for additional examples.
29	c
30	a
31	d
32	b
33	b
34	b
35	d
36	Any six of the following: control access to the lab; decontaminate trash and/or work surfaces; no mouth pipetting; no eating, drinking or smoking; wear gloves, lab coats, closed shoes, etc. and remove them when leaving the lab; minimize aerosols and wear goggles, face shields or masks if they are unavoidable; display Biohazard symbol on lab, trash, refrigerators, etc.; don't recap needles; use Class I or II biological safety cabinets if aerosols or large amounts of biohazards are present; wash hands with disinfectant even after wearing gloves; autoclave trash; insect and rodent control program
37	a
38	b
39	Standard/Universal Precautions; Transmission-Based Precautions
40	false
41	d
42	vertical, chained, empty, separated, oldest, fittings or regulator
43	gamma, lead, license, half-life, Curies or Becquerels, rem, dosimeter, documented or recorded
44	
45	a
46	d
47	d
48	b
49	SEGREGATION of hazardous waste from non-hazardous waste, PLANNING to minimize discarding expired materials and incorporating non-hazardous materials when possible and REDUCING, REUSING and RECYCLING

50	a
51	b
52	d
53	d
54	d
55	c
56	b
57	b
58	a
59	a
60	d
61	f, e, d, b
62	i, b, h, e, a, d, c, f, g
63	b

INDEX